CW00684176

PROFICIENCY
EXPERT
STUDENT'S RESOURCE BOOK

Megan Roderick and Carol Nuttall with Nick Kenny

Contents

Contents

Module	Section	Vocabulary development 1	Use of English	Language development 1	Listening
6 Travel (p.61)	**A** Sense of adventure	Adjectives; collocations: describing places of interest; verbs of movement: going on foot (p. 61)	**Paper 1 Part 1** Multiple-choice cloze *Fashions in sightseeing* (p. 62) **Paper 1 Part 2** Open cloze *Snowboarding in the Himalayas* (p. 64)	Present subjunctive; past subjunctive and unreal past (p. 63)	**Paper 3 Part 1** Multiple choice: *Three extracts about travel experiences* (p. 65)
7 The way we live (p. 72)	**A** Communities	Collocations; idioms with *give* and *get*; building communities (p.72)	**Paper 1 Part 1** Multiple-choice cloze *Is a simple life better?* (p. 73) **Paper 1 Part 2** Open cloze *Social fitworking* (p. 75)	Relative clauses; reduced relative clauses with participles and *to* infinitives; omitting the relative pronoun; reduced non-defining descriptive clauses (p. 74)	**Paper 3 Part 2** Sentence completion: *CycleAware* (p. 76)
8 Changing fashions (p. 83)	**A** A question of style	Prepositions; different structures/ buildings; expressions and phrasal verbs: *draw* and *drop*; art: personality types (p. 83)	**Paper 1 Part 1** Multiple-choice cloze *Art on approval* (p. 84) **Paper 1 Part 3** Word formation *The big squeeze* (p. 86)	Common words and expressions: verb phrases + -*ing* (p. 85)	**Paper 3 Part 4** Multiple matching: *Five short extracts about a work of art* (p. 87)
9 Fitness and nutrition (p. 94)	**A** How far can you go?	Idioms: sport; word formation (p. 94)	**Paper 1 Part 1** Multiple-choice cloze *Improving athletics teaching in schools* (p. 95) **Paper 1 Part 3** Word formation *The fascination of tennis* (p. 97)	Sentence adverbials; gradable and ungradable adjectives; adverb-adjective collocations; collocations (p. 96)	**Paper 3 Part 2** Sentence completion: *Sports Psychology* (p. 98)
10 Broadening your horizons (p. 105)	**A** Professional concerns	Collocations; idioms: success at work; verb phrases; word formation: adjectives and adverbs with *in-* or *un-* (p. 105)	**Paper 1 Part 1** Multiple-choice cloze *How a small company grows* (p. 106) **Paper 1 Part 2** Open cloze *No logo* (p. 108)	Direct to reported speech; phrasal verbs for reporting and rephrasing; verbs for reporting and summarising; rephrasing and summarising: impersonal report structures (p. 107)	**Paper 3 Part 3** Multiple choice: *Attitudes to work* (p. 109)

Vocabulary development 1

> **CB** pp. 10–11

Words connected with the performing arts

1 Replace the words in bold with a word or phrase from the box.

denouement   flashbacks   prequel   score   sequel
stage fright

1 The award-winning drama serial ended with a lot of questions left unanswered, so we're expecting to see a **continuation of the story**. *Sequel*
2 On her first night, Kara suffered from **an acute attack of nerves** just before the performance but managed to overcome it once she got onto the stage. *Stage fright*
3 The **exciting last part** of *The Bourne Ultimatum* had the audience on the edge of their seats. *denouement*
4 The film starts in the middle of the story and events are gradually explained through a series of **scenes showing what happened before that**. *flashbacks*
5 Although released subsequently, *The Hobbit* is the **film that tells you what happened prior** to *The Lord of the Rings* trilogy. *prequel (opp. sequel)*
6 Ennio Morricone has written the **music** for numerous well-known film productions. *score*

Collocations

2 Complete each sentence by using a word from Box A and a word from Box B to form collocations.

A box   film   lead   rave   silver   standing

B adaptation   office   ovation   reviews   ~~role~~   screen

1 The Australian actor's big break came when he was cast in the **lead role** of a Hollywood blockbuster.
2 The **film adaptation** of the Broadway musical is skilfully directed, and much of the original choreography has been retained.
3 The show opened last week and received **rave reviews** from the critics.
4 Scott's film received a ten-minute **standing ovation** after its debut screening.
5 The controversial play proved to be a huge **box office** hit, making the production company a tidy sum, and earning both director and playwright Olivier awards.
6 Many young hopefuls flock to Hollywood each year dreaming of achieving fame on the **silver screen**, only to become disillusioned.

Verbs of movement

3 Use a dictionary to find out the meaning of the verbs in italics. Then complete each sentence by circling the most suitable verb.

1 The ballerina *curled / expanded /* (*stretched*) out her arms to receive her partner's embrace.
2 The king (*hobbles*) */ saunters / strides* onto the stage bent double, leaning heavily on a walking stick, appearing as a careworn, old man.
3 John expertly grasped his partner and (*hoisted*) */ piled / winched* her onto his shoulders.
4 In the scene, the protagonist *ambles /* (*clambers*) */ trudges* across the rooftops in hot pursuit of the murderer.
5 The dancers' feet seemed to (*glide*) */ skid / sprint* effortlessly across the floor.
6 Their full skirts flared out as the dancers *slid / tripped /* (*twirled*) round and round at great speed.

Nouns and prepositions

4 Complete the text with suitable prepositions.

=== Etienne Decroux ===

In the 1920s, an aspiring young actor named Etienne Decroux became fascinated by the art of mime. He saw the body as the actor's chief tool, the fundamental instrument **(1)** *for/in* creating action, thought and emotion, and developed what is known as corporeal mime – the art of movement. By mastering total control **(2)** *of/over* his body, the mime artist is able to captivate his audience by conveying feeling with a turn of his head, while the actor can lend clarity to the execution of his lines or facial expression with a simple shift within his body.

Decroux opened a school of corporeal mime in 1940, and was to train many talented students, among them the well-known mime artist, Marcel Marceau. In the 1950s and 60s, he gained worldwide recognition **(3)** *for* his contribution **(4)** *to* the theatre and is regarded by many as the father of modern mime. Evidence of his enduring influence **(5)** *on* acting techniques can be seen today in the work of comic actors such as Rowan Atkinson, whose ability **(6)** *to* amuse lies as much in their physical presence as it does in their vocal delivery.

Use of English (Paper 1 Part 1)

Multiple-choice cloze

1 Read the whole text quickly to get the general meaning, ignoring the gaps for the moment.

EXPERT STRATEGY

For this task, you need a good knowledge of how vocabulary is used, including fixed expressions, collocations and the grammatical forms which complement different words.

2 Re-read the text carefully and think about the type of word that will fit in each gap. Can you predict the answer without looking at the multiple-choice options?

3 Now look at the options A–D and choose the one which you think fits best. Use the Help clues if necessary.

4 Read through the text again when you've finished with your chosen options in place. Does it make complete sense?

For questions **1 – 8**, read the text below and decide which answer (**A, B, C** or **D**) best fits each gap. There is an example at the beginning **(0)**.

Tech Music School

London's Tech Music School has an unrivalled (0) __A__ [track] offers a Diploma in Commercial Music Production. This record. Since its foundation in 1983, it has (1) __D__ [turned] course (4) __D__ [provides] students with hands-on training in areas out some of Europe's best-known musicians, including such as song-writing and the composing of music for film Marina Diamandis of Marina and the Diamonds, Frank and TV. (5) __A__ [Meanwhile], the Diploma in Music Business gives Colucci and Radiohead's Phil Selway, to (2) __B__ [name] but a students the chance to (6) __C__ [gain] a thorough grounding in few. The school offers the next generation of performers business principles whilst working alongside artists, record training from industry professionals, and (3) __D__ [boasts] strong labels and the music press. connections with the music industry. Recent guest tutors With such courses on offer, the school is (7) __B__ [effectively] a have included musicians who have worked with the likes microcosm of the music industry, where it is possible of Stevie Wonder and Robbie Williams. to be at the cutting (8) __A__ [edge] of the latest techniques and

In addition to courses in performance skills, the school developments.

HELP

➤ Q1 Which word followed by *out* makes a phrasal verb meaning 'to produce'? *turn out*

➤ Q2 Look in the text before the comma for a clue.

➤ Q3 All the options have a similar meaning, but only one of them can be used in a positive sense.

➤ Q4 Only one option can be followed by the preposition *with*. Which one?

0	A track	B success	C field	D hit
1	A passed	B carved	C checked	D turned
2	A say	B name	C call	D refer
3	A brags	B flaunts	C touts	D boasts
4	A enables	B allows	C delivers	D provides
5	A Meanwhile	B Whereas	C Otherwise	D Albeit
6	A grasp	B win	C gain	D capture
7	A exceptionally	B effectively	C eventually	D especially
8	A edge	B margin	C verge	D fringe

EXPERT LANGUAGE

Look back at your answers. Find one which tests your knowledge of:
a a collocation *gain a qualification*
b a fixed expression *to name but a few*
c a dependent preposition *provides students with*

Language development 1

➤ CB p. 13, **GR** p. 172

State verbs review

1 Complete each sentence by circling the correct verb form from each pair in italics.

1 Aunt Giselle *adores* / *is adoring* ballet – she goes at least three or four times a year.

2 Dance is all about expressing your inner emotions through physical movement. *Do you see* / *Are you seeing* what I mean?

3 I'm afraid *I didn't notice* / *wasn't noticing* the name of the soloist – could I borrow your programme, please, to check?

4 It was tough at first, but I *enjoy* / *am enjoying* this course more and more every day!

5 It's fantastic to perform in front of an audience that *appreciates* / *is appreciating* all your hard work and effort.

6 According to the critics, last night's performance *lacked* / *was lacking* in verve and energy.

7 Jack *is* / *is being* very annoying these days – I can't persuade him to forget his stage-fright and get out and perform!

8 If you *promise* / *are promising* to commit to six months of intensive rehearsals, I can offer you the position.

Present perfect and past perfect tense review

2 Complete the second sentence by circling the correct verb form from each pair in italics so that it means the same as the first sentence.

1 Ben always seems to be at hip-hop classes these days.
Ben *has been doing* / *has done* a lot of hip-hop classes lately.

2 I only started singing classes recently but I can already see an improvement.
I *haven't been attending* / *hadn't been attending* singing classes for long but I can already see an improvement.

3 As soon as I walked into the room, the judges stopped talking.
I knew as soon as I walked into the room that the judges *have been talking* / *had been talking* about me.

4 This is my first solo performance in front of so many people.
I *have never performed* / *had never been performing* a solo in front of so many people before!

5 It would have been nice to know that most performers suffered from stage fright.
No one *had told* / *has been telling* me that stage fright was such a common phenomenon.

6 Only a few months after James started dancing professionally, he broke his leg.
James *has only been dancing* / *had only been dancing* professionally for a few months when he broke his leg.

Time words

3 Complete each sentence with a time word from the box. There are six words you do not need.

currently   ever   first   just   just now   last   lately
later   long   never   occasionally   since   still   yet

1 I saw Jake at the shops _just now_ . He said he had an audition _later_ .

2 Liz was unemployed for some time but she's _currently_ on tour with a theatre company in China.

3 I've _never_ been so humiliated in all my life as when I fell over on stage in full view of the audience.

4 What have you been up to _lately_ ? It seems a long time _since_ we went to that rap concert together.

5 They _still_ haven't decided on a venue for the jazz weekend – I hope it will be somewhere nice.

6 I used to play the trumpet in an orchestra but I only play _occasionally_ these days – I just don't have time anymore!

Past and present tense review

4 Complete the text with the correct form of the verbs in brackets.

Lift the mind
and the body will follow

Britt Tajet-Foxell has been the Royal Ballet's resident psychologist for nearly 20 years, working alongside its physiotherapists and body-control experts to lead dancers to realise their full potential. Her skills in the context of rehabilitation from significant physical injury (1) _have also earned_ (also / earn) her an outstanding reputation in the world of sport.

Tajet-Foxell originally (2) _trained_ (train) as a physiotherapist at St Thomas' Hospital in London in the early 1970s. She (3) _joined_ (join) the Royal Ballet at a time when a specific science of dance physiotherapy (4) _did not exist_ (not exist). 'The theoretical models were all drawn from sport. Before then, nobody (5) _gave_ (give) any thought to what dancers (6) _was continually asking_ (continually / ask) their bodies to do,' she recalls. 'Now there's much more awareness. Working on the mechanics of dancers' injuries, I (7) _became_ (become) increasingly fascinated by their psychology. It was amazing how two dancers with the same injury could respond to it in completely different ways.' So Tajet-Foxell (8) _embarked_ (embark) on a psychology degree and (9) _came_ (come) out with a double-sided perspective that is, she (10) _believes_ (believe), unique in the field.

Use of English (Paper 1 Part 2)

Open cloze

EXPERT STRATEGY

For this task, you need a good knowledge of sentence structure, as well as fixed expressions and the grammatical forms which complement different words. Remember to add new words and phrases to your vocabulary notebook.

1 Read the title of the text. What does *on the edge of our seats* mean?

2 Read the whole text quickly to get the general meaning, ignoring the gaps for the moment.

3 Re-read the text carefully, thinking about the type of word that will fit each gap.

4 Complete the gaps, looking carefully at the whole sentence that contains the gap. Use the Help clues if necessary.

5 Read through the text again when you've finished, with your chosen words in place. Does it make complete sense?

HELP

➤ Q2 You need to add a preposition to make a phrasal verb.
➤ Q3 Which word completes this common adverbial phrase? It indicates that an additional point is being made.
➤ Q4 Look at the whole sentence. What type of structure is this?
➤ Q5 Which form of the auxiliary do we need before the past participle in this position?

EXPERT LANGUAGE *come (to a conclusion)*

Look back at the text.
a Find the verbs which collocate *have (a tendency),*
with the nouns *conclusion, follow (a pattern)*
tendency and *pattern.*
b Are there any other verbs which commonly collocate with these nouns? Do they need different prepositions? *reach/arrive at a conclusion (preposition = at)*

Show/demonstrate/display a tendency (no preposition required), conform to a pattern (preposition = to)

For questions **1 – 8**, read the text below and think of the word that best fits each space. Use only one word in each space. There is an example at the beginning **(0)**.

What keeps us on the edge of our seats at the cinema?

According (0) _____TO_____ James Cutting, a psychologist at Cornell University, film-makers are getting better at constructing films in (1) __Such__ a way that they hold our attention. He points (2) __out__ that the viewer's attention is held more effectively in films which feature shots of a similar length. What's (3) __more__ , this effect is enhanced (4) __Such__ those shots recur in a regular pattern throughout a film. (5) __Having__ analysed over a hundred Hollywood movies, he has come to the conclusion that, the more recent they are, the more closely their shot lengths have a tendency to follow the same mathematical pattern that also describes human attention spans.

Cutting suggests that following such a pattern (6) __Could/might__ *may* well make films more gripping because they resonate (7) __with__ the rhythm of natural attention spans. However, he doubts that directors are deliberately using mathematics in the making of movies. Instead, he thinks films that happen to be edited in this way tend to be successful, (8) __which__ in turn encourages others to copy their style, explaining why more recent films tend to conform to the pattern.

Listening (Paper 3 Part 1)

Multiple choice

EXPERT STRATEGY

Read the questions carefully to know what you are listening for. Each question will focus on a different aspect of the recording. Some questions will be about specific parts of the text and others about the text as a whole.

HELP

➤ Q1 You are listening for the main point she is making. Which option best matches this?

➤ Q2 Listen for what the man's colleague said to him.

➤ Q3 You are listening for the woman agreeing with an idea the man expresses. She uses the word *indeed* to show this.

➤ Q4 This answer comes in the second half of the recording, when they are talking about lists. Listen for the phrase *If you ask me*; the woman's opinion follows this.

EXPERT LANGUAGE

Look back at the multiple-choice questions. Find an example of:
a a phrasal verb
b a verb and noun collocation
c a dependent preposition

EXPERT WORD CHECK

*pick and choose   flunked   busted
raucous chuckle   a glib response
the shifting sands   a hook to hang it on
alluring   gladiatorial
a running commentary*

1 Read the instructions for the task and the questions.

a How many extracts are you going to hear?

b What is each extract about?

2 Look at the questions for Extract One. How much do you find out about the topic and speakers from the rubric and from the questions?

3 Underline the main words in each question stem and in the Options A, B and C.

4 Listen to the recording and choose the correct option. Use the Help clues if necessary.

You will hear three different extracts. For questions **1 – 6**, choose the answer (**A**, **B** or **C**) which fits best according to what you hear. There are two questions for each extract.

Extract One

You hear two actors discussing their careers.

1 The woman advises drama students
  A to take what opportunities are available.
  B to hold out for the right opportunity.
  C to avoid wasting opportunities.

2 What does the man's story about the bank illustrate?
  A Success in a job requires real commitment.
  B Acting experience is useful in other walks of life.
  C Real-life experiences can inform the work of an actor.

Extract Two

You hear two radio presenters talking about pop music.

3 The woman agrees that the structure of the film she made
  A was designed to provoke a reaction.
  B involved a difficult selection process.
  C would have benefited from more thought.

4 What does the woman think about lists of favourite songs?
  A People use them to bolster an image of themselves.
  B Their contents can reveal a lot about somebody.
  C They shouldn't be taken too seriously.

Extract Three

You hear part of a media-studies lecture on the subject of reality TV.

5 What is the speaker doing in this part of the lecture?
  A explaining why the genre developed
  B describing how the genre has changed
  C accounting for the effectiveness of the genre

6 What is the programme *The X Factor* given as an example of?
  A the power of the advertising industry in television
  B a formula for attracting large numbers of viewers
  C the lessons that can be learnt from other media

Vocabulary development 2

Prepositions

1 Complete each sentence with a preposition from the box. There are two prepositions you do not need.

at	back	for	in	into	on	to	towards

1 Most performers thrive _____on_____ positive recognition but react badly to negative criticism.
2 The organisers were hard-pressed _____for_____ new ideas for evening entertainment, so when I suggested a classical evening at a club, they thought it was great!
3 A professional pianist, Boris really enjoyed getting his teeth _____into_____ challenging pieces by Bartok or Shostakovich.
4 Why is it that the older generation always hark _____back_____ to the good old days of the 60s and 70s music scene?
5 As part of the breakdancing team, we spent months working _____towards_____ a common goal.
6 Sally took _____to_____ her new hobby of amateur theatricals like a duck to water!

Music idioms

2 Complete each sentence with the correct form of an idiom from the box. The meaning is given in brackets at the end of each sentence.

blow your own trumpet	change your tune
go for a song	play it by ear	pull out all the stops
ring a bell		

1 Someone said he was a well-known actor but his name doesn't _ring a bell_ . (= sound familiar)
2 That acrobatic display was fantastic! They certainly _pulled out all the stops_ (= tried their very best)
3 Leila spent the whole meeting _blowing her own trumpet_ instead of listening to other people's opinions! (= talking about her own achievements)
4 Their old gymnastic equipment _went for a song_ on a well-known online auction site. (= was sold very cheaply)
5 Phil insisted that he loathed any form of dance but after seeing the Cuban dancers performing live, he quickly _changed his tune_. (= expressed a different opinion)
6 I'm not sure exactly what I'm going to say to Lisa about her performance but I'll _play it by ear_ and see how she reacts. (= see how a situation develops before deciding what to do)

mediocre /ˌmiːdiˈəʊkə/ a. not very good syn second rate: mediocrity n. [U]

Word formation: nouns and adjectives

rave reviews/ notices/ reports strong praise for a new play, book etc, esp in a newspaper or magazine.

3 Complete each sentence with a suitable word formed from the one given in brackets.

1 In my view, there is no room for _mediocrity_ (mediocre) in the world of the performing arts today. It's a highly _competitive_ (compete) field where a certain amount of _ruthlessness_ (ruthless) is required in order to succeed.
2 Stella's performance really _bowled me over_ tonight! *phr v to surprise, please, or excite some very much* All the various _subtleties_ (subtle) of gesture and mood were evident in her performance and I'd be amazed if she doesn't get _rave reviews_ after all the _setbacks_ (set) she's had to overcome recently.
3 The noise level was _deafening_ (deaf) at the rock concert but everyone seemed to be having a good time.
4 Do you think all performers have two sides to their personality? The ones I know seem to be very _outgoing_ (go) on stage but in real life they have a _tendency_ (tend) to be quite introverted and anti-social!

Collocations

4 Complete the text with words from the box.

bar	come	dabbling	ease	potential
sampling	significant	wider		

MUSIC

Webcasting – the way forward?

Top classical festivals are very expensive and difficult to get into. But now a mouse-click may be all you need.

Europe's elite classical music festivals do not, as a rule, **(1)** _come_ cheap. Many have dizzying ticket prices; some are habitually so over-subscribed that it's nearly impossible to get in even if you can afford it. Now though, you can beat financial pressure by **(2)** _sampling_ such events from the comfort of your home computer: some savvy organisations have set out to reach a **(3)** _wider_ audience for the events via webcasting.

The technology has made **(4)** _significant_ progress since the first opera webcast in 1999. The Berlin Philharmonic's pioneering, year-round Digital Concert Hall has set the **(5)** _bar_ high in terms of standard and many more orchestras and opera houses have since started **(6)** _dabbling_ with online streaming. Festivals are no exception; their webcasts are making rapid gains in both quality and quantity.

For them the advantages of webcasting are obvious. More viewers mean more **(7)** _potential_ attendees, while the **(8)** _ease_ of access dilutes any suggestion of elitism.

novice l'nɔvɪs/ n. [C] 1. Someone who has no experience in a skill, subject, or activity [SYN] beginner:

Reading (Paper 1 Part 7)

Multiple matching

EXPERT STRATEGY

Always read the questions first in this task. You must read the text carefully, but you should do that with the questions already in mind.

1   Read the title of the text and the subtitle and look at the photo. What is your mental image of the group?

2   Read the rubric for the exam task and the questions (1–10). Highlight the key words in each question.

rubric/n. [C] 1. formal a set of instructions or an explanation in a book, examination paper etc.

3   Read through all the sections quickly to get an idea of how the text is structured and in which sections different issues are discussed. What is the main focus of each section?

4a Read Question 1 again. Find the sections of the text that talk about the energy of the performers – look for words and expressions that describe energetic movements. Write the question number in the margin next to these sections so you can find them again quickly.

b   Then read these sections carefully and decide which section matches the exact wording of Question 1.

5   Repeat the procedure for the other questions. Use the Help clues if necessary.

HELP

➤ Q1 There are lots of words describing energetic movements in Section A, but it is not the answer. Which other section talks about *energy*?

➤ Q2 Money is mentioned in Sections A and D, but which one talks about *an initiative*?

➤ Q3 Be careful. The word *novice* occurs in Section A, but this is not the answer. Look for references to somebody being reassured.

➤ Q4 You are looking for one person's opinion, which the writer mentions.

EXPERT LANGUAGE

Look back at Sections A and B. Find words which describe ways of moving in these categories:
a ways of climbing
b ways of jumping
c types of move

EXPERT WORD CHECK

acrobatics contortion confer buckle alight on bough cheesy spine falter verbal

You are going to read an article about a group of circus performers from Africa. For questions **1 – 10**, choose from the sections (**A – D**). The sections may be chosen more than once.

In which section does the writer mention

the performers maintaining a constant level of energy throughout the visit?	1 D
a way of generating income for a related initiative?	2 A
an attempt to give a novice reassurance?	3 B
the unique feature of the group's style of performance?	4 C
a move that is unexpectedly challenging?	5 B
an example of the stamina demanded by a routine?	6 D
a shift away from the conventions of a genre?	7 C
a feeling of relative inadequacy?	8 B
an appreciation of the faith performers have in each other?	9 B
the contrasting pace of elements of the performance?	10 A

6   Find words and expressions in the text that mean:
1 has two roles (Section A) — *doubled as*
2 real practice (Section A) — *hands-on experience*
3 volunteering for something (difficult)(Section A) — *letting myself in for*
4 comes to an end (Section A) — *draws to a close*
5 very weak (Section B) — *incredibly puny*
6 a fresh start (Section C) — *a new lease of life*
7 relaxes (Section D) — *winds down*
8 give up (Section D) — *throw in the towel*

Cirque
Mandingue

A circus troupe from Guinea in West Africa is bringing its meld of acrobatics, contortion and dance to Europe.

A Cirque Mandingue is both a circus school and a touring company; money earned touring helping to fund the training of thirty young performers back in Guinea. Junior Camara, leader of the acrobatics
5 troupe, doubles as the school's director. I've come to meet them and to get hands-on experience of what they do. I'll be learning how to become part of a human pyramid. But first I watch their show to see what I'm letting myself in for. Bantering performers – gymnasts, contortionists
10 and acrobats – crowd the stage, dancing and leaping to the insistent sound of live *djembe* drumming. Scenes move between a blur of frenetic handstands and incredibly fast leaps, with performers flipping themselves on to each other's shoulders, to slower, intricately choreographed contortion
15 routines. As the show draws to a close, it's my turn. As I head backstage, Junior approaches me enthusiastically, 'You've done this before, right?' 'Err no, I haven't.' This prompts some conferring among the team as to what's safe to do with a novice.

20 **B** I'm told to clamber on to the shoulders of a gymnast called François. I've no idea what's about to happen, so there's little choice but to go with it and hope I don't break my neck. I manage to scramble up but then I'm instructed to hold my legs at a right angle and point my toes upwards.
25 This isn't as straightforward as it sounds. My thighs are aching and I'm ready to buckle but more performers are attaching themselves to the chap below me. 'Hurry up!' I yell, 'I can't hold it much longer.' They insist that what we're doing is quite safe but I'm not entirely convinced. I also feel
30 incredibly puny next to the real acrobats, who aren't shy about demonstrating either their physiques or their immense strength. Their training takes years and most of them started young. As I concentrate on staying more or less upright, I realise too that the kind of acrobatics I've watched on stage
35 depend totally on a mix of confidence and trust. To be able to flip so precisely that you land on someone's shoulders as easily as a bird alights on a bough requires fearlessness, true but you also have to know that your partner won't let you down.

40 **C** Regis Truchy, a French clown, performs in and choreographs part of the show and his narrative humorously highlights artistic differences between western and African cultures, particularly in music. Some scenes see Truchy's cheesy western pop pitched against Guinean
45 hip-hop. Truchy, 38, has worked as both a ballet dancer and a figure skater and says Cirque Mandingue has given him a new lease of life. For him, the stand-out element of the show is the way it mixes contortion with dance. Contortion is an ancient practice found across the world
50 and the technique tends to remain very traditional. 'These guys,' says Truchy, 'mix it up a bit.' In the current show, one of the guys mixing it up is Naby, 25, whose feats of contortion make one fear for his spine. He started learning acrobatics when he was ten and, as well as contortion, he
55 dances and plays the *djembe*.

D Aboubacar, 26, also started aged ten, at first learning from friends on the beaches of Conakry. At 15, his hard work paid off when he started working with Junior. He says touring can be hard on artists' families, but, 'It's a chance
60 for me to have a job and make some money for them.' With my attempt to be one of the gang now concluded, the group winds down for dinner. I'd been warned that even when the troupe relaxes, the vibe never falters and sure enough I find myself in the middle of a full-on rap show,
65 Guinean-style; the table shaking as everyone joins in a fast and furious battle of rhythm and rhyming. It's rather like a verbal version of their passionate physical skills. They tell me about a festival where the troupe was joined by some French performers who asked to warm up with them. The
70 group's daily warm-up takes at least two hours and is followed by four hours of practice – acrobatics, contortion, hand-balancing and traditional dancing. Barely an hour into the session exhaustion forced their guests to throw in the towel. Somehow, I'm not surprised.

banter n. [U] friendly conversation in which people make a lot of jokes with, and amusing remarks about, each other.
insistent a. 2 making a continuous pattern of sounds that is difficult to ignore:
frenetic /frɪˈnetɪk/a frenetic activity is fast and not very organized [SYN] frantic;
handstand n. [C] a movement in which you put your hands on the ground and your legs in the air.
Conferring n discussion

Language development 2

> CB p. 18, GR pp.173–174

Future tense review

1 Complete each sentence by choosing the correct option.

1 By this time next week, we _____B_____ filming on location and be back in the studio.
A are finishing   B will have finished
C will be finishing

2 Thanks for your email. I _____A_____ you this afternoon to discuss the matter further.
A will call   B should call
C am calling

3 We've just finished touring with the show in Australia actually and _____B_____ on a new production back in the UK.
A will start   B are about to start
C should start

4 Call whatever time of the day or night you like, Mr Cameron. I _____B_____ to hear from you.
A am going to wait   B will be waiting
C will have waited

5 Let's meet to discuss the best candidate for the leading role at the end of the week. I _____C_____ more of an idea of the person I'm looking for by then.
A 'll be having   B 'm having   C should have

6 I _____B_____ in rehearsals until eight o'clock and then we could grab a bite to eat, if you like.
A 'm due   B 'll be   C 'll have been

7 The director _____A_____ the choreographer at the theatre tomorrow morning at half past nine.
A is meeting   B will have met
C is bound to meet

8 I'm really sorry to hear that you didn't get the part. What _____C_____ now?
A are you doing   B will you have done
C are you going to do

2 Complete each sentence with a preposition from the box. There is one preposition you do not need.

after	by	for	in	of	to	until

1 Study the script well, Gina, and I'll see you _in_ two weeks.

2 We're due to start rehearsals on Monday, so I hope we'll have finished auditioning _by_ then.

3 The sequel is due _~~to~~ for_ release in November of this year.

4 We don't expect Jill to return to the stage _until_ the end of the month.

5 There is now little likelihood _~~for~~ of_ the three-time Oscar winner accepting the role.

6 All those here for the audition are _~~of~~ to_ wait outside until called.

Other forms with future meaning

3 Complete each sentence by circling the correct word or phrase from each pair in italics.

1 Daniel was _(supposed)_ / thought to be performing in Les Misérables this week but he's gone down with the flu.

2 The French director stands / _(is expected)_ to retire from making action movies after finishing his latest film.

3 She was _(due)_ / intended to give a press conference this afternoon but had to cancel it because of poor health.

4 The winner of the talent show is bound / _(set)_ to star in a new stage production of Cabaret.

5 Oliver is due to / _(on the verge of)_ making a deal with Pixar.

6 Given that it has a great cast and spectacular dance sequences, the show is _(bound)_ / about to be a success.

7 I thought I ought to / _(might)_ go for a career in acting when I finish college. What do you think?

8 John's got the looks, the talent and the charisma for show business, so he _(should)_ / may do well in auditions.

4 Complete each sentence with a suitable phrase formed from the word given in brackets. Make any other changes that are necessary.

1 The way the choreographer pushes the dancers, there _is bound to be_ (bound) an accident before long.

2 Cecilia Bartoli _was supposed to be_ (supposed) performing at the Royal Albert Hall this autumn but has unfortunately had to cancel.

3 Diana! I _was about to_ (about) call you! There's been a change of plan and we're not rehearsing the scene in the library today.

4 The singer _was to appear_ (be) appear at the festival this weekend but is suffering from laryngitis.

5 The popular TV series _is set to be_ (set) adapted for the stage.

6 The band's manager _stands to_ (stand) make a lot of money if the record deal goes through.

5 Complete the sentences in your own way, using the correct form of the words in brackets.

1 The whole cast were absolutely outstanding; the film _is bound to be a huge success_ . (bound)

2 Andy looked devastated when he heard he'd been turned down; I thought he _was going to cry_ (going to)

3 It's already twenty past. Where on earth is Johnny? He _should have been_ (be) here by now.

4 Ciaran is a rising star. He _is set to become very famous_ (set)

5 I'm sorry I can't answer your questions; the director _is supposed to be here to answer them himself_ (supposed)

6 I don't think Heather can take any more; she looks as though _she is on the_ . (point)
point of giving up

Use of English (Paper 1 Part 4)

Key word transformations

EXPERT STRATEGY

This task tests your ability to express ideas in different ways, using different structures and syntax, but without changing the meaning. When you've written your answer, check carefully that both sentences have exactly the same meaning.

HELP.

➤ Q1 You need to use the word *time* and the past perfect tense.

➤ Q2 You need a noun that conveys the same idea as 'better'.

➤ Q3 You need to introduce a negative idea here in the first part of the sentence.

➤ Q5 You need to use a collocation which includes the word *difference*.

1 Read the task instructions carefully and look at the example. Think about how the two sentences are different and notice how the meaning has not changed.

2 Now answer Questions 1–10, using the Help clues if necessary.

For questions **1 – 10**, complete the second sentence so that it has a similar meaning to the first sentence, using the word given. **Do not change the word given.** You must use between **three** and **eight** words, including the word given. Here is an example (**0**).

0 Would you mind if I brought a friend to your party?
objection
Would __you have any objection to my bringing__ a friend to your party?

1 Luke had never been invited to a film premiere before.
first
It _was the first time that_ ^Luke had an invitation to a film premiere.

2 Did the cast dance any better in last night's performance?
in
Was _there any improvement_ ^in the cast's dancing in last night's performance?

3 I wasn't at all surprised when I heard that Melanie had got the part in the show.
hear
It came _as no surprise (to me)_ ^to hear that Melanie had got the part in the show.

4 Dario was just about to leave for the theatre when the phone rang.
point
Dario _was on the point of_ ^leaving for the theatre when the phone rang.

5 Camilla doesn't mind whether she dances on stage or in a TV show.
no
It _makes no difference_ ^to Camilla whether she dances on stage or in a TV show.

6 Fiona impressed the director enormously in her first audition.
made
Fiona _made an enormous_ ^impression on the director in her first audition.

7 Finally, Barry concluded that he wasn't very likely to get a job in computer animation.
came
Finally, Barry _came to the conclusion_ ^that he was unlikely to get a job in computer animation.

8 Graham doesn't intend to tolerate any further rudeness from his students.
has
Graham _has no intention_ ^of tolerating any further rudeness from his students.

9 Soap opera fans get very excited at the prospect of a wedding.
great
The prospect of a wedding is a source _of great excitement to_ soap opera fans.

10 Paul's mother finds it hard to accept that her kids are grown up.
terms
Paul's mother has _difficulty coming to terms_ ^with the fact that her kids are grown up.

Writing: essay (Paper 2 Part 1)

➤ **CB** pp. 14 and 20–21, **WR** pp. 192–193

Understanding the writer's viewpoint

> **EXPERT STRATEGY**
>
> Use a variety of verbs and expressions in your summary and try to avoid repetition as far as possible. Make full use of your knowledge of reporting verbs, the passive and verb or noun phrases.

1 Read the task and the two texts below. What opinion is the writer expressing in each text?

> Read the two texts below.
> Write an essay summarising and evaluating the key points from both texts. Use your own words throughout as far as possible and include your own ideas in your answers.
> Write your answer in **240 – 280 words**.
>
> > **1 Comic book movie adaptations**
> > Fundamentally, animation and comics are false siblings. They resemble one another but they're two completely different things. The relationship a reader has with a comic is nothing like the one a viewer has with a film. When you read a comic, you're always active because you have to imagine all the movements that happen between the frames. In a film, you are passive: all the information is there. Granted, cinema and comics both use images. However, in comics, you write with images, something like pictograms. In a movie, you combine those images with movement, sound and music – all those things that are not considerations when making comics.
> >
> > **2 Film versions – to be feared or not?**
> > When it is announced that a much-loved novel is going to be made into a film, ardent admirers of the book become extremely nervous. Who will play their beloved characters? Will the film-makers capture the spirit of the novel? Can the film possibly be as good as the book? But why do people care so much? Of course a film is going to be different to a book – they are entirely different art forms. In film, one of the most powerful and exciting media, special effects and computer-generated imagery can take the printed word to a completely different level. However, your connection to the book is unchanged. The words remain the same.
>
> Write your **essay**.

2a Complete each summary sentence with a word from the box.

accessible	comparisons	connection
demands	enhance	present	similarities

A The writer also implies that modern digital technology can **(1)** _____ a novel and bring other exciting dimensions to it.

B The writer suggests that films made from books are more **(2)** _____ to the general public.

C The writer also points out that there are elements to an animation that are not **(3)** _____ in a comic book, such as music, movement and sound.

D The writer underlines the **(4)** _____ between certain types of books and films.

E The writer emphasises that **(5)** _____ between comic books and animated cartoons should not be drawn since they are very different in the **(6)** _____ they make on the viewer or reader: the reader has to make much more effort than the viewer.

F The writer questions why people get so concerned over film adaptations of books since, whatever the film is like, the reader's **(7)** _____ to the book is not in any way affected.

b Decide which two sentences in Exercise 2a summarise Text 1 and which two sentences summarise Text 2. There are two sentences which are not applicable.

c Underline the different summarising verbs that are used in the sentences, e.g. *implies*, *suggests*.

Formulating your opinion

3 In order to evaluate the texts and give your own ideas on the topics, you need to formulate an opinion. Here are some useful phrases you can use for expressing opinion. Write one or two sentences about Texts 1 and 2, agreeing or disagreeing with what the writer says. Use the phrases below to help you.

as far as I am aware	*I have to say that*
I'm not entirely sure whether I agree with	*in general*
in my experience	*personally speaking*
to a certain extent	*up to a point*

Writing task

4 Now do the task in Exercise 1.

Vocabulary development 1

> **CB** pp. 26–27

Word formation: nouns ending in -ion

1 Complete each sentence with a noun ending in -ion formed from one of the words from the box. Make any other changes that are necessary.

decimate	evaporate	evolve	forest	proliferate
saline				

1 The _____ of the rabbit population in certain areas was largely a result of disease.
2 The process of removing salt from seawater to make it drinkable is called _____ .
3 It is important that policies of _____ are implemented in areas where many trees have been cut down.
4 The theory of _____ is constantly being amended in the light of new discoveries.
5 In the waters of the Caribbean, the _____ of different species of fish of all colours and sizes is a wonder to see.
6 Salt is obtained from seawater through a process of _____ .

Verbs describing sounds

2 Complete the text with words from the box.

claps	crunch	lapping	patter	roar
scrabbling	twittering	whistling		

Sounds of nature

Amidst the noise of today's world, take a few moments to listen to the sounds of nature, whenever you get the chance. Take a walk in the park and listen to the birds (1) _____ in the trees – how many different songs can you hear? Stroll through the forest in the autumn and enjoy the (2) _____ of the dry leaves under your feet. Was that a small creature you could hear (3) _____ in the undergrowth? Or go down to the seashore and listen to the gentle (4) _____ of the waves. Go to sleep at night and hear the distant (5) _____ of the ocean. Enjoy the power of nature in a thunderstorm and relish those huge (6) _____ of thunder, the wind (7) _____ through the trees and the (8) _____ of rain on the windowpane. So many sounds – if we would only listen.

Word formation: adjectives ending in -ic

3 Find adjectives ending in -ic to match the definitions.

1 related to science
2 living in or having to do with the water
3 having disastrous consequences
4 having a connection with the large seas
5 using energy generated by water power
6 very happy and excited about something good
7 possible to achieve
8 relating to a particular country or to the home

Collocations

4 Complete the text with words from the box.

captivity	contact	evolved	forces	grounds
natural	treatment	variety		

Rights for whales and dolphins

Research into the very complex behaviour of cetaceans – whales, dolphins and porpoises – is revealing that these sea mammals are so highly (1) _____ that they deserve special protection. As a result, marine biologists and philosophers have joined (2) _____ to support a controversial declaration of rights for whales and dolphins on the (3) _____ that their astonishing intelligence and emotional empathy puts them on a par with humans. It has been observed, for example, that dolphins and whales are able to learn an amazing (4) _____ of behaviours when they come into (5) _____ with humans.

The declaration of rights for cetaceans states that every individual dolphin, whale and porpoise has the right to life and liberty and that none should be kept in (6) _____ or be subjected to cruel (7) _____ . It calls for the legal protection of their (8) _____ environment and a ban on any activity that disrupts their acoustic communications.

Use of English (Paper 1 Part 1)

Multiple-choice cloze

1 Read the title of the text. How might sugar be used as a fuel?

2 Read the whole text quickly to get the general meaning. Then choose the best option A–D to fit each gap, using the Help clues if necessary. Don't forget that the four options will have a similar meaning, but only one will fit the gap perfectly.

3 Read through the text again when you've finished with your chosen options in place. Does it make complete sense?

EXPERT STRATEGY

Make sure that you read the text before and after each gap, noticing any prepositions or words which might collocate with your answer.

For questions **1 – 8**, read the text below and decide which answer (**A, B, C or D**) best fits each gap. There is an example at the beginning (**0**).

Sugar: the fuel of the future?

Brazil has a good track (0) __A__ in research in many areas of science and technology. It is in the field of bio-energy, however, that the country (1) _____ to make its biggest contribution. Brazil is the world's largest producer of sugar and since 1975 has been fermenting sugar-cane juice into a substance called ethanol, which can be used as motor fuel. For many years, the programme (2) _____ in virtual isolation from the rest of the world, using fairly low-tech methods. Recently, however, the government has been investing (3) _____ in research aimed at improving all stages in the process from sugar-cane biology to engine efficiency.

Whilst the motivation for the investment is largely (4) _____ by energy needs rather than environmental concerns, the fuel's green (5) _____ are now also being emphasised. Net emissions of carbon dioxide from a car (6) _____ on sugar ethanol are just 20 percent of those from a petrol-fuelled vehicle. (7) _____ , the bio-energy programme aims to achieve a significant increase in supply without a corresponding rise in the amount of farmland (8) _____ to sugar cane.

HELP

➤ Q1 Only one of the options can be followed by the infinitive to create the meaning 'has a good chance of succeeding'.

➤ Q2 You are looking for a phrasal verb which means 'continued'.

➤ Q3 Only one of these adverbs collocates with the verb to invest.

➤ Q7 You need a word that indicates addition rather than contrast.

0	A record	B story	C reputation	D success
1	A stands	B sets	C rests	D ranks
2	A took place	B held forth	C carried on	D kept up
3	A highly	B strongly	C vastly	D heavily
4	A driven	B stemming	C drawn	D arising
5	A endorsements	B credentials	C testaments	D referrals
6	A performing	B working	C running	D burning
7	A Nonetheless	B Furthermore	C Otherwise	D Instead
8	A occupied	B applied	C consigned	D devoted

EXPERT LANGUAGE

Look back at the text. Find three compound adjectives in noun phrases.

Language development 1

➤ **CB** p. 29, **GR** pp. 174–175

Passive forms

1 Complete the text with the correct passive form of the verbs in brackets.

Restoring habitats

Plans **(1)** _____ (currently / make) for one hundred of the most endangered habitats in the world **(2)** _____ (restore). They are some of the world's most threatened natural landscapes, which **(3)** _____ (devastate) by decades of pollution and deforestation. Now a major new project is aiming to restore them to their former glory.

In 2012, The Ecological Restoration Alliance, which includes botanic gardens from around the world including China, Brazil, Hawaii, Kenya, Mexico, South Africa and Venezuela, **(4)** _____ (form) in response to a United Nations call to restore at least 15 percent of the world's damaged ecosystems by 2020. Among the landscapes they are hoping to save are the arid huarango woodlands in southern Peru, which **(5)** _____ (almost completely / turn) to desert after **(6)** _____ (cut down) to make way for farm land.

Dr Bruce Pavlik, from the Royal Botanic Gardens in Kew, said, 'One of the main causes of degradation is fragmentation, where agriculture has impinged on an area of forest and it has become isolated. Mining is also a problem as soil **(7)** _____ (often / remove) and the organisms that live in that soil go with it, so restoring that land is difficult.' The scientists will use seed banks like Kew's Millennium Seed Bank, which now has specimens from more than 10 percent of the world's wild plant species, to help replant the habitats. In some cases species from the last remnants of the habitat **(8)** _____ (also / cultivate) and transferred to repopulate the land being restored.

2 Complete each sentence with ONE word.

1 The laws against hunting should _____ enforced more strictly.
2 The scientists were really worried about young chimpanzees _____ taken away from their mothers.
3 _____ been asked to lead the expedition, Dave could hardly say no.
4 All our wildlife generally _____ protecting from those who would wish to destroy it for their own purposes.
5 According to the rules, we weren't _____ to approach the mountain gorillas on our trek in Rwanda, so we watched them from afar.
6 Action could have _____ taken earlier to deal with the illegal poaching in the area.

Impersonal use of the passive

3 Complete each sentence with the correct passive form of the words in brackets.

0 Scientists _are reported to have said_ (report / say) that it will take a hundred years to complete an assessment of the diversity of life on earth.
1 The speaker promised that _____ (something / do) about the dwindling numbers of orangutans, if further financial aid can be procured.
2 During the conference, it _____ (point out) that a lot of valuable conservation projects have been the work of concerned individuals.
3 There _____ (say / be) millions of new species of plants and animals yet to be discovered.
4 Alice _____ (rumour / carry out) research somewhere in the jungles of Borneo at the moment.
5 There _____ (think / be) a lot more seabirds in that area in the past than there actually are now.
6 It would _____ (consider) very foolish to go into the jungle without a guide.
7 For many years, humans _____ (assume / be) the only species to use tools but discovery of tool use by chimpanzees refuted the assumption.
8 In the 80s, it _____ (estimate) that there were 8,000 tigers across Asia but by 2011 that figure was fewer than 4,000, in spite of campaigning by conservationists.

Have / Get something done

4 Complete each sentence with the correct form of *have / get* + past participle. Use the verb you think is most common in each case. In some cases, both verbs may be possible.

1 The local farmers _____ (their fields / sow) with organic crops in recent months.
2 Through his tireless campaigning, the TV celebrity _____ (the fishing quotas / increase), which meant that fishermen didn't have to throw the fish they'd caught back into the sea.
3 The council is planning to _____ (that piece of wasteland / convert) into a communal garden.
4 Due to the potential impact on the neighbouring conservation area, we _____ (currently / the project / manage) by an environmental expert.
5 By next year, they hope that they _____ (their application / approve) by the authorities.
6 My brother and his wife are thinking of _____ (a wind turbine / install) on their land. I wonder how much that will cost?

Use of English (Paper 1 Part 2)

Open cloze

1 Read the title of the text. Why might these two ideas be in opposition?

2 Read the whole text quickly to get the general meaning, then read again carefully. Try and identify any words which might collocate with the missing word. Write one word in each gap. Use the Help clues if necessary.

3 Read through the text again when you've finished with your chosen words in place. Does it make complete sense?

EXPERT STRATEGY

Make sure that you read the text before and after each gap. Think about the structure of the sentences and how the ideas are linked together.

HELP

> Q1 You need a modal verb in this gap. Which one makes sense in this context?

> Q5 Which preposition is needed here?

> Q6 You need a verb that collocates with *pressure*.

> Q8 *By all means* and *by no means* are common fixed phrases. Which makes sense in the context of the whole sentence?

EXPERT LANGUAGE

Look back at the text and find two examples of the passive voice.

For questions **1 – 8**, read the text below and think of the word that best fits each space. Use only one word in each space. There is an example at the beginning (**0**).

Food production vs biodiversity?

A life of poverty and famine is all (**0**) _____TOO_____ common a problem in Africa. For the foreseeable future, it (**1**) _____ seem that agricultural development provides the only means of alleviating the situation and the prospect of agricultural expansion is certainly welcome. (**2**) _____ , however, threats to sustainability (**3**) _____ to be avoided, any such development will need to be carefully managed. For example, although Africa retains much of its biodiversity, agricultural expansion into sensitive areas (**4**) _____ well aggravate declines that are already becoming apparent. Increased agricultural production is needed to feed the world's growing population but brings (**5**) _____ it the risk of knock-on effects, such as an increase in greenhouse gas emissions. Every such increase brings us closer to an ecological crisis point and so (**6**) _____ added pressure on the global life-support systems upon (**7**) _____ agriculture itself depends. Such tensions are, of course, by (**8**) _____ means unique to Africa and new approaches to the problem are clearly needed on a worldwide scale.

4 Write the verb forms of these nouns.
   1 expansion   _____
   2 threat   _____
   3 emission   _____

5 What is the difference in meaning between each pair of words / phrases?
   1 famine / hunger
   2 foreseeable / foreseen
   3 alleviating / aggravating
   4 by no means / not by any means

Listening (Paper 3 Part 4)

Multiple matching

EXPERT STRATEGY

In this task, you are listening for each speaker's main idea – you are not expected to understand every word. Read the two tasks carefully. Make sure you know what you are listening for in each task.

1 Read the instructions for Task One carefully. Think about the vocabulary and expressions you would expect to hear connected with zoos and reasons for visiting them.

2 Read Task Two carefully and highlight the key words in options A–H.

3 Listen to the recording and answer as many questions as possible on both tasks.

4 Listen to the recording again and try to answer the remaining questions. Use the Help clues if necessary.

You will hear five short extracts in which people are talking about visiting a zoo.

Task One

For questions **1 – 5**, choose from the list (**A – H**), what reason each speaker gives for visiting a zoo.

Task Two

For questions **6 – 10**, choose from the list (**A – H**), what made the greatest impression on each speaker during their visit.

While you listen, you must complete both tasks.

Task One		Task Two	
A having guests to entertain		A the lack of space	
B an unexpected gift		B the behaviour of other visitors	
C positive reports in the media	Speaker 1 [1]	C the educational resources	Speaker 1 [6]
D a wish to see rare animals	Speaker 2 [2]	D the condition of the animals	Speaker 2 [7]
E a desire to enter into debate	Speaker 3 [3]	E the research facilities	Speaker 3 [8]
F an official invitation	Speaker 4 [4]	F the attitude of the staff	Speaker 4 [9]
G wanting to appear open-minded	Speaker 5 [5]	G the design of the enclosures	Speaker 5 [10]
H a commitment to certain issues		H the interaction between animals and humans	

HELP

➤ Q1 The speaker says he received something *out of the blue*. Which option contains a word that matches the meaning of this expression?

➤ Q3 Which option matches the idea of *a letter … formally asking us*?

➤ Q6 Listen for the phrase *what really struck me*. The answer follows this.

➤ Q7 The speaker mentions *tiny cages, the information for visitors* and *families on day trips*. Which of these things really surprised her?

➤ Q8 Be careful – the speaker uses the word *behave* but Option B is not the answer.

5 Match the expressions from the recordings (1–10) with their definitions (A–J).

1 steer clear of (Speaker 1)
2 have a soft spot for (Speaker 2)
3 stumble across (Speaker 2)
4 be anathema to me (Speaker 3)
5 leave a bit to be desired (Speaker 3)
6 bridle (Speaker 4)
7 be blown away by (Speaker 4)
8 eat my words (Speaker 4)
9 grant you (Speaker 5)
10 take issue with (Speaker 5)

A feel fond of
B feel completely against an idea
C take offence
D take back a negative comment
E be very impressed by
F acknowledge another view
G avoid
H find by chance
I not as good as it should be
J disagree with a point of view

Reading (Paper 1 Part 5)

Multiple choice

EXPERT STRATEGY

For this task, you need to read each section of text carefully and answer the corresponding question. You have to make sure you choose the option which answers the question by reflecting the exact meaning of the text.

HELP

➤ Q2 Look at the phrase *quite disproportionate significance* – the answer follows this.

➤ Q3 *Galling* is another way of saying 'irritating'. Read the section around the word to find out what the writer found most *galling*.

➤ Q6 Remember to read the whole text. Underline the parts that seem to show the writer's attitude. Which of the options does her attitude seem closest to?

EXPERT LANGUAGE

Look back at the text and questions and find:

a four adjectives ending in *-ic*

b eight nouns ending in *-ion*.

EXPERT WORD CHECK

devil-may-care festering rancid busted bolshy po-faced paranoia wind up pipe up cut (me) dead

1 Read the title of the text. What do you think it is going to be about? Can you predict the writer's attitude to the topic?

2 How many different words can you find that express the idea of 'rubbish'. Why have different words been used?

3 Now read Question 1. Read the text carefully to find the section which contains the answer. Then find the option which is closest in meaning to your selection.

4 Repeat the procedure for the rest of the questions. Use the Help clues if necessary.

You are going to read an article about recycling household rubbish. For questions **1 – 6**, choose the answer (**A, B, C** or **D**) which you think fits best according to the text.

1 The writer says that visitors to New York often gain the erroneous impression that
  A it takes refuse collection more seriously than other cities.
  B its refuse collection policies aren't implemented rigorously.
  C its citizens fail to comply with its refuse collection regulations.
  D it smells of rubbish despite having a highly effective refuse collection system.

2 In the second paragraph, the writer is emphasising
  A the shortcomings of the arrangements at her own accommodation.
  B the impact that rubbish collections have on the rest of her life.
  C the need to develop strategies to get round the system.
  D the inconvenience of the timing of rubbish collections.

3 What did the writer find particularly irritating about the fines she received?
  A the amount which was levied
  B the way she was informed of them
  C the triviality of some of the offences
  D the reaction of her neighbours to them

4 On hearing about how her infringements of the rules had been uncovered, the writer
  A realised she had no choice but to comply in future.
  B resolved to avoid putting certain items into her rubbish.
  C became worried about what else her garbage revealed.
  D decided to pay more attention to the detailed instructions.

5 In the final paragraph, the writer admits to being most resentful of
  A the attitude of her fellow citizens towards recycling.
  B the public money that is wasted on recycling projects.
  C the attempts of her neighbours to advise her about recycling.
  D the fact that recycling schemes do not always achieve their aims.

6 In the text as a whole, the writer's tone is
  A politely tentative.
  B righteously indignant.
  C light-hearted and ironic.
  D restrained and reasonable.

The whole rotten business of rubbish

Visitors to New York are often shocked when they first encounter its powerful summertime stink of rotting garbage. Breathing in the miasmic odours and observing the mountainous piles of refuse that line the streets each night, newcomers are apt to reach the conclusion that New York is rather relaxed and devil-may-care about matters of refuse and refuse collection. But nothing could be further from the truth. The city may look and smell like a compost heap a lot of the time, but it is home to some of the most draconian garbage rules and regulations known to modern man.

Every neighbourhood in New York has three designated garbage pick-up days a week and residents are allowed to put their refuse out no earlier than 5p.m. on the eve of each pick-up day. If you live in a smaller apartment building with no garbage storage in the basement, your pick-up days take on quite disproportionate significance. Miss a day, and you have to live with your festering garbage bags in your apartment until the next scheduled pick-up. Once or twice, over the years, I have become so desperate to get rid of some rancid piece of chicken, or left-over Indian take-away, that I have crept out under cover of night and illicitly dumped the bags in another neighbourhood where pick-up was due the next morning.

Then there are the elaborate and fiercely policed recycling protocols. Plastic and glass and metal go in a blue bag, paper and cardboard in a transparent bag, and everything else in a black bag. Black bags can go out on any of the three days, but the recyclables can only be put out on Friday. Failure to observe these – and a whole raft of infinitely more subtle particulars – results in heavy fines. When I first moved to the city, and had not yet been initiated into the mysteries of the garbage laws, I was constantly being busted for improperly wrapped or sorted refuse. And as if that wasn't sufficiently galling in itself, the fines were then issued to my building superintendent, who would then post them on my front door, like a plague sign, for all my neighbours to see. Once or twice a month, I would return home to find a gnomic account of my latest infraction – 'Two bottles found in black bag' or 'Newspapers improperly tied' – together with a demand for a hundred bucks.

One day, in a bolshy mood, I asked the superintendent how the garbage police could be so sure that the delinquent bottles and inadequately tied newspapers were mine and not someone else's. He trudged down to the basement and came back brandishing an empty bottle of prescription drugs with my name on it. 'They found this in the bag,' he said. Knowing that one's garbage stands a strong chance of being gone through, piece by piece, by a po-faced enforcement agent does tend to encourage compliance. It also produces a certain amount of paranoia. Over the past 17 years, I have spent more time than I am happy to admit standing over my recycling bins, cutting up receipts and scribbling over labels to obscure evidence of my dodgier self-medication habits and lingerie purchases.

I deeply resent all this. It's not just that the economics of the city's recycling are highly questionable – which they are – or even that an estimated 40 percent of New York's recyclable stuff winds up in landfills, anyway – which it does: there's something maddening about the elevated status that recycling enjoys – as if it were an absolute good. To question its worthiness is to put yourself beyond the pale of common civic values. One recent Friday night, as my children and I were hauling garbage bags down to the street, we met a neighbour in the elevator. Observing my untidy bag of unflattened cardboard boxes, he offered to give me some packing tips. 'We do all our sorting and packing as a family on Thursday nights. It's kind of fun and the kids love it.' I smiled and nodded. 'Mom thinks recycling is crap,' my daughter piped up. 'She wishes we could go back to landfills.' The neighbour's eyes grew watery with anguish, or perhaps suppressed rage. 'Well, I'm sorry she feels that way,' he murmured. He has cut me dead ever since.

Vocabulary development 2

Synonyms and antonyms

1 Complete each sentence with the antonym of a word from the box.

*detrimental   far-sighted   inferior   intellectual
permanent   straightforward*

1 Any sort of work is tiring but _____ work is physically exhausting.
2 The meat we bought from the local farmer was definitely _____ to what I usually buy from the supermarket.
3 When we're dealing with the environment, the last thing we need is _____ policies that only focus on the immediate problem.
4 The ideal solution is one that is _____ to both the producers of foodstuffs and the consumer.
5 We agreed to give _____ shelter to some hens that were going to be re-homed, but we had no space to keep them, unfortunately.
6 The procedure involved in the manufacture of recycled garments is actually quite _____.

Binomials (word pairs)

2 Match the beginnings of the word pairs (1–10) with their endings (a–j).

1 by and _____	a breadth
2 hard and _____	b cons
3 ins and _____	c fast
4 length and _____	d fro
5 peace and _____	e joy
6 pride and _____	f large
7 pros and _____	g outs
8 safe and _____	h quiet
9 sick and _____	i sound
10 to and _____	j tired

3 Complete the text with word pairs from Exercise 2.

1 There are many _____ to keeping livestock but _____ I'm in favour! Of course some days I get _____ of cleaning them out and getting up at the crack of dawn to feed them. However, there's nothing to compare with the _____ of the countryside.
2 The other day, a horse we had on our smallholding went missing! Panic! He must have jumped over the fence – but the problem was we lived near a main road. It was a disaster waiting to happen. The horse was our _____ , since he'd won several show-jumping cups. Having searched the _____ of the fields around the farm, we set off in the car to look for him. Fortunately, after five minutes we found him _____ , quietly grazing by the side of the road. Obviously, the grass looked greener to him there!

Ways of walking

4 Think of a verb to fit each definition and situation described.

1 to walk proudly in a way that shows you think you are important; male peacocks do this when they open their tail feathers to impress a female
2 to roll around in mud, water, etc.; hippos do this to keep cool
3 to walk through deep water; people may do this to cross a river
4 to follow a person or animal quietly in order to attack them; cats do this when they try to catch birds

Adjectives and adverbs

5 Complete the text with an adjective or adverb from the box.

*absent   acutely   apparently   asymmetric   confined
faint   general   magnetic   precisely   remotely
truly   visible*

Sense and sensibility – according to birds!

You think you know the world, at least the **(1)** _____ shape of it, the way it works, yet sometimes you are struck by just how far you are from **(2)** _____ comprehending it in all its glorious peculiarity. For example, have you ever **(3)** _____ considered that above the surface of the ocean might be drifting immense blocks or plumes of smells appearing and disappearing like mists? The **(4)** _____ empty marine vastness, which seems so featureless, is not really featureless at all – if you can sniff your way around it.

Seabirds such as petrels and albatrosses, whose sense of smell is **(5)** _____ sensitive, can pick up **(6)** _____ odours such as that of a chemical given off by plankton; and following them upwind, they can find food supplies, or they can even find their way home, sometimes over thousands of miles of empty water. Smell is a key feature of their lives. Yet fifty years ago, most scientists thought that a sense of smell was **(7)** _____ or minimal in nearly all birds.

It has also become clear that another way birds navigate is by sensing the earth's **(8)** _____ field; and they also orientate themselves by using the sun in the day and the stars at night. Some birds are even capable of flying around inside **(9)** _____ spaces in pitch blackness by using echolocation – giving off sounds and picking up their echoes, just as bats do.

But even the more familiar senses can be developed in birds to levels far beyond what humans are capable of. Shrikes, which are small predators, can see larger predators such as falcons miles away, before they are at all **(10)** _____ to the human eye. The great grey owl of the Far North can detect scurrying mice and voles under several inches of snow by using its **(11)** _____ ears – one sited at two o'clock on its head, the other at seven o'clock – which pinpoint **(12)** _____ the direction the sound is coming from.

Language development 2

➤ **CB** p. 34, **GR** p. 175

Verb phrases

1 Complete each pair of sentences with a different form of the same verb.

1 a Could you please _____ me up-to-date with the most recent research findings in this area?

  b The sight of the baby animal without its mother _____ tears to my eyes.

2 a The actor was such a formidable opponent of animal testing in the cosmetics industry that the management knew they had _____ their match.

  b Do you think the Save Energy campaign will _____ its objectives?

3 a I'm afraid that Sam's recent accident has _____ paid to his idea of going to work in Africa.

  b By next month we'll be _____ our new plan into action.

4 a Conservationists nowadays _____ a lot of importance on the protection of endangered wildlife.

  b The school has recently _____ an order for two new recycling bins.

5 a If you run a business, it makes sense to _____ your stationery in bulk to secure a discount.

  b We _____ ourselves more time to reach an agreement by requesting further information.

6 a Ben and Hilary _____ exception to the fact that the chickens from next door were getting into their garden!

  b When is the farm open day _____ place? Is it next Sunday?

Collocations

2 Complete each sentence by circling the correct word from each pair in italics.

1 Our dog seemed to be feeling lonely so we bought another one to *keep / make* her company.

2 The local wildlife protection society thanked all its members for *making / lending* their support to their latest public awareness campaign.

3 Have you *given / taken* into consideration how much it costs to feed your animals over a year? Do you think you will be able to *do / make* a profit in the end?

4 Certainly, the government is *making / taking* steps to improve the situation.

5 I'm trying to *take / get* hold of a really good pair of second-hand binoculars. Maybe I'll try on eBay.

6 How much time will it *take / do* to get approval to buy that piece of land?

Prepositional phrases

3 Complete each sentence with a suitable preposition.

1 _____ all likelihood, they'll be opening a new recycling plant fairly soon.

2 I was proud to be invited to give a talk about my conservation work and I accepted _____ pleasure!

3 _____ occasion, they have seen seals in the sea near their holiday cottage.

4 We were asked to take in our friends' pets _____ short notice so it was difficult to refuse.

5 Are any particular species _____ decline in your country?

6 Jack has been banned from gardening after digging up his mother's favourite dahlia _____ accident!

7 _____ the strength of her qualifications in environmental studies, Lucy was accepted onto the research team.

8 If you're feeling _____ the end of your tether and you can't take the stresses and strains any longer, go and have a walk by the sea – it works wonders!

Phrases with *have*, *do* and *give*

4 Complete each sentence with a word from the box. Then underline the verb phrases.

conscience consequences doubts harm impression opinion priority scruples thought without wonders

1 I really have grave _____ about Simon's capacity to get this job done properly.

2 Many scientists agree that pesticides and other chemicals do significant _____ to the environment as well as having serious _____ for our health.

3 To be honest, if a person gives _____ to the welfare of other living creatures, then they can have a clear _____ .

4 If we give some _____ to our modern way of life, it seems that most people would find it difficult to do _____ certain luxuries.

5 It was interesting to listen to someone like Harry, who has an informed _____ on the question of renewable energy sources.

6 They say that talking to flowers does _____ for their rate of growth!

7 I don't want to give people the _____ that I'm only interested in making money.

8 Poachers have no _____ about killing animals in danger of extinction in order to make money from their tusks or skins.

Use of English (Paper 1 Part 3)

Word formation

EXPERT STRATEGY

This task tests your knowledge of how vocabulary is used in context, including prefixes, suffixes and compound words. You must also know the spelling rules which apply when building new words.

HELP

➤ **Q1** You need to add a prefix here to form a word that together with the preposition *for* means 'gives an explanation'.

➤ **Q3** How do you make this kind of verb into an adjective?

➤ **Q6** You need to make a compound verb here by adding a prefix before *light*.

➤ **Q7** Read the whole sentence carefully to see whether a positive or negative prefix is needed here.

EXPERT LANGUAGE

Look back at the text. Find set phrases which include prepositions.

1 Read the title of the text. What can you guess about orangutans from this?

2 Read the text quickly to get the general meaning.

3 Read it again carefully and complete the gaps, using the Help clues if necessary. The words you create must fit the grammar of the sentence in terms of tense, pluralisation, etc.

4 Read through the text again when you've finished with your chosen words in place. Does it make complete sense?

For questions **1 – 8**, read the text below. Use the word given in capitals at the end of some of the lines to form a word that fits the space in the same line. There is an example at the beginning **(0)**.

The last orangutans

The orangutan is our closest living **(0)** _RELATIVE_ among the animal species. There is just a two percent difference in our DNA and this perhaps **(1)** _____ for the number of tourists flocking to the rainforests of south-east Asia in the hope of seeing the creatures in close proximity. Just glimpsing one is an **(2)** _____ experience. With logging and oil-palm production destroying their precious habitat at an ever **(3)** _____ pace, the animal is on the brink of extinction. Mass tourism itself must take part of the blame for the creature's demise, but for anyone determined to see one, a **(4)** _____ centre offers the chance to do so in a regulated environment. The recent discovery of a new population of orangutans in a largely **(5)** _____ area of Borneo is a bit of positive news in an otherwise bleak situation. A team of conservationists has **(6)** _____ the need to protect the group, both by **(7)** _____ unwanted tourists, and by ensuring the remote region remains **(8)** _____ by the sort of development that has done so much damage elsewhere.

RELATE

COUNT

FORGET

QUICKEN

REHABILITATE

ACCESS

LIGHT
COURAGE
TOUCH

5 Find words and expressions in the text that mean:

1 going in great numbers _____
2 up close, nearby _____
3 catching sight of _____
4 almost, nearly _____
5 the end (of something) _____
6 without much hope _____

Writing: article (Paper 2 Part 2)

➤ **CB** pp. 30 and 36–37, **WR** pp. 196–197

> **EXPERT STRATEGY**
> Remember to address all of the points mentioned in the exam task and do so in the most interesting and imaginative way possible. Put yourself in the position of the reader – would you want to read what you have written?

Analysing the task

1 Read the exam task below and think about the following questions.

a Who is your target reader?

b What register will you use?

c What does your article need to include?

d How will you make it interesting?

e What type of language will you use?

> A local English-language entertainment magazine has requested articles about events of interest that have taken place in your area recently. You have decided to write about a one-day event organised by a local college, which was part of a public campaign to raise awareness of environmental issues. The article should include an outline of the activities that were available at the event and an assessment of how successful the event was.
>
> Write your answer in **280 – 320 words**.

Developing ideas

2 Brainstorm ideas for the task. Which of the following activities would you like to include in your article?

Illustrated talks / demonstrations

Recycling ☐

Deforestation ☐

Sustainable energy ☐

Endangered species ☐

Pollution ☐

Practical workshops

Eco-farming/organic farming ☐

Bee-keeping ☐

Wood carving using recycled wood ☐

Tree-planting ☐

Green household products ☐

Other? ☐

Planning your answer

3 Organise your ideas and write a short plan.

Features of good writing

4 Read the paragraph below, which is taken from the main body of an article written for this task. Did you find the extract interesting to read? Why/Why not?

> Coming from one corner of the college grounds could be heard a variety of loud noises: squawks, screeches and other animal noises. Intrigued, I made my way across the beautifully-kept college lawns. Indeed, there on its perch, was a lovely brightly-coloured parrot which was attracting a lot of attention from the younger members of the public. The thought did cross my mind as to why these birds were ostensibly here in captivity and not being allowed to fly around freely in their native habitat but the people in charge hastened to explain that the birds were on loan from a local bird sanctuary where they were kept in conditions similar to their normal surroundings. In combination with the bird attraction, leaflets were being handed out outlining how the parrots' habitat is endangered and how members of the public can get involved in conservation projects. It was all fascinating and well-researched. I couldn't fault it.

5 Find examples of the following features in the paragraph in Exercise 4.
  • **Vocabulary:** use of precise descriptive vocabulary, interesting verb phrases, phrasal verbs, collocations, appropriate topic vocabulary, good use of advanced adjectives and adverbs
  • **Grammar:** use of the passive, appropriate tenses
  • **Register:** formal
  • **Sentence structure:** complex, varied

Writing task

6 Now do the task in Exercise 1.

3 Surviving and thriving

3A | Who's in control?

Vocabulary development 1

> **CB** pp. 42–43

Word formation: prefixes

1 Complete each sentence with the correct form of a word from the box. You must add the correct prefix to each word.

approval   conceptions   confrontational   decision
logical   personal   respective   understanding

1 _____ of how he or she feels, a psychiatrist needs to show a calm exterior at all times.
2 When faced with a conflict, starting a sentence with 'I' rather than 'you' is a _____ way to express what you want without criticising the other person.
3 Sophie wasted a lot of time because of her chronic _____ over matters of importance.
4 I hope you don't have any _____ about the nature of the job – you will find it extremely demanding.
5 Since much of a doctor's role involves interacting with others, they must have strong _____ skills and be effective communicators.
6 There was a _____ amongst the staff and Ben found himself having to explain the situation to the boss.
7 Do you find his argument _____ ? There's a flaw in it somewhere, but I can't put my finger on it.
8 Dan was determined to become an actor despite his parents' _____ of his chosen career.

Word formation: noun suffixes

2 Complete each sentence with a suitable noun formed from the word given in brackets.

1 George made quite clear his _____ (satisfy) with the way he had been treated. He felt that his _____ (accomplish) and his _____ (qualify) should be more highly regarded.
2 In their letter to me, they expressed their _____ (appreciate) for my _____ (thoughtful) and _____ (consider) during their stay.
3 It's difficult to find any _____ (justify) for Imogen's unreasonable behaviour.
4 Giving personal advice to others can sometimes be seen as an _____ (intrude), so it's just as well to tread carefully.

3 Add prefixes to these words to give them the opposite meaning.

belief   comprehensible   literate   rational   respect
secure   stable   verbal

Words connected with psychology

4 Complete the text with words from the box. There are two extra words you do not need.

analytical   control   dysfunctional   insights
intention   interact   make-up   manifest   modify
mutually   precursor   premise   rationalise
revert   stance   unconsciously

Transactional analysis (P) (A) (C)

Courses in assertiveness training very often include an analysis of people's psychological **(1)** _____ , since this is seen as a necessary **(2)** _____ to any attempt to **(3)** _____ set patterns of behaviour. Transactional analysis is one method that attempts to provide **(4)** _____ into the way people act and **(5)** _____ with each other.
Transactional analysis is based on the **(6)** _____ that human beings move, usually **(7)** _____ , through three different ego states: Child, Parent and Adult. When in the Child state, people react emotionally to events and are unable to **(8)** _____ or stand back from a given situation. In the Parent mode, people will **(9)** _____ to an authoritarian **(10)** _____ observed in a parent figure during their childhood and this may well **(11)** _____ itself through a tendency to **(12)** _____ others. Finally, the Adult ego state, as might be expected, is one where the mode of behaviour is more **(13)** _____ . Transactional analysis aims to bring about improvement in **(14)** _____ behaviour by raising awareness of the psychological forces that are at work within us from our childhood years. Once that is achieved, methods of being assertive without being aggressive can be learnt.

Use of English (Paper 1 Part 1)

Multiple-choice cloze

EXPERT STRATEGY
Read through the text again when you've finished with your chosen options in place to make sure it makes complete sense.

1 Read the title of the text. What is *status* and why do people worry about it?

2 Read the whole text quickly to get the general meaning, and then read again carefully and choose the best word to fit each gap.

For questions **1 – 8**, read the text below and decide which answer (**A**, **B**, **C** or **D**) best fits each gap. There is an example at the beginning (**0**).

Should we worry about status?

In recent decades, there has been (0) __A__ evidence that an individual's well-being is significantly affected by that person's place in the social pecking (1) _____ . In other words, given that the world is (2) _____ up of winners and losers, counting ourselves amongst the latter can open up an uncomfortable gap between the way things are and the way we'd like them to be. Frequently, we think the solution (3) _____ in achieving more: if we managed to (4) _____ a better salary, house, body or whatever, we'd be able to drop the competing game and feel contented. But this (5) _____ risks landing us on a treadmill from which it is impossible to step off. There will always be people who, to our (6) _____ , have achieved more than us and we'd constantly be running to try and catch up with them. (7) _____ of slavishly following our instincts, however, we would do better to use our (8) _____ for reflection to help us decide for ourselves what gives meaning to our life and is therefore worth doing.

HELP

➤ Q1 Only one of the options collocates with *pecking* to form a common collocation.

➤ Q5 You are looking for the word that means 'way of doing things to achieve a goal'.

➤ Q7 You are looking for the linker that makes a contrast.

➤ Q8 Only one of the options can be followed by *for*.

EXPERT LANGUAGE
Look back at the text. Find three phrasal verbs.

0	A mounting	B rising	C piling	D building
1	A structure	B layer	C strata	D order
2	A comprised	B made	C composed	D done
3	A lies	B stays	C abides	D sits
4	A secure	B confirm	C effect	D fulfil
5	A policy	B device	C strategy	D scheme
6	A opinion	B view	C mind	D belief
7	A ahead	B In spite	C By means	D Instead
8	A competence	B capacity	C ability	D expertise

3 Find words and expressions in the text that mean:

1 good health and happiness _____
2 last mentioned of two things _____
3 lifestyle characterised by routine _____

4 Which prepositions follow each of the options in Question 8?

Language development 1

> CB p. 45, GR p. 176

Conditionals

1 Finish each sentence by choosing the correct option or options.

1 I wouldn't have spoken to him …
   a if I hadn't wanted to.
   b if he wanted to.
   c if it hadn't been for you.
2 If she wasn't such a good friend, …
   a she wouldn't have tried to make me look stupid.
   b I'd say she was being rather stupid.
   c I'd think she was trying to make me look stupid.
3 If I were in your shoes, …
   a I'd have said something by now.
   b I'm going to say something.
   c I'll say something.
4 The conference wouldn't have been a success …
   a if he hadn't contributed.
   b if his contribution was better.
   c but for his brilliant contribution.
5 If you aren't feeling strong, …
   a you aren't arguing.
   b it's best to avoid any arguments.
   c don't get into any arguments.
6 I might have been able to hear better …
   a had there been less noise.
   b if there hadn't been so much noise.
   c should there be less noise.

2 Complete the text by circling the correct word or phrase from each pair in italics.

 Are you in need of an energy boost?

Sometimes you may feel as if you're dragging yourself around, without much enthusiasm for anything. So what steps can you take **(1)** *unless / if* this is the case? Firstly, let go of any negative thoughts about the past. It **(2)** *would / will* be a pity if you **(3)** *were / would* be weighed down by past mistakes. Your energy levels will increase by leaps and bounds **(4)** *unless / without* all those negative and useless thoughts that prevent you from being true to yourself. Secondly, are you involved in something you don't really enjoy? **(5)** *If so / In case*, get out of it as fast as you can! And **(6)** *what / how* if your friends don't really appreciate you? Join in new activities and meet new people – no one wants to be around energy 'vampires', **(7)** *assuming / whether* or not they're your so-called friends! Finally, **(8)** *were / should* you ever find yourself getting too busy, slow down. Listen to your inner voice, your intuition – that's where the wisdom and the energy lie.

3 Complete the dialogue with suitable words or phrases.

Trish: So what would you say are the most important qualities for creating and maintaining good friendships, Gaby? It's not the easiest thing to do nowadays when we're all so busy!

Gaby: I agree! Well firstly, I think you need to show a true interest in your friends. If absolutely **(1)** _____ , set aside an hour a week when you make contact with them or do something special for them. **(2)** _____ if that sounds silly, it actually ensures that you will think of your friends regularly!

Trish: If I had to choose one quality of friendship, it **(3)** _____ be loyalty, I think. I just can't stand it when so-called friends talk about you behind your back to other people.

Gaby: Absolutely! There's nothing worse! And something else – I must say that if I can't have a good laugh with a friend, then in a way, I **(4)** _____ really make the effort to see that person so much the next time the opportunity arises. It sounds bad but I think you need your friends to be positive, don't you?

Trish: Yes, I think so. Of course, it goes without saying that if your friend **(5)** _____ to ask for your advice when they're in a difficult situation, you're not going to tell him or her simply to cheer up and be happy!

Gaby: Sure. Well, we probably **(6)** _____ be such good friends if we **(7)** _____ shared some difficult times together.

Trish: I think you're right there, Gaby.

Alternatives to *if*

4 Complete each second sentence with ONE word so that it means the same as the first sentence.

1 Tim would never have been so successful if Kelly hadn't given him so much help.
   Tim would never have been so successful _____ Kelly's help.
2 Even if you don't believe me, take my advice and get out of that relationship fast!
   Take my advice and get out of that relationship fast, _____ or not you believe me.
3 I would never have heard about him if my brother hadn't told me.
   Were it _____ for my brother I would never have heard about him.
4 Madge says she'll only go to see the counsellor if you go with her.
   Madge says she won't go to see the counsellor _____ you go with her.

Use of English (Paper 1 Part 3)

Word formation

1 Read the title of the text. What do you think it is going to be about?

2 Read the whole text quickly to get the general meaning, ignoring the gaps for the moment.

3 Read the text again carefully and think about the type of word that will fit in each gap.

4 Complete the gaps, looking carefully at the whole sentence that contains the gap. Use the Help clues if necessary.

5 Read through the text again when you've finished with your chosen words in place. Does it make complete sense?

HELP
- ➤ Q1 Change this noun into an adjective and then into an adverb.
- ➤ Q5 You are looking for a plural noun here.
- ➤ Q6 Change this verb into a noun.
- ➤ Q8 Add a prefix to create a word meaning 'to emphasise'.

EXPERT LANGUAGE

Look back at the text. Find two nouns that have the suffix -ing.

For questions **1 – 8**, read the text below. Use the word given in capitals at the end of some of the lines to form a word that fits the space in the same line. There is an example at the beginning (**0**).

The stress-busting gene

It seems an (0) <u>INESCAPABLE</u> fact of life that some people are much better than others at dealing with stress. This ability has long been linked with personal qualities like optimism and, more (1) <u>Controversially</u> with high levels of self-esteem. Although such (2) <u>Psychological</u> resources are known to run in families, their genetic basis <u>remained obscure</u> until 2011. That's when (3) <u>researchers</u> at the University of California announced they had identified a gene that influences self-esteem. This gene is found in a hormone that plays a role in behaviours including social (4) <u>recognition</u> and bonding, as well as aggression. At a particular location in its DNA sequence, the gene can have various (5) <u>characteristics</u> and people carrying what is called the 'A variant' report lower levels of self-esteem, whilst having a greater (6) <u>tendency</u> to report depressive symptoms than those carrying the so-called 'G variant'. It is now thought that genetic influences account for between 30 and 50 percent of individual differences in self-esteem. Although it will (7) <u>doubtlessly</u> ^{undoubtedly} also be affected by other genes, the finding (8) <u>underline</u> the importance of biology in human psychology.

ESCAPE

CONTROVERSY

PSYCHOLOGY

RESEARCH

RECOGNISE

CHARACTER

TEND

DOUBT
LINE

6 Find words and expressions in the text that mean:
  1 a positive outlook   _____
  2 a good opinion of yourself _____
  3 be hereditary   _____
  4 forming a close relationship _____
  5 a slightly different version _____
  6 these indicate an illness   _____

Listening (Paper 3 Part 2)

Sentence completion

EXPERT STRATEGY

Although you won't hear exactly the same words as you can see in the list of statements, the actual word or phrase you need to complete the gap will be exactly as it is heard in the recording. The statements follow the same order as the information in the recording. Your answers need to fit into the sentences grammatically, and be spelled correctly.

HELP

➤ Q2 Be careful. Two words are used which could describe states of this type – only one of them describes Amy.

➤ Q4 Listen for a word that indicates that Amy is surprised.

➤ Q7 You are listening for two words – but *emotions* isn't one of them.

➤ Q8 Be careful – is the answer a noun or an adjective?

➤ Q9 The speaker lists three emotions, but only one of them is linked to poor performance.

EXPERT LANGUAGE

Look back at the statements in this task. Find two words with negative prefixes.

EXPERT WORD CHECK

hectic   nurture   millet   porridge
utmost   fatigue   erratic   incense
pondered   plumped   drift off

1   Read the instructions for the exam task.

a   Who is going to be speaking?

b   What will that person be talking about?

2   Read the sentences. How much do you find out from the sentences about the topic of the listening?

3   Try and predict the missing words which you have to find. For example:

a   Which answers are likely to be nouns?

b   Which answers are likely to be adjectives?

c   Which answer is likely to be plural?

4   Listen to the recording and complete the sentences. Use the Help clues if necessary.

You will hear a journalist called Amy Freville talking about her trip to a centre for ayurvedic treatments. For questions **1 – 9**, complete the sentences with a word or short phrase.

Ayurvedic treatments

Amy says that the atmosphere at the centre where she stayed was similar to that of a **(1)** _____ .

Amy uses the word **(2)** _____ to describe her physical and mental state before going to the centre.

Amy uses the English word **(3)** _____ to give us an idea of what 'doshas' are.

Amy was surprised to be asked about her **(4)** _____ in a questionnaire.

Amy would define herself as a **(5)** _____ sleeper by nature.

Amy was pleased to hear that her diet would feature **(6)** _____ tasting foods as well as sweet things.

Amy gives **(7)** _____ as an example of emotional imbalance caused by an inappropriate diet.

When asked, Amy named **(8)** _____ as the negative emotion that she would most like to eradicate.

Amy denies experiencing feelings of **(9)** _____ during the guided yoga sessions with her therapist.

Vocabulary development 2

Words connected with emotions

1 Complete each sentence by circling the correct word from each pair in italics.

1 Andy was feeling tired and *cranky / mellow*, and snapped at Kate when she asked him what he'd like for dinner.

2 Paula felt increasingly *moody / restless* and, unable to sit still, she got up and started pacing the room.

3 Harry gave a *bitter / wistful* look at his old school as he drove past, suddenly missing his happy days there.

4 Jane was *resentful / thoughtful* of her new roommate, who seemed to be so popular with everyone in the college, while Jane went about largely unnoticed.

5 Jill looked down at Paul as she covered him with a blanket, and suddenly felt very *tender / sensitive* towards him.

6 Tony was *outraged / adamant* that he'd been right about the problem, and was determined to prove it.

Prepositions

2 Complete the text with suitable prepositions.

Yoga with Lucy

Lucy Chang is a person with a social conscience who has decided to act on it. A physiotherapist **(1)** _____ profession, she specialises **(2)** _____ work-related health problems such as repetitive strain injury (RSI), caused more often than not by spending too many hours working **(3)** _____ a computer. What is special about Lucy, however, is that she devotes her spare time **(4)** _____ giving yoga classes free **(5)** _____ charge to working mothers in the inner city.

'Many women in this area are struggling to raise a family **(6)** _____ their own,' she says. 'They suffer from various stress-related problems which are detrimental **(7)** _____ their health. Yoga is particularly good **(8)** _____ such women, but they can rarely afford to join a class. I was lucky enough to be able to take up classes ten years ago, and felt so much better **(9)** _____ them that I decided to train as a yogi master in order to help others. While I realise that many people may prefer a more vigorous form of exercise **(10)** _____ the slower pace of yoga, I'm delighted to be able to offer at least some of these women a solution **(11)** _____ their problems.'

If you're interested **(12)** _____ finding out about Lucy's classes, go to her website at www.lchang.com.

Words connected with the mind

3 Complete the text with words from the box.

conventional   correlation   disturbing   light
linked   overcome   processing   recall
subconscious   suppress

Dreaming is good for you

Why do we dream when we sleep, and how important is it that we do so? Researchers have found that dreaming is strongly **(1)** _____ to mood swings. Studies show that people who dream and remember their dreams are able to **(2)** _____ negative moods more quickly than those who cannot **(3)** _____ dreaming at all. Some researchers believe there is a **(4)** _____ between a 'loss of dreams', as opposed to loss of sleep, and the development of depression. They argue that dreams represent the mind's way of **(5)** _____ and dealing with the various emotions and events the individual has experienced during the day, and that bad dreams, although **(6)** _____ at the time, act as a kind of catharsis, allowing the **(7)** _____ to tackle the individual's stress and negative emotions head-on and initiate recovery. Therefore, we should view dreams, both good and bad, in a positive **(8)** _____ . If this theory is correct, **(9)** _____ medicine will need to reconsider its methods for treating depression, since many widely used medications for treating both depression and insomnia actually **(10)** _____ dreaming.

Idioms with *mood*

4 Replace the words in bold with a phrase from the box.

*be in no mood for   get into the festive mood
lighten his mood   mood swings
when the mood takes him*

1 After those disastrous exam results, I **don't feel at all like** celebrating.

2 Adolescents are often susceptible to sudden **emotional changes**, as a result of hormonal changes.

3 Why don't we take Peter out to **cheer him up** a little, and stop him feeling sorry for himself?

4 Sarah loves Christmas, and really **livens up during that period**, going to parties and having fun.

5 Will is likely to suddenly go off on a trip **if he feels like it**, so don't be surprised if he's not there when you call.

Reading (Paper 1 Part 6)

Gapped text

EXPERT STRATEGY

Read the text before and after each gap, underlining key vocabulary and checking all reference words that refer to previous or later paragraphs. Look out for words like these in the options A–H as well.

EXPERT LANGUAGE

Look back at the main text. Find seven words which include prefixes.

EXPERT WORD CHECK

autistic   mnemonic   seizure   catastrophic   neurological   stroke   fleeting   at face value   honed   dead on   impaired   anew

1 Read the title and subtitle of the text. How do you think people can remember so much?

2 Read the main text quickly and answer these questions:

a Who is Jill Price? James McGraugh? Marilu Henner?

b How do people react to Jill's '*gift*'?

c Who or what was HM?

d Where does most of our understanding of memory come from?

3 Think about the correct answer for Gap 1.

a Read the text before Gap 1. What is it about?

b Read the text after Gap 1. What does it describe?

c Which of the missing paragraphs contains a description of the first meeting between Price and McGraugh?

4 Now look at Questions 2–7 and repeat the procedure.

> You are going to read a magazine article about memory. Seven paragraphs have been removed from the extract. Choose from the paragraphs **A – H** the one which fits each gap (**1 – 7**). There is one extra paragraph which you do not need to use.

A 'Some of them are really good,' says McGaugh. For instance, one subject claimed she could recall what she was thinking when brushing her teeth on a particular date. 'She said: "Oh yes, I was thinking about going to dinner." I can't confirm that, but from all the other testing that we've done, I do believe her.'

B McGaugh invited his correspondent to his lab, making sure he had to hand a copy of *Twentieth Century Day by Day*, a book that lists important events by date. He opened the book to random pages and asked what had happened on those days. 'Whether it was some elections or a movie star doing an outrageous thing, she was dead on,' he recalls. 'Time and again.'

C Price also concedes her gift helps in her job as a religious education coordinator. 'My memory helps me remember anything I need to know about the students,' she says. 'And my co-workers know that if they need anything, I will be able to find it.'

D Intrigued by these findings, I arranged to visit McGaugh's lab at the University of California, to find out how these people live with such unusual abilities – and what it's like for the researchers working with them. 'It never ceases to amaze me,' says McGaugh's colleague, Aurora LePort. 'Some of them can remember every day you give them.' She says studying people whose powers of recall seem to be enhanced, rather than impaired, offers us a new tool to explore memory.

E So how much, exactly, can such people remember? McGaugh has begun a long-term tracking project to see how their memories might fade over time. Wondering how my own memory might stack up against their awesome abilities, I volunteer to be one of the control subjects.

F Interviewing Price on the phone, I ask what it feels like to have this ability. 'My memory really has ruled my life,' she says. 'It's brought me great joy, but it has tormented me. Being able to hold on to all of the amazing moments is something that gives me comfort. But you remember the sad things, too.'

G Such memories can be subdivided into semantic ones to do with concepts, such as the fact that London is the UK capital, and autobiographical memories, about everyday events that we experience. Price has no special abilities with regard to her short-term or semantic memory, but when it comes to autobiographical memory, her scores are off the chart.

H Although still able to recall his early life, this individual was no longer able to lay down memories of things that happened after the surgery. Every day, the researchers studying the condition had to introduce themselves anew. Intriguingly, though, tasks that used short-term memory, like retaining a phone number for a few minutes, were not a problem.

The amazing memory marvels

There are people who can recall what happened on almost every day of their lives

It was an email that memory researcher James McGaugh found hard to believe. The sender, a thirty-four-year-old housewife named Jill Price, was claiming that she could recall key events on any date back to when she was about twelve, as well as what she herself had done each day. 'Some people call me the human calendar,' she wrote, 'while others run out of the room in fear. But the one reaction I get from everyone who finds out about this 'gift' is amazement. I run my entire life through my head every day and it drives me crazy!'

1 _____

McGaugh's group has worked closely with Price ever since and has discovered she is one of a select few with similar abilities. These individuals are neither autistic savants nor masters of mnemonic-based tricks of recall, yet they can remember key events from almost every day of their lives. Learning more about their abilities and how their brains are wired should lead to insights into the nature of human memory.

2 _____

It's certainly fair to say that most of our knowledge of the subject derives from looking at memory loss. The classic case is that of a patient known as 'HM', who had surgery nearly sixty years ago to treat severe epilepsy. In a misguided attempt to remove the source of the seizures, several parts of the brain were cut out, including both hippocampi, curled up ridges on either side of the brain. For HM, the consequences were catastrophic.

3 _____

Thanks to HM and many other people with neurological problems caused by head injuries and strokes, we now know that there are different kinds of remembering. Our short-term memories last up to about a minute, unless they are reinforced, or 'rehearsed' through further repetition. While much about the neuroscience of memory remains mysterious, our hippocampi seem to be involved in turning these fleeting impressions into long-term memories, which are thought to be stored in the temporal lobes on either side of the brain.

4 _____

Naturally, however, McGaugh's team did not take these recollections at face value. In a routine they have since honed on other individuals, they check facts using subjects' diaries and photo albums, interviews with their families, and online research. For instance, they might check someone's description of their first home against images on Google Street View and the family photo album.

5 _____

In 2007, McGaugh's team published their findings about Price in the journal Neurocase (vol 12, p 35), concluding that she was the first known case of someone with highly superior autobiographical memory (HSAM). They have since discovered thirty-three others with similar talents. As with Price, the detailed memories date back to around the age of ten.

6 _____

The next one of McGaugh's HSAMers I speak to is more upbeat. Marilu Henner, an actor who is perhaps best known for her role in the 1980s US TV series *Taxi*, says her abilities have been invaluable professionally. 'In acting classes, people would ask, "How are you able to cry or to laugh so easily?" I'd be right back at that emotional moment, with all of my senses engaged, looking out through my eyes.'

7 _____

McGaugh says most HSAMers do see their talent in a positive light. 'None of them has said they would wish away the ability if they could,' he says. 'When I ask what they do when they have a sad memory, they say they conjure up a happy one.'

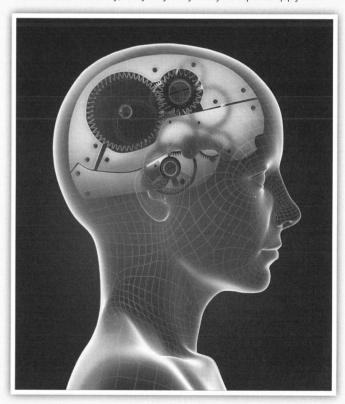

Language development 2

> **CB** p. 50, **GR** p. 177

Introductory and emphatic *it*

1 The word *it* is missing from some of the sentences. Add *it* where necessary.

Tips for avoiding neck and back strain at work

1 In an office, is easy to get into bad habits with regard to the way you sit at your desk, and this can lead to unnecessary tension and strain being placed on your neck and back.

2 Avoiding tension in your neck, shoulders and wrists at work is a matter of maintaining the right posture.

3 Before sitting down at your desk is important to consider how you are going to sit in order to avoid slumping or sitting at an awkward angle.

4 A lot of people forget how vital is to have a good chair when sitting at a desk for long hours.

5 Adjust your chair in such a way that your lower arms and hands are at a right angle when placed on the surface of your desk, especially if you are working at a computer.

6 Remember is essential that you keep your head, neck and back aligned as you work, otherwise you will create strain in these areas.

7 If you are working at a computer or laptop, is a question of using your eyes to look at the screen, rather than leaning your neck and shoulders towards it.

8 You will probably find difficult to maintain a good posture once you become absorbed in what you are doing, but makes a difference if you do so.

9 Finally, is worth mentioning that you should keep both your feet flat on the floor and avoid the temptation to cross your legs.

---

2 Rewrite each sentence with a suitable phrase with *it* and the word in brackets so that it means the same as the first sentence. Make any other changes that are necessary.

1 I'm sorry you missed the party on Saturday, as we had a great time! (shame)

2 I'm surprised that Karen's depressed, because she seems to have everything she could want. (find)

3 Once you've admitted that you need to make some changes in your life, the thing to do is to get started as soon as possible. (matter)

4 I suddenly realised that I no longer felt tired in the mornings. (dawned)

5 I heard about Laughter Clubs from Melanie. (who)

6 I don't care who you go to see, as long as you get some professional help! (difference)

7 There's no point in feeling sorry for yourself. You're the one to blame for this, and you know it! (good)

8 You need to think 'outside the box' to solve this problem. (question)

Inversion

3 Complete each sentence by circling the correct verb form from each pair in italics.

1 Little *she realised / did she realise* just how stressed out she was.

2 Only after *she had / had she* consulted a psychotherapist did she begin to take control of her life again.

3 If *should you / you should* need to talk to someone, give me a call.

4 Never *have I / I have* seen such a confused young man!

5 Not until *had he / he had* left did I realise how upset I was.

6 So devastated *was she / she was* at the loss of her dog that John couldn't leave her alone.

7 Only *was Howard / Howard was* aware of how serious Caroline's condition was.

8 On no condition *should you / you should* take those pills without consulting a doctor.

9 Rarely *she had / had she* been shown such kindness by a total stranger.

10 I would have called you *had I / I had* known about the incident.

4 Complete each sentence with a word or phrase. Use inversion where possible.

1 No sooner _____ phoned the police than Laura arrived home, much to our relief!

2 So determined _____ not to give up that he took pills to keep him awake.

3 Never _____ such a poor excuse for missing a lecture!

4 No-one but Sara _____ the police a description of the burglars, for she was the only one who had seen them.

5 Were Amy _____ a therapist, she might not be in such a state now.

6 You might have managed to work things out with Mike, _____ my advice.

7 When I first met James, little _____ he would become such an important part of my life.

8 Such _____ anxiety over the problems at work that Kevin couldn't eat or sleep.

9 At no time during the presentation _____ how nervous she was.

10 Only when _____ her new job did she realise how unhappy she had been at her previous one.

11 Not only _____ Mike's advice and take up T'ai Chi, but it helped me so much that I decided to become an instructor.

12 Had it not _____ the Laughter Club, I might never have got over my depression.

Use of English (Paper 1 Part 4)

Key word transformations

EXPERT STRATEGY

When you have finished, read both sentences again to ensure that they have exactly the same meaning.

HELP

➤ Q1 You need to use a common verb that collocates with *objections*.

➤ Q3 You need to use the noun form of the verb *recur*.

➤ Q5 You need to use the noun *attention* in a phrase which means 'become aware'.

➤ Q7 The expression with *fear* is followed by the gerund.

1 Look at the key word. Think about how this word can be used to express the same idea as the first sentence in a different way.

2 Write between three and eight words in the gap including the key word. The words must complete the sentence logically and grammatically. Remember, contractions count as two words.

3 Now answer Questions 1–8, using the Help clues if necessary.

For questions **1 – 8**, complete the second sentence so that it has a similar meaning to the first sentence, using the word given. **Do not change the word given.** You must use between **three** and **eight** words, including the word given.

1 Unless anyone objects, I intend to start a self-help group for new employees.
   nobody
   Providing _____ objections, I intend to start a self-help group for new employees.

2 Without that book on assertiveness, I wouldn't have coped in the new job.
   it
   Had _____ that book on assertiveness, I wouldn't have coped in the new job.

3 The pain in my back never recurred after I went to see the acupuncturist.
   of
   There _____ pain after I went to see the acupuncturist.

4 What explanation can we offer for the consistent success rate of alternative remedies?
   account
   How _____ that alternative remedies have a consistent success rate?

5 Ursula had been told that some people in her department felt bullied.
   brought
   It _____ that some people in her department felt bullied.

6 The increase in the number of dance therapy classes in the area has been marked.
   rise
   There _____ the number of dance therapy classes in the area.

7 Chloe didn't drive her father's car because she was scared she might scratch the paintwork.
   fear
   Chloe didn't drive her father's car _____ the paintwork.

8 Zac soon realised that confessing to his error was his only option.
   no
   Zac soon realised that _____ up to his error.

Writing: essay (Paper 2 Part 1)

➤ **CB** pp. 46 and 52–53, **WR** pp. 192–193

> **EXPERT STRATEGY**
> Making notes can help you to organise your answer and think about using your own words. Try to replace key words in each text with synonyms as you note them down.

Analysing the input texts

1 Read the task and the two texts below and make notes on:

a how they are connected.

b how they differ.

c your opinion of them.

> Read the two texts below.
> Write an essay summarising and evaluating the key points from both texts. Use your own words throughout as far as possible, and include your own ideas in your answers.
> Write your answer in **240 – 280 words**.
>
> **1 To nap, or not to nap**
> A recent study suggests that taking a short nap during the day may boost people's short-term memory. A group of adults tackled a demanding learning task, achieving similar results. Then, half of them were allowed to take a short nap, after which the tests were repeated. Those who had slept scored higher than those who had not. It seems that sleep enables the brain to assimilate incoming information and file it away in the memory, at the same time freeing up space for further incoming messages. So, students cramming for exams should perhaps take note!
>
> **2 Does coffee help you concentrate?**
> Some studies have found that drinking coffee tends to make an individual's brain more alert, enabling swotting students to stay awake for long hours during examination periods. However, the evidence that caffeine in coffee enhances concentration is as yet inconclusive. Some research suggests that drinking coffee improves the attention span of sleep-deprived students, while other studies have concluded that drinking a lot of coffee makes people more easily distracted, and can have adverse effects on their sleep patterns. It would seem, therefore, that coffee affects individuals in different ways. One thing researchers generally do agree on, however, is that caffeine intake does not improve a person's memory.

Write your **essay**.

Planning your answer

2 Read the paragraph below. Which of the two essay plans does it follow?

Plan A
Para 1: Introduction
Para 2: Summary of both texts
Para 3: Evaluation of both texts
Para 4: Conclusion

Plan B
Para 1: Introduction
Para 2: Text 1 – summary & evaluation
Para 3: Text 2 – summary & evaluation
Para 4: Conclusion

> Text 1 **(1) suggests** taking a short nap during the day in order to **(2) boost** your memory, and **(3) mentions** a recent **(4) study** which showed that people who napped after studying performed better on tests afterwards. Undoubtedly, a short sleep or rest during the day can be **(5) helpful** but the writer fails to **(6) consider** the fact that people have different sleep patterns and needs according to their lifestyle. For instance, people who get at least eight hours **(7) continuous** sleep at night may not need to sleep during the day in order to **(8) work** well. Others may find that they wake up from a midday nap feeling tired and unable to work effectively afterwards. A lot depends on the way an individual sleeps and how much rest he or she needs.

3 Decide which plan you would prefer to follow. Organise the notes you made in Exercise 1 under the paragraph headings.

Varying your language

4 Replace the words in bold in the paragraph in Exercise 2 with a word or phrase from the box.

advocates beneficial cites enhance experiment perform take into account uninterrupted

Writing task

5 Now do the task in Exercise 1.

4 Information

4A Too much of a good thing?

Vocabulary development 1

➤ **CB** pp. 58–59

News and points of view

1   Complete each sentence with a word from the box.

bias   censorship   editorial   expose   mindset
objectivity   scrutinise   sensationalise

1   The newspaper expresses fairly conservative views which reflect its readers _____ .
2   Some editors routinely _____ news items in order to make them more appealing to the public.
3   The decision to _____ the scandal was taken only after the story had been thoroughly investigated.
4   A certain amount of _____ on the internet is necessary if children are to be protected from unsuitable content.
5   It is virtually impossible for news articles to be totally free from _____ .
6   It is the sub-editor's responsibility to _____ . all articles for spelling and grammatical errors.
7   People who post comments online in response to an article frequently complain about the lack of _____.
8   It was once widely accepted that political views and other opinions of the newspaper owners or editor should be confined to the _____ pages.

2   Rewrite each sentence using the correct form of the phrase in brackets. Make any other changes that are necessary.

1   How do you feel about the government's proposal to raise the retirement age further?
_____ (your position on)
2   The journalist believes that there needs to be greater freedom of the press.
_____ (hold the view)
3   Party members fiercely disagree over what the policy on climate change should be.
_____ (be deeply divided on)
4   I totally disagree with the reporter's conclusion that the riot was caused by students.
_____ (take issue with)
5   The government has decided to crack down on football hooliganism.
_____ (adopt a tough stance on)
6   People get worked up about the dangers of children playing computer games but we should try and look at the issue more realistically.
_____ (keep things in perspective)

Word formation

3   Complete the sentences with different forms of the word given in bold.
1   inform
    a   The company website is interesting and very _____ .
    b   The journalist paid an _____ to provide him with details of the company's business activities in the area.
    c   It is advisable to read more than one newspaper in order to have an _____ view of current affairs.
    d   I'm afraid your reporter has been _____ about the company's policy. You will have to retract that comment in the article immediately.

2   represent
    a   Many people think women should have greater _____ in Parliament.
    b   The demonstration was _____ of a broader feeling of dissatisfaction among the labour force.
    c   The artist's _____ drawing gives us a detailed view of life in the eighteenth century.

3   invent
    a   Leonardo Da Vinci had one of the most _____ minds the world has ever known.
    b   Journalists were subsequently forced to admit that the story was pure _____ .
    c   Konrad Zuse is credited with being the _____ of the first working programmable computer.

4   mind
    a   Eva and Paul are just two of a growing number of _____ people who believe we need to develop a community website.
    b   _____ of the potential repercussions involved in commenting on controversial matters, many bloggers take steps to disguise their identity.
    c   Robots have taken over many of the repetitive, _____ jobs on the production line.

5   investigate
    a   The _____ journalist is trying to discover the truth behind the allegations that the MP has been accepting bribes.
    b   The police are to launch a full-scale _____ into the cause of the crash.
    c   Accident _____ have been at the scene this morning trying to piece together what happened.

Use of English (Paper 1 Part 1)

Multiple-choice cloze

1 Look at the title of the text. What might *teething problems* be?

2 Read the whole text quickly to get the general meaning. Then read again carefully, choosing the best option A–D to fit each gap. Use the Help clues if necessary.

For questions **1 – 8**, read the text below and decide which answer (**A**, **B**, **C** or **D**) best fits each gap. There is an example at the beginning (**0**).

Touchscreen teething problems

The (0) __A__ of touchscreen typing didn't suit everyone initially. Some people who had grown (1) _____ to using a conventional keyboard, missed the physical feedback on whether they had hit the correct key or not. They found the touchscreen slow to use, whilst the text they produced was (2) _____ with errors, a situation that was (3) _____ if the text was produced on the (4) _____ using a smartphone.
Researchers at Maryland University found that many of these errors resulted from (5) _____ in each individual's typing style. For example, a user might be (6) _____ to hitting the bottom of a key rather than the centre, increasing the likelihood that they would also hit the key below by mistake, (7) _____ producing so-called 'fat finger' errors. They also found that if typing and walking simultaneously, there was a tendency for people to hit a different part of the key if the tap coincided with their foot striking the ground. The data produced by the team eventually allowed designers to (8) _____ these very human characteristics into account in the next generation of touchscreen keyboards.

HELP

➤ Q4 The word you need is part of a phrase with *on the*, which means you are travelling.

➤ Q6 Only one of these words can be followed by *to* plus a gerund.

➤ Q7 The word you need means 'in this way'.

➤ Q8 The correct answer collocates with *into account* to form verb phrase that means 'to consider something'.

EXPERT LANGUAGE

Look back at the text. Find three adverbs that tell us when something happened.

	A	B	C	D
0	advent	onset	input	upshot
1	familiar	accustomed	comfortable	proficient
2	strewn	caked	stashed	clogged
3	amplified	deteriorated	exacerbated	incensed
4	haste	transit	foot	move
5	whims	kinks	glitches	quirks
6	prone	apt	inclined	liable
7	therein	otherwise	thereby	likewise
8	hold	take	put	bring

3 Find words and expressions in the text that mean:
1 information about how you do something _____
2 probability _____
3 when two things happen at the same time _____

4 Which prepositions precede each of the options in Question 4?

5 Complete each sentence with one of the options from Question 6.
1 My internet connection is _____ to be rather slow in the evening.
2 The road is _____ to flooding in wet weather.
3 The site is rather _____ to attack by hackers.
4 Sally is _____ to make mistakes if she tries to type too fast.

Language development 1

➤ **CB**, p. 61, **GR** pp. 177–178

Modals: obligation and necessity

1 Complete each sentence by circling the correct word or phrase from each pair in italics. In some cases, both options may be possible.

1 You *mustn't / needn't* interrupt me while I'm playing *League of Legends*!

2 I simply *have to / must* work out a better system for dealing with my daily emails.

3 I *needn't / feel obliged* to answer my emails as soon as they come in.

4 We *have to / must* send this information to the lab right away, according to Professor Plum's instructions.

5 You *mustn't / don't have to* phone me, just send me a text.

6 You *needn't / mustn't* have bought me such an expensive ipod. I hardly ever use it.

7 Fortunately, I *needn't have revealed / didn't need to reveal* the identity of my source to the police, as they found evidence to back up my story.

8 Mobile phones *are / need* to be switched off in the library.

Modals: advice and criticism

2 Complete each sentence by crossing out the modal verb which doesn't fit.

1 I think it *should / would / could / might* be a good idea to install a tool to filter your incoming emails more carefully.

2 It *could / would / should / might* be worth talking to John Brooks about the problem; he knows a lot about computers.

3 You *should / would / might* have told me you'd won the Young Journalist of the Year award; we could have gone out to celebrate!

4 One thing you *should / could / would / might* do is join the open science project, and share your ideas online. Someone may be able to help.

5 You *could / would / might* have let me know the information was wrong! I looked such a fool in class today!

6 The conference is going to be packed this year, so you *ought to / should / would* book your tickets well in advance.

7 I *should / would / could* do a search for open research sites, if I were you.

8 You *might / would / could* do worse than set up your own blog, if you want to draw attention to your research.

Modals: other ways of expressing obligation, necessity and advice

3 Rewrite each sentence with the word or phrase in brackets so that it means the same as the first sentence. Make any other changes that are necessary.

1 You're responsible for making sure you list all your sources when you send in that report.

_____ (up to)

2 Sally should have made sure she downloaded all the notes of the lecture she missed before going to see the professor.

_____ (onus)

3 It might be better to browse several travel websites in order to find the best holiday deals.

_____ (if I were you)

4 I don't think you should upload that photo on your *Facebook* ™ wall.

_____ (better not)

5 It's not necessary to reveal all your personal information when you sign up for a social networking site.

_____ (not need)

6 All students must wear protective glasses during the experiment.

_____ (are to be)

4 Complete the dialogue with suitable words.

> **Anna:** Here you go, Tim. I've written up our proposal.
>
> **Tim:** Oh no, Anna! You (1) _____ have bothered, because management have ditched the project.
>
> **Anna:** What? Well, they (2) _____ better have a good excuse, after all our hard work! When did they tell you this, then?
>
> **Tim:** On Friday evening. They said they had no choice with all the cutbacks they've (3) _____ to make.
>
> **Anna:** Well, you (4) _____ have told me! I (5) _____ have wasted all my weekend working!
>
> **Tim:** Yes, you're right. I (6) _____ have called you straightaway. I'm sorry, but I (7) _____ to rush off to that Future Technologies conference, and it kind of slipped my mind. You (8) _____ be too angry with me, though, because I made some useful contacts there, and a guy from Logitech expressed interest in our idea!
>
> **Anna:** Tell me more!

Use of English (Paper 1 Part 3)

Word formation

EXPERT STRATEGY

For this task, remember to write one word only and to check that it has been spelled correctly.

HELP

➤ Q1 This word means the date by which something must be done.
➤ Q2 Add a negative prefix and make the word into a past participle.
➤ Q3 Add two suffixes – one to make an adjective, then another to make an adverb.
➤ Q8 There are two adjectives which can be formed from the verb *sense* but which one fits the meaning here?

EXPERT LANGUAGE

Look back at the text. Find:

a a modal verb that expresses probability

b a modal verb that expresses obligation

1 Read the title of the text. What does the word *mania* in *Informania* suggest about the topic?

2 Read the whole text quickly to get the general meaning, then read again carefully and complete the gaps. Use the Help clues if necessary.

3 Read through the text again. Does it make complete sense?

For questions **1 – 8**, read the text below. Use the word given in capitals at the end of some of the lines to form a word that fits the space in the same line. There is an example at the beginning (**0**).

Informania

Does this sound like a familiar (0) _SCENARIO_ ? I'm at my desk trying to meet the (1) _____ on a college assignment when I hear that little popping noise. It tells me that somebody, somewhere wants to get hold of me. Unable to resist the temptation, I have a quick look to see who it is. Before I know it, I've wasted hours idly chatting, and my urgent assignment remains (2) _____ . Annoyed with myself, I wonder how I manage to (3) _____ fall into the same trap. The answer may be that I'm an 'informaniac'. That's the new term for people whose use of text messages, emails and social networking sites has become (4) _____ to the point where it dominates their lives. Another symptom is (5) _____ checking your phone in case somebody you know has (6) _____ their status. To say I spend a lot of time looking at my phone and my tablet would be an (7) _____ . I urgently need to get a grip on myself and do the (8) _____ thing – ration my use of them

SCENE
LINE

DO
REPEAT

COMPULSION

CONTINUE
DATE

STATE

SENSE

4 Find words and expressions in the text that mean:

1 a piece of written work _____
2 to contact _____
3 with no real purpose _____
4 take control of one's actions _____
6 use less of something _____

5 What is the difference in meaning between each pair / group of words?

1 repeatedly / continuously / continually
2 update / up-to-date
3 state / status
4 sensible / sensitive

Listening (Paper 3 Part 4)

Multiple matching

EXPERT STRATEGY

Some people like to do Task One on the first listening and Task Two on the second listening. Other people prefer to do both tasks at the same time. Practise both ways to see which is best for you.

1 Read the instructions for the task. Think about the vocabulary and expressions you would expect to hear when people discuss buying things online.

2 Read both tasks carefully and highlight key words in the options A–H. Can you predict what kind of problems somebody might have when buying things like this online?

3 Now listen and do the tasks. Use the Help clues if necessary.

You will hear five short extracts in which different collectors are talking about buying a valuable object online.

Task One

For questions **1 – 5**, choose from the list (**A – H**) what led each speaker to buy the object online.

Task Two

For questions **6 – 10**, choose from the list (**A – H**) what aspect of the purchase caused a problem for each speaker.

While you listen, you must complete both tasks.

A a heavy work schedule	
B a remote location	
C a shortage of funds	Speaker 1 [ ] 1
D a recommendation	Speaker 2 [ ] 2
E an attractive website	Speaker 3 [ ] 3
F a temporary disability	Speaker 4 [ ] 4
G limited availability	Speaker 5 [ ] 5
H the chance to get a second opinion	

A the delivery arrangements	
B the packaging charges	
C damage to the item in transit	Speaker 1 [ ] 6
D delay in receiving the item	Speaker 2 [ ] 7
E arranging the payment	Speaker 3 [ ] 8
F obtaining insurance	Speaker 4 [ ] 9
G the seller's returns policy	Speaker 5 [ ] 10
H the condition of the item	

HELP

➤ Q1 Listen for what the speaker says about her colleague.

➤ Q2 Why did this speaker do something he wouldn't usually do?

➤ Q3 Why couldn't this speaker drive? This tells you the answer.

➤ Q9 What did this speaker get into a *lengthy argument* about?

➤ Q10 Listen out for the problem that wasn't resolved successfully.

4 Match the expressions from the recordings (1–10) with their definitions (A–J).

1 the small print (Speaker 1)	A a long distance to travel
2 quite a hike (Speaker 2)	B with nothing much to do
3 with a fine toothcomb (Speaker 2)	C rather expensive
4 crumpled (Speaker 3)	D cheated or overcharged
5 at a loose end (Speaker 3)	E to blame for an error
6 ripped off (Speaker 4)	F with spare cash to spend
7 at fault (Speaker 4)	G slightly damaged from being folded
8 in funds (Speaker 5)	H in great detail
9 a bit steep (Speaker 5)	I edges slightly damaged from use
10 dog-eared (Speaker 5)	J the detailed terms and conditions

EXPERT WORD CHECK

*brooch   courier   depot   in transit
garment   wrist   invoice   figurine
costs an arm and a leg   memorabilia*

Reading (Paper 1 Part 5)

Multiple choice

EXPERT STRATEGY

In this task you need to distinguish between similar viewpoints or reasons in the options. Read the question and study the text to find your own answer before comparing the options.

HELP

➤ Q1 The writer uses the phrase *I cannot share this view* to show disagreement. What does this phrase refer to?

➤ Q2 This question is testing your understanding of the whole second paragraph. Why are blogs and bloggers mentioned?

➤ Q3 Find the name in the text. You have to read the whole paragraph in order to answer the question.

➤ Q6 The first sentence of the paragraph summarises the main idea of the paragraph. You can find the answer there.

EXPERT LANGUAGE

Look back at the text. Underline all the uses of the words *so* and *such*. Which instances indicate:
a a degree of something?
b a reference to something already mentioned?
c a conclusion?

EXPERT WORD CHECK

dubbed   on the fringes   mainstream
by the dozen   incongruent
dig their heels in   fixed in stone
seminal   cocoon   banter

1 Read the title and subtitle of the text. What do you think *pro-science bloggers* are? Why do you think they are *defending reason*?

2 Read the text quickly to see whether your predictions were correct.

3 Then read carefully and answer the Questions 1–6. Use the Help clues if necessary.

4 When you have chosen the best option (A, B, C or D), read again carefully to check why the other options are wrong.

You are going to read an article about science on the internet. For questions **1 – 6**, choose the answer (**A**, **B**, **C** or **D**) which you think fits best according to the text.

1 In the first paragraph, the writer disagrees with scientists who
   A continue to see alternative medicine as insignificant.
   B have themselves embraced the ideas of alternative medicine.
   C use pejorative language when referring to alternative medicine.
   D feel it's no longer worth challenging claims made by alternative medicine.

2 What point does the writer make about scientific discussions on blogs?
   A It has meant more laypeople are joining scientific debates.
   B It has weakened the position of those who would defend science.
   C It has tended to give too much credence to unscientific viewpoints.
   D It has encouraged people to become too passionate about scientific issues.

3 The quote from Fahad Manjoo illustrates the point that the Internet
   A attracts people with very fixed points of view.
   B can reinforce people's existing beliefs and prejudices.
   C causes people to take the beliefs of others more seriously.
   D allows people to check out the facts behind accepted theories.

4 The writer suggests that proponents of discredited ideas in alternative medicines
   A are not always consistent in the arguments they bring forward.
   B feel that they are treated unfairly by the scientific community.
   C remain keen to gain the approval of the scientific community.
   D tend to ignore the contrary evidence produced by scientists.

5 The writer mentions the work of Cole Campbell to support his view that
   A there are very few absolute truths in the world of science.
   B reasoned arguments have the power to change people's opinions.
   C scientists themselves can learn from informed debate with lay people.
   D certain groups of people will never be convinced by scientific theories.

6 In the final paragraph, the writer stresses the need for pro-scientists to
   A relate any discussions on the internet to relevant research data.
   B follow up lively discussions on the internet with formal written reports.
   C avoid getting into heated discussions with non-scientists on the internet.
   D maintain the integrity and exposure of scientific viewpoints on the internet.

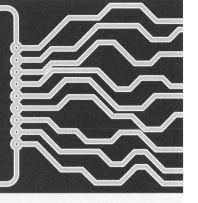

A popular enlightenment

Pro-science bloggers are doing a better job than scientists of defending reason

Alternative medicine has never enjoyed such popularity and respect as it does today. Therapies once dubbed 'pseudoscience' or 'quackery' are now typically referred to as 'alternative', 'complementary' or 'holistic'. Practices that used to circulate on the fringes are now accepted as mainstream. But the rise of alternative medicine poses a problem for defenders of science. Many see the fight-back as a lost cause, but I cannot share this view because the factors that allow quackery to prosper can and are being harnessed for a counter-revolution in defence of science itself.

In the past, those exploring alternative lifestyles joined groups of like-minded people and subscribed to counter-cultural magazines. They now participate in online communities and surf the Internet, where they encounter alternative websites and blogs by the dozen, but also come across mainstream scientific viewpoints. In other words, the defence of science is also increasingly being undertaken by members of the public because the web has proved to be a crucial mobilising instrument for pro-science activists. Such defence was once conducted primarily by scholars; today the battle is often fought at an individual level via cut-and-thrust debate in blog postings. This social phenomenon of 'angry nerds' and 'guerrilla bloggers', dedicated to defending evidence-based medicine and challenging quackery, is important. Rather than relying on scientists to defend the boundaries of science, we are seeing a much more socially embedded struggle – a popular enlightenment project. Can such a project work? Reasserting goals of progress through reason and evidence is one thing, but whether it has any effect remains an open question. How easy is it to persuade people through factual corrections?

The answer seems to depend a great deal on the individual. For example, according to recent research, providing people who are ideologically committed to a particular view with incongruent information can backfire by causing them to dig their heels in and support their original argument even more strongly. This problem is a general one. A substantial body of psychological research suggests that humans tend to seek out and evaluate information that reinforces their existing views. The digital revolution has exacerbated the problem because, as journalist Farhad Manjoo writes, you can now 'watch, listen to and read what you want, whenever you want; seek out and discuss, in exhaustive and insular detail, the kind of news that pleases you; and indulge your political, social or scientific theories ... among people who feel exactly the same way'.

I believe such pessimism goes too far, though. The boundary between mainstream and alternative knowledge may have become more permeable but the world has yet to enter what political scientist Michael Barkun of Syracuse University in New York calls 'complete epistemological pluralism'. The fact that quacks keep trying to get the imprimatur of science for their discredited ideas, by trying to publish their work in peer-reviewed journals, for example, speaks to the continued public prestige and power of science. Furthermore, their support base is far from fixed in stone. Some people are so committed to unorthodox views that they cannot be moved, but they are the exception. People motivated to explore the 'cultic milieu' – that fluid countercultural space in which alternative therapies and conspiracy theories flourish – are open to changing their minds.

In his seminal work on the cultic milieu, sociologist Colin Campbell of York University in the UK, stresses that it is not a space where firm opinions are held but rather a 'society of seekers' – people who 'do not necessarily cease seeking when a revealed truth is offered to them'. This creates the space for pro-science activists to compete for attention. When they do so, the internet becomes a tougher place for people to sequestrate themselves in a comfortable cocoon of the like-minded. This is good news for the enlightenment project. People may be biased in favour of interpretations that align with their prejudices but this does not mean that they just believe what they like. Faced with information of sufficient quantity or clarity, people do change their minds.

So the challenge for the pro-science movement is to keep an active and credible online presence. The web is an anarchic space where defence of science ranges from ridicule and banter to serious discussion about findings along with links to scientific articles and reports. It looks, in other words, like the space that used to be the preserve of the cultic milieu – but with greater informational depth. The weapons of science and reason are still very much in contention.

Vocabulary development 2

Words connected with working together

1 Complete each sentence by choosing the correct option.

1 If space exploration is to move on in the twenty-first century, we need to think _____ and create bolder visions of a sustainable research station in space.
A beyond the pale   B outside the box
C in the open

2 Researchers from two reputable universities are _____ to work on the project.
A joining forces   B combining
C rooting together

3 The professional network website LinkedIn operates on the _____ that making contact with other professionals helps you broaden your horizons in the business world.
A foundation   B thought   C premise

4 The Open Science movement is a global _____ to make scientific data accessible to the general public, allowing more widespread involvement in scientific research.
A scheme   B process   C initiative

5 The CERN Institute is a shining example of successful international scientific _____, with 20 European member countries conducting research into particle physics.
A collaboration   B combination
C collusion

6 In the 1980s, the United Nations Environment Programme _____ with the World Meteorological Organisation to identify and communicate the seriousness of the threat to the ozone layer.
A got in   B teamed up   C took up

7 Through the college's online student network, students can _____ resources to facilitate access to information and advice on anything from course work to finding a part-time job.
A join   B pool   C connect

8 All in all, the internet has managed to _____ barriers in several areas of research, by facilitating the sharing of information free from corporate restraints.
A break down   B bring out
C force through

Compound words

2 Complete the spidergram with words that combine with *news* to form compound nouns. Add as many as you can think of.

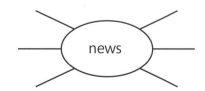

3 Replace the words and phrases in bold with a compound word from the box.

> avant-garde   breakthrough   cutting-edge
> diehard   mind-boggling   mind-blowing

1 The complexity of the computer data that appeared on the screen in front of me was **very confusing**.
2 Jenny's discovery marked a major **step forward** in genetic research.
3 The university's department of technology has contributed to a number of **the latest** technological developments.
4 Many of Leonardo Da Vinci's ideas were **extremely modern** for the time, and some people found them shocking.
5 There are still some **fierce** opponents to technological gadgets, who flatly refuse to use them, but they are becoming increasingly isolated.
6 The potential benefits to nuclear research of the Large Hadron Collider, the most complex scientific instrument ever built, are truly **amazing**.

Words connected with ideas about the future

4 Complete the text with words from the box.

> alternative   bleak   blueprint   conceived
> generate   inject   innovative   inspiration
> realise   stagnating

The role of science fiction in technological innovation

Science fiction has often been cited as a source of (1) _____ for technological developments, and fine examples abound. Jules Verne (2) _____ the idea of submarines in *Twenty Thousand Leagues Under the Sea* and Neal Stephenson's 1992 novel *Snow Crash* helped Philip Rosedale (3) _____ his dream of creating the virtual community *Second Life*.

Yet Stephenson himself believes that the genre is currently (4) _____ and in need of a shake-up. He criticises contemporary science fiction writers for their tendency to paint a rather (5) _____ picture of the future. 'They need to (6) _____ some optimism into their stories,' he says, 'and come up with big visions that make sense, so that scientists can be inspired to build them into reality.' Science fiction should not only motivate young people to study science but at its best, it should provide scientists with a (7) _____ for an (8) _____ world, in which new technologies work, and illustrate how (9) _____ ideas can be applied to daily life. With this in mind, Stephenson has created *Project Hieroglyph*, an online platform for writers and innovators to exchange ideas, publish stories and (10) _____ discussion in the hope of inspiring a more positive vision of the future.

Language development 2

> **CB** p. 66, **GR** pp. 178–179

Modals: ability

1 Tick (✓) the correct sentences. Correct those which contain mistakes.

1 Students can access the internet from their room, as the halls of residence have Wi-Fi facilities.

2 You might not use your mobile phone here, as there's no signal.

3 May you lend me a flash drive?

4 We weren't able to access that website you told us about.

5 Gill may not help checking her emails every five minutes when she's supposed to be working on something.

6 Hey, Sal! I'm not able to find the earphones for my iPod. You haven't taken them, have you?

7 Anil couldn't resist buying the new smartphone that's just come onto the market.

8 I'd appreciate it if you can send me an email with all the relevant information.

Modals: possibility and probability

2 Complete each sentence with the correct form of *can*, *could*, *should* or *might* and the verb in brackets. In some cases, more than one answer may be possible.

1 I _____ (buy) some new apps for my smartphone when I go into town today; I'll see what's available.

2 They _____ (receive) the survey report by now, as Karen told me she sent it through this morning.

3 We're surrounded by mountains here, so you _____ (not get) a signal for your phone.

4 Professor Daniels assured me she posted the notes from the seminar yesterday, so you _____ (have) no trouble accessing them.

5 When she sent the email, it _____ (be) that she forgot to copy you in on it.

6 Rosie _____ (be) a little absent-minded sometimes, so she _____ (forget) to attach the file to the email. It happens all the time!

7 It _____ (not be) Mike who posted that photo of you on *Facebook* ™. He doesn't have an account any more.

8 At this time of day, Stephen has usually had his break, so he _____ (be) in the canteen.

9 The accident _____ (not happen) if he hadn't been feeling so tired after studying all night, but who knows?

3 Complete the text by circling the correct word or phrase from each pair in italics.

Dispelling the myths about video games . . .

Contrary to popular belief, playing video games **(1)** *can / will* be good for you. So let's lay some misconceptions to rest.

Myth 1: Computer games isolate people. With the development of online interactive games, people **(2)** *would / may* now play together, and chat via Skype or MSN. Location is no longer a barrier, so friends **(3)** *are able to / should* team up and play against other people from anywhere in the world. Through the games, people **(4)** *can / must* form new friendships, and **(5)** *should / are able to* maintain old ones with people who have moved away.

Myth 2: Individuals who play from a young age become socially inept. The reality is that many games involve problem-solving and strategy-planning through teamwork. A code of fair play also means that players **(6)** *may / couldn't* report someone who repeatedly breaks the rules. So, gamers **(7)** *would / are likely to* be well-adjusted.

Myth 3: Habitual gamers don't get enough exercise and **(8)** *are able to / can* become obese. While this **(9)** *may / would* be true of some people, it does not apply to everyone. A lot of gamers also play sport, or go to a gym. Someone who spends all their time reading books **(10)** *might / should* also become overweight, yet they are rarely criticised for it. As with any activity, there is a need for balance.

Myth 4: Video games with violent content fuel aggressive behaviour in real life. The same **(11)** *should / could* be said for TV cartoons such as *Tom and Jerry,* and gory stories such as Shakespeare's *Macbeth*, not to mention most of Greek mythology. Video games **(12)** *are not likely to / are no more likely to* trigger violent acts than any of these forms of entertainment.

So, suppressed gamers, take heart!

Modals: deduction

4 Rewrite each sentence with *must*, *can't* or *couldn't* so that it means the same as the first sentence. Make any other changes that are necessary.

1 The only possible explanation is that I deleted the file by mistake.

2 The figures don't add up, so that answer isn't possible.

3 Your email isn't anywhere in my inbox, so in all likelihood it's in my spam folder.

4 Charlie's on holiday in the Bahamas, so it definitely wasn't him you saw at the conference.

5 Your contribution was instrumental in helping us make the breakthrough. Without you, we'd still be struggling to find a solution.

6 I'm certain it was Christine I saw secretly copying the project files onto a memory stick.

Use of English (Paper 1 Part 4)

Key word transformations

EXPERT STRATEGY

Don't forget that you must not change the key word in any way. You also have to include all the information from the first sentence in your answer, so check that nothing has been left out.

HELP

➤ Q2 The phrase you need includes the word *mind*.

➤ Q6 You need to use the phrase *a clear distinction* as part of your answer.

➤ Q7 Use *in* + gerund after *alone*.

➤ Q8 You need to use a collocation with *make* that means 'decide'.

➤ Q10 You need to use the word *never*.

EXPERT LANGUAGE

Look back at the sentences. Find examples of single words which are compound nouns.

1 Look at the key word. How can this word be used to make the second sentence mean the same as the first sentence?

2 Now answer Questions 1–10, using the Help clues if necessary.

For questions **1 – 10**, complete the second sentence so that it has a similar meaning to the first sentence, using the word given. **Do not change the word given.** You must use between **three** and **eight** words, including the word given.

1 Simon's friends persuaded him to buy the latest smartphone.
   talked
   It was _____ the latest smartphone.

2 It never occurred to me that I might be able to fix the computer myself.
   crossed
   The idea that I might be capable _____ mind.

3 According to rumours, the company is about to make a big technological breakthrough.
   verge
   The company is _____ making a big technological breakthrough.

4 When buying a laptop, the choice of software package is left to the customer.
   up
   It is _____ the software package when buying a laptop.

5 The new laboratory is unlikely to be ready for the start of the new term.
   chances
   The _____ the start of the new term are slim.

6 The lecturer was pointing out clearly that science and technology were different things.
   drawing
   The lecturer _____ between science and technology.

7 Peter wasn't the only person who found the blogger's comments offensive.
   alone
   Peter _____ offence at the blogger's comments.

8 Sally really should have come to a decision about her future career before now.
   mind
   It's high _____ about her future career.

9 People can only access the database if they have a password.
   restricted
   Access _____ password holders.

10 Dennis could play computer games all day long.
   tires
   Dennis _____ computer games.

Writing: report   (Paper 2 Part 2)

➤ **CB** pp. 62 and 68–69, **WR** p. 198 and p.200

EXPERT STRATEGY

To write a report, use the question to help you organise your paragraphs. There is no underlining in actual exam questions. So, underline the key points you need to address and use these to help you form your paragraph headings. Keep headings to two to three words.

Analysing the task

1   Read the exam task below and think about the following questions.

a   Who is your target reader?

b   What register will you use?

c   What information should you include in your report?

d   What recommendations can you make?

> Your tutor has asked you to write a report on the benefits and drawbacks of your college website. You should consider the <u>visual appeal</u> of the website, the <u>quality and relevance of news and information</u> it provides to students, and <u>how easy</u> it is for students to <u>find what they are looking for</u>. Make recommendations for improvement.
>
> Write your answer in **280 – 320 words**.

Developing ideas

2   Consider a college website you use, or know of. If possible, look at it critically and add to the following notes.

1 **Visual appeal:** use of colour, artwork and photographs
  Good points: Home page visually attractive, photos and bright colours
  Weak points: little colour or interesting artwork on other pages of the website

2 **Quality and relevance of information:** news, events, advice, useful information about college services, etc.
  Good points: Useful help page for new students, advice on student finance
  Weak points: information pages rather wordy, with long sections of text, difficult to read. No personal student stories

3 **Ease of navigation:** how easy is it to access specific pages or information?
  Good points:
  Weak points:

3a   Complete these sentences using information from your notes in Exercise 2.

1 Generally speaking, the home page of the website …
2 A major drawback, however, is that …
3 One particularly positive aspect of the site is that it offers …
4 Furthermore, there is a really useful section on …
5 Nevertheless, the information pages are in need of improvement, due to the fact that …
6 Another area which needs improvement is …

b   Add to the sentences you wrote in Exercise 3a to create the three paragraphs that will form the main body of your report. Use the headings (1–3) from Exercise 2 or create your own.

Making recommendations

4   Your final paragraph should include recommendations for improvement. Complete these sentences to create an opening for your final paragraph.

1 In light of the observations made above, it would be a good idea to ….
2 Those responsible for the website could do a number of things to improve its appeal ….
3 In view of the observations made above, there are several things that could be done to ….

Writing task

5   Now do the task in Exercise 1.

5 Language and literature

5A It's all in a word!

Vocabulary development 1

> **CB** pp. 74–75

Types of language and language use

1 Complete each sentence with a word from the box.

burr   dialect   Estuary   jargon   lingua franca
slang

1 The words and phrases used in a particular profession or subject and which are difficult for other people to understand are called _____ .
2 _____ English is a way of speaking English that is common in London and the southeast of England.
3 Delegates at international conferences who cannot speak each other's first language often use English as a _____ in order to communicate.
4 Andrea Camilleri is quite a difficult author to read in the original Italian since he uses a lot of words in the Sicilian _____ .
5 This is a type of very informal language, often used by young people. For example, 'well jel' is _____ for 'really jealous'.
6 People from Scotland and Somerset speak with a _____ – that is, they pronounce the 'r' in their words strongly, quite often rolling it.

Word formation: multiple affixation

2 Complete each sentence with an appropriate word formed from the one given in brackets.

1 Chinese is _____ (deny) one of the most difficult languages to learn to write!
2 Do you find that sometimes the blurb on the back cover of a book can be somewhat _____ (lead)?
3 The author lives in a rather _____ (access) part of the country; up a hill and down a long winding track, far away from any other signs of civilisation.
4 At school, we had a language teacher who was a bit of a dragon. She used to mark any _____ (accurate) in our spelling or grammar with a huge red cross!
5 I'm afraid to say that the poetry recital we went to was neither _____ (impress) nor _____ (memory).
6 Fortunately, in most parts of the world, levels of _____ (literate) are declining.

Idiomatic language

3 Complete each sentence with ONE word.

1 Amy racked her _____ trying to think of the boy's name, but it eluded her.
2 Off the top of my _____ , I'd say you've got around 1,000 books on your bookshelves!
3 On this particular issue, I don't intend to budge an _____ .
4 More _____ you if you ever think that learning a language is going to be child's _____ .
5 The striker's over-inflated opinion of himself made him a laughing _____ among supporters.
6 Sara has an engaging personality and disarming smile, but don't be fooled, she's as tough as _____ underneath.

Words connected with linguistics

4 Complete the text with words from the box. There are two extra words you don't need.

alphabet   consonants   linguist   literate   minority
official   print   spelling   tongue   transcribe
translation   word

Language is more than the spoken word!

Africa is a linguistically-rich continent where **(1)** _____ languages abound. In Zambia, for example, over 70 languages are spoken, though English is Zambia's **(2)** _____ language, mainly used by an educated elite. Those who do not speak English use other local languages as a lingua franca. Steps are currently being taken to codify some of the lesser-known languages that have, until now, been transmitted solely by **(3)** _____ of mouth.

One such language is spoken by the Shanjo people, a community numbering around 20,000. Local farmers from the community have been receiving training in **(4)** _____ techniques and they are being helped in their attempt to **(5)** _____ the language by a retired professional **(6)** _____ . The farmers already had a knowledge of English so they were able to apply that understanding of the system of vowels and **(7)** _____ to their own language. Gradually, they compiled a **(8)** _____ system and a first basic dictionary was produced.

For both young and old in the Shanjo community, this new project has been a huge achievement. One young farmer described seeing his language in **(9)** _____ for the first time as being quite miraculous! Now, he feels, the young men who write songs in their mother **(10)** _____ can be confident that they are using the language correctly. For the older members of the community, it is a comfort to know that the threat of the language becoming extinct has diminished

Use of English   (Paper 1 Part 1)

Multiple-choice cloze

1   Read the title of the text and think about what you are going to read. What does the word *OK* mean? What do you think it stands for?

2   Read the whole text quickly to get the general meaning. Then read again carefully, choosing the best option A–D to fit each gap. Use the Help clues if necessary.

For questions **1 – 8**, read the text below and decide which answer (**A**, **B**, **C** or **D**) best fits each gap. There is an example at the beginning (**0**).

OK?

The word *OK* is ubiquitous in modern English but its origins remain (0) __A__ in mystery. Over the years, many theories have been (1) _____ regarding its derivation but none of them is (2) _____ convincing. The first recorded written use of OK was in 1839, when it appeared in a newspaper article in Boston, Massachusetts. There was a (3) _____ for wacky acronyms at the time, just as today's text messages use things like 'LOL', and *OK* allegedly originated as a misspelling of *All Correct*. But (4) _____ many of these acronyms flourished briefly and then gradually (5) _____ out of use, *OK* has proved to be remarkably (6) _____ . It first reached England in 1870, where it appeared in the words of a popular song, and today is in (7) _____ use across the English-speaking world. As part of a phrase '... rules OK', it has been a mainstay of urban graffiti since the 1930s and in 1969 it had the (8) _____ of being the first word spoken on the moon. In short, it's a phenomenally useful word.

HELP

➤ Q1   You need the phrasal verb that means 'suggested' or 'proposed'.
➤ Q3   You need the word that means 'completely'.
➤ Q4   Only one of these words fits the sentence grammatically.
➤ Q8   Only one of these words can be followed by *of being*.

EXPERT LANGUAGE

Look back at the text. Find three examples of multiple affixation.

0	A shrouded	B smothered	C clothed	D draped
1	A laid out	B put forward	C drawn up	D brought about
2	A widely	B mainly	C wholly	D largely
3	A hype	B craze	C rage	D whim
4	A despite	B albeit	C whereas	D providing
5	A slipped	B faded	C crept	D strayed
6	A resolute	B stalwart	C steadfast	D resilient
7	A staunch	B relentless	C durable	D constant
8	A credit	B pride	C honour	D acclaim

3   Find words and expressions in the text that mean:

1 found everywhere   _____
2 eccentric, crazy   _____
3 a word formed from the first letters of
   the words in a phrase   _____
4 a key element   _____
5 to a very great extent   _____

4   Write the noun forms of these adjectives.

1 ubiquitous   _____
2 relentless   _____
3 durable   _____
4 constant   _____

Language development 1

➤ **CB** p. 77, **GR** pp. 179–180

Words with a similar meaning

1 Complete each sentence by circling the correct word from each pair in italics.

1 I think we'll have to *abandon / abolish* our plans to go for a walk – it's raining cats and dogs!
2 I'm afraid on that subject I beg to *vary / differ*.
3 What's the *equal / equivalent* of 100 pounds in dollars?
4 Teachers emphasise the *obligation / necessity* for good planning and classroom management.
5 If you have the *chance / occasion*, read her autobiography – it's quite illuminating.
6 The Hay Festival was *originated / launched* in 1988.
7 The chair *proposed / suggested* that the literature campaign be got under way within the next two years and the vice-chair seconded.
8 It's difficult to put a *worth / value* on his contribution to the field of linguistics.

Easily confused words

2 Complete each pair of sentences with the correct pair of words from the box. Make any other changes that are necessary.

censor / censure	disposable / disposal
extend / expand	insistent / persistent
negligent / negligible	variable / varying

1 a The difference in price is _____ , so just take the one you think looks best.
 b I'm afraid he was found to have been _____ in his duties and was subsequently fired.
2 a The only way to cater for such a large crowd is to have _____ plates and cutlery.
 b A limousine and driver will be put at your _____ for the whole week.
3 a Have you heard that the chain of bookshops is _____ and opening two new outlets?
 b Could we possibly _____ the deadline for this project?
4 a Some films are _____ in order to meet classification guidelines for younger viewers.
 b The TV channel was publicly _____ for its inappropriate coverage of the event.
5 a Our tutor was most _____ that we should spend our holidays reading Shakespeare.
 b The _____ pressure of handing in assignments was quite difficult to handle.
6 a Tests of _____ levels of difficulty were given to the students.
 b The _____ nature of the English climate means that people spend a lot of time talking about the weather!

3 Complete the text by circling the correct word from each pair in italics.

The Hay Festival

Each year, the small town of Hay-on-Wye in mid-Wales plays host to a major literary festival. Many **(1)** *illustrative / illustrious* names from the world of literature, as well as showbiz personalities and film stars such as Ralph Fiennes, Rob Lowe and Goldie Hawn have made appearances there over the years. Visitors to the festival can rub **(2)** *shoulders / backs* with these celebrities at the same time as gaining **(3)** *insight / hindsight* into the process of creating a novel or a film. The literature scene here isn't solely **(4)** *defined / confined* to fiction or autobiography; there are books on business, sustainability and history, together with poetry and plays.

The Hay Festival was purely a literary and arts festival until 2001 when the organisers decided to invite Bill Clinton to give a talk. That set a **(5)** *president / precedent* and from then on, each year the list of celebrities has got longer. In other words, Hay, as it is commonly referred to, has become a **(6)** *heady / brainy* mixture of **(7)** *institutional / inspirational* talks on just about the whole **(8)** *gamut / gambit* of human experience. **(9)** Rich *takings / pickings* indeed for those who are lucky enough to be able to **(10)** *assist / attend*!

Homophones

4 Find one incorrect homophone in each sentence. Correct the spelling.

1 The children spent all day whining about the whether.
2 When we were in Paris last year, we made sure we saw all the main tourist cites.
3 James poured over the newspaper looking at the Situations Vacant page.
4 The boat drew up to the key and the passengers disembarked.
5 You need to way up the pros and cons, and decide which is the best course for you.
6 The book was made into a very popular cereal that was shown on TV last year.
7 It's no mean feet to write an account of a painter's career that is neither dull nor pretentious.
8 He wrote about his parents, who had been together threw thick and thin for sixty years.

Use of English (Paper 1 Part 2)

Open cloze

1 Read the title of the text. What do you think it is going to be about?

2 Read the whole text quickly to get the general meaning, then read again carefully and complete the gaps. Use the Help clues if necessary.

3 Read through the text again when you've finished, with your chosen words in place. Does it make complete sense?

HELP

➤ Q1 The word *back* forms the second part of this phrasal verb.

➤ Q4 You need a verb here to complete the phrase ... *by the name of Tara.*

➤ Q7 Which relative pronoun do you need here?

➤ Q8 You need one word which means 'that which'.

EXPERT LANGUAGE

Look back at the text. Find two idiomatic phrases beginning with common verbs.

For questions **1 – 8**, read the text below and think of the word that best fits each space. Use only one word in each space. There is an example at the beginning (**0**).

A language-teaching avatar

One of the trickiest tasks for an adult studying another language is (0) __GETTING__ your tongue around unfamiliar sound patterns. Poor pronunciation often (1) _____ learners back, preventing them from being fully effective (2) _____ it comes to actually using the language. Priya Day of Sheffield University may have (3) _____ up with a solution to this perennial problem. She has designed a talking avatar which (4) _____ by the name of Tara. Tara shows people the precise mouth movements they should be making in (5) _____ to produce a given word in the target language. (6) _____ with an external view of Tara's head, the system also displays the internal workings of her mouth and tongue as the words are spoken. These images were generated from magnetic resonance images taken from Day's own head and neck as she was speaking. In a small pilot trial with learners (7) _____ first language was Arabic, Day found that Tara helped improve their pronunciation much more than simply listening and repeating (8) _____ had been heard.

4 Find words and expressions in the text that mean:

1 most difficult _____

2 is always present _____

3 first attempt to use something to see if it works _____

5 Which of the groups of words does **not** share the same vowel sound?

1 fully, woolly, wholly, pull

2 mouth, enough, around, loud

4 those, whose, shows, throws

Listening (Paper 3 Part 3)

Multiple choice

1 Read the instructions for the task. How many main speakers will you hear?

2 Read through the questions. What are some of the things the speakers are going to talk about?

3 Listen to the recording and choose the correct option. Use the Help clues if necessary.

EXPERT STRATEGY

In this task, you will hear two or three people speaking together. One of them is usually just a presenter. Make sure you know which main speaker you are listening for in each question. Some questions may focus on the views of both main speakers.

HELP

➤ Q1 Simon uses the words *got to* on two occasions. Listen for what he thinks young authors have *got to* do.

➤ Q2 Naomi talks about all these things, but which of them does she think must be *avoided*?

➤ Q3 When Naomi says *So yes, it's best …* she is agreeing with Simon's earlier point, which she then goes on to repeat.

EXPERT LANGUAGE

Look back at the questions. Find:
a six verbs with dependent prepositions
b strong verb and noun collocations

EXPERT WORD CHECK

*media-savvy   quirky   tap into
displacement activities   beguile
bash out a whole raft of
a whole different ballgame
volume of sales   dumbed down
walk a tightrope*

You will hear an interview with two authors called Simon Chirk and Naomi Glenn, who are talking about getting started as a novelist. For questions **1 – 5**, choose the answer **A**, **B**, **C** or **D** which fits best according to what you hear.

1 Simon thinks that young would-be authors should
   A attempt to get known in another field first.
   B secure the support of a publisher from the outset.
   C devote themselves to the more lucrative types of writing.
   D have sufficient intrinsic motivation to meet the challenge.

2 Naomi suggests that unpublished writers need to avoid
   A trying to combine writing with another occupation.
   B exhausting themselves with a gruelling routine.
   C attempting to work with outdated equipment.
   D becoming distracted from the task in hand.

3 Naomi agrees with Simon's point that a first novel should
   A explore an aspect of a glamorous lifestyle.
   B reflect the writer's own personal experience.
   C seek to replicate elements of recent bestsellers.
   D feature appealing characters in an everyday setting.

4 Naomi and Simon disagree about the extent to which young novelists should
   A do research into unfamiliar subject areas or periods.
   B aim for established genres with large readerships.
   C allow prospective publishers to suggest a theme.
   D concentrate on producing a strong narrative.

5 What point does Naomi make about teenage fiction?
   A Feedback from readers can be very stimulating.
   B Novels need to deal with sophisticated issues.
   C The long-term rewards can be worthwhile.
   D It's easy to develop a loyal following.

---

4 Match the expressions from the recording (1–5) with their definitions (A–E).

1 gruesome
2 humdrum
3 jumping on the bandwagon
4 mainstream
5 dumbed down

A doing something because other people do
B very horrible
C rather boring
D over-simplified
E not specialised

Vocabulary development 2

Book idioms

1 Replace the words in bold with the correct form of an idiom from the box.

be in sb's good books (not) *judge a book by its cover*
read between the lines *read sb like a book*
speak volumes *take a leaf out of sb's book*

1 On first acquaintance, your boss might seem to be laid-back and easy-going but be careful! **Appearances can be deceptive!**

2 I'm afraid that Ricky doesn't hold many surprises for me – **I know exactly what he's thinking most of the time**.

3 Well, in Jen's last email she sounded really upbeat but **I get the feeling that** she might not be quite as happy as she makes out.

4 Having handed in all my assignments on time, I think **my tutor's quite pleased with me** at the moment.

5 Why don't you **follow Dan's example** and go jogging every day? Getting fit would help your concentration, you know.

6 The fact that Tom gives up some of his spare time to help children with reading problems **says a lot** about the type of person he is.

Ways of speaking

2 Use a dictionary to find out the meaning of the verbs in italics. Then complete each sentence by circling the correct verb or phrase from each pair in italics.

1 They *coaxed / wheedled* the baby to take its first faltering steps across the room.

2 'I can't stand fried food,' Ken *whined / muttered* under his breath at the dinner table.

3 The person I was introduced to *murmured / babbled* something polite and then moved away to join another group. What had I done wrong?

4 Max tends to rant and *whinge / rave* if he doesn't get his own way – what sort of behaviour is that?

5 I'm wondering if Lisa was trying to *whine / insinuate* that I'm anti-social simply because I have a lot of work on at the moment.

6 Once he got on to his favourite topic, Harry could go *rabbiting on / gabbling* for hours!

3 Put the verbs from the box into five categories.

babble coax gabble insinuate mumble murmur
mutter rabbit rant wheedle whine whinge

1 talk fast or a lot   _____
2 persuade   _____
3 complain   _____
4 suggest   _____
5 speak in a low voice   _____

Collocations

4 Complete each sentence with a word from the box.

attentive celebrated discerning fluent
prolific voracious

1 A _____ writer is someone who produces an unusually high number of written works during his or her lifetime.

2 What I like about my friend Veronica is that she's a very _____ listener; she rarely interrupts or tries to say her bit.

3 Holly's aim is to be a _____ speaker of at least two or three foreign languages.

4 I would say that I'm a _____ reader – I make my choices according to the quality of the writing.

5 My sister's always been a _____ reader with a compulsion to finish everything she starts.

6 Needless to say, the creative writing course led by the two _____ writers was fully booked up within a few days.

Words connected with language and communication

5 Complete the text with words from the box.

colloquialisms communication conversations
dialect identify imitative input phenomenon
picked up put forward speechless tête-à-tête

Am I hearing things?

In parts of Australia recently, people have been left (1) _speechless_ with surprise to hear strange (2) _conversations_ issuing from the trees in their gardens. It seems that certain parrots, formerly household pets, had escaped from captivity and had been 'teaching' the phrases they had (3) _picked up_ to their wild counterparts! The younger wild parrots were particularly receptive to this (4) _input_ and, given the (5) _imitative_ skills of parrots generally, were capable of reproducing (6) _colloquialisms_ such as 'Hiya darling! How are things?' It must indeed be startling to witness two parrots having a lively (7) _tête-à-tête_ in the garden.

Some scientists have (8) _put forward_ the hypothesis that this (9) _phenomenon_ could potentially spread throughout the parrot population, due to the fact that parrots rely on a type of (10) _dialect_ to enable them to easily (11) _identify_ any outsiders to the flock. Thus, this novel form of (12) _communication_ could conceivably become part of wild parrots' social repertoire.

55

Reading (Paper 1 Part 7)

Multiple matching

EXPERT STRATEGY

Many of the questions contain more than one idea. The relevant piece of text must match the whole meaning of the question – not just part of it.

HELP

➤ **Q2** What is an 'analogy'? How many can you find in the text? Read carefully around these ideas.

➤ **Q3** Look for a mention of something which people often do when they feel anxious.

➤ **Q6** Be careful – Sections B, C and D all talk about *interactivity* – the word itself appears in Section B – but it is not the answer. Read C and D carefully to see which one matches the question.

EXPERT LANGUAGE

Look back at the text. Find seven words with prefixes.

EXPERT WORD CHECK

*codex   hand-wringing
dodo   geometric pattern   margin
congregate   node   painstakingly
dog-eared   akin to*

1 Read the title and subtitle of the text. What issues do you think will be raised?

2 Read the instructions for the exam task. Then read all the questions and underline the key words in each question.

3 Underline the sections of text that deal with the ideas mentioned in the questions and read these very carefully.

4 Complete the exam task. Use the Help clues if necessary.

You are going to read an article about electronic books and reading. For questions **1 – 10**, choose from the sections (**A – D**). The sections may be chosen more than once.

In which section does the writer mention

an example of superseded technology that still has a certain appeal?	1
an analogy used to emphasise how seriously an idea is taken?	2
an anxiety she shares with other like-minded people?	3
a development that questions our assumptions about what reading actually entails?	4
the willingness of writers to experiment with new ideas?	5
the idea that books have always been part of an ongoing interactive process?	6
a seeming contradiction in her own attitudes?	7
a belief that the fundamental nature of reading will change?	8
finding pleasure in another readers' reactions to a book?	9
a view that a prediction is somewhat exaggerated?	10

---

5 Find words or expressions in the text that mean:
   1 book fan (Section A)   _____
   2 be a supporter of (Section A)   _____
   3 with various features (Section B)   _____
   4 becoming less clear (Section B)   _____
   5 an organisation which creates theory (Section C) _____
   6 an extra feature (Section C)   _____
   7 the basis of something (Section C) _____
   8 beginning of something (Section D) _____
   9 in a way that never lets you down (Section D) _____
   10 wrote quickly and unclearly (Section D) _____

6 Rearrange the groups of letters to create words from the text.
   1 light / ful / de   4 a / abor / tive / coll
   2 nent / mi / im   5 no / ed /an / tat
   3 in / a / por / cor / ting   6 tors / men / com / ta

THE BOOK IS DEAD – LONG LIVE THE BOOK

Electronic books are blurring the line between print and digital

A A lot of ink has been spilled on the supposed demise of the printed word. Ebooks are outselling paper books. Newspapers are dying. To quote one expert: 'The days of the codex as the primary carrier of information are almost over.' This has inspired a lot of hand-wringing from publishers,

librarians, archivists – and me, a writer and lifelong bibliophile who grew up surrounded by paper books. I've been blogging since high school, I'm addicted to my smartphone and, in theory, I should be on board with the digital revolution – but when people mourn the loss of paper books, I sympathise. Are printed books really going the way of the dodo? And what would we lose if they did? Some commentators think the rumours of the printed word's imminent demise have been rather overstated. Printed books will live on as art objects and collector's items, they argue, rather in the way of vinyl records. People may start buying all their beach novels and periodicals in ebook formats and curating their physical bookshelves more carefully. It is not about the medium, they say, it is about

people. As long as there are those who care about books and don't know why, there will be books. It's that simple.

B Meanwhile artists are blending print with technology. *Between Page and Screen* by Amaranth Borsuk and Brad Bouse is a paper book that can be read only on a computer. Instead of words, every page has a geometric pattern. If you hold a printed page up to a webcam, while visiting the book's related website, your screen displays the text of the story streaming, spinning and leaping off the page. Printed books may need to become more multi-faceted, incorporating video, music and interactivity. A group at the MIT Media Lab already builds electronic pop-up books with glowing LEDs that brighten and dim as you pull paper tabs, and authors have been pushing the boundaries with 'augmented reality' books for years. The lines between print and digital books are blurring, and interesting things are happening at the interface.

C Beyond the page, ebooks may someday transform how we read. We are used to being alone with our thoughts inside a book but what if we could invite friends or favourite authors to join in? A web tool called SocialBook offers a way to make the experience of reading more collaborative. Readers highlight and comment on text, and can see and respond to comments that others have left in the same book. 'When you put

text into a dynamic network, a book becomes a place where readers and sometimes authors can congregate in the margin,' said Bob Stein, founder of the Institute for the Future of the Book, a think tank in New York. Stein showed how a high-school class is using SocialBook to read and discuss *Don Quixote,* how an author could use it to connect with readers, and how he and his collaborators have started using it instead of email. Readers can open their books to anyone they want, from close friends to intellectual heroes. 'For us, social is not a pizza topping. It's not an add-on,' Stein says. 'It's the foundational cornerstone of reading and writing going forth into the future.'

D The tools might be new, but the goal of SocialBook is hardly radical. Books have found ways to be nodes of human connection ever since their inception. That's why reading a dog-eared volume, painstakingly annotated with thoughts and impressions is unfailingly delightful – akin to making a new like-minded acquaintance. The MIT Rare Books collection has kept a copy of John Stuart Mill's 1848 book *Principles of Political Economy,* not for its content but for the lines and lines of tiny comments a passionate but unknown user scrawled in the margins. Maybe ebooks are taking us where print was trying to go all along.

Language development 2

➤ **CB** p. 82, **GR** pp. 180–181

Cleft sentences

1a Complete each sentence with ONE word.

1 _____ I've ever wanted is a place of my own by the sea.
2 _____ really annoys the tutors is bad spelling from the students.
3 _____ is nothing I'd like better than a hot drink at the moment!
4 _____ a good supply of books to read is of the utmost importance to her.
5 The _____ I most appreciate about the creative writing course is the access we gain to some extremely helpful ideas and guidance.
6 The _____ why she speaks German so well is that her mother was born and brought up there.

b Now write six sentences about yourself, using the structures from Exercise 1a.

2 Rewrite each sentence so that it means the same as the first sentence. Use cleft sentences and make any other changes that are necessary.

1 People really admire JRR Tolkien for his creative imagination.
What _____ .
2 Colin prided himself on knowing everything about English idioms.
There wasn't _____ .
3 It's quite difficult to produce a novel a year, but many authors do it.
Producing _____ .
4 I don't know many quotations from Shakespeare, but I do know *To be, or not to be*!
The only _____ .
5 The tutor was happy if we gave our work in on time.
All _____ .
6 Liz really wished she could meet JK Rowling.
The person _____ .

Nominal relative clauses

3 Complete each sentence with a word from the box. There are two words you do not need.

how   that   what   when   whenever   where
which   whichever   whoever   why

1 The trouble with Kate is that you never know _what_ she's going to come out with next!
2 I'm happy to invite _whoever_ you like to the party, provided you look after the catering.
3 I can't remember _where_ I put my library book – and it's due back today.
4 Paul had an article accepted by a highly respected journal, _which_ was quite a breakthrough for him.
5 Do you by any chance know _why_ he turned down the invitation to speak at the conference? It seems a bit strange to me.
6 I can't understand _how_ anyone could learn a foreign language in less than a year.
7 There were only one or two people at the reception _when_ we got there.
8 _Whichever_ essay you choose to write in the exam, make sure you keep an eye on the time.

Noun collocations with *of*

4 Complete each sentence by using a word from Box A and a word from Box B joined with *of*.

A	B
lapse	day
matter	fame
offer	help
point	memory
price	opinion
sign	success
time	time
waste	view

1 One _____ is having the freedom to make choices.
2 My _____ is that all great literature appeals to the emotions.
3 It's a _____ trying to attract his attention – he's too busy signing books!
4 The _____ is the loss of anonymity.
5 Thanks for your _____ but I've sorted the problem out now.
6 My grandmother has the occasional _____ now she's nearly 90.
7 What _____ do you find is the best for you to work productively?
8 It's a _____ whether e-readers are more convenient than books.

Use of English (Paper 1 Part 3)

Word formation

1 Look at the title of the text. Can you predict any benefits?

2 Read the whole text quickly to get the general meaning, then read again and complete the task. Use the Help clues if necessary.

HELP

➤ Q1 You need to change the personal noun into the abstract noun.

➤ Q3 You need to add both a prefix and a suffix to form a word meaning 'it makes no difference'.

➤ Q7 Add a prefix to make a noun meaning 'the beginning of something'.

➤ Q8 Add a prefix to make a verb meaning 'to complain about'.

EXPERT LANGUAGE

Look back at the text. Find two noun phrases which include compound adjectives.

/

For questions **1 – 8**, read the text below. Use the word given in capitals at the end of some of the lines to form a word that fits the space in the same line. There is an example at the beginning (**0**).

The benefits of being bilingual

The (0) <u>DOMINANCE</u> of English as a global language may be something of a mixed blessing for mother-tongue speakers of the language. Because English is the lingua franca of science, technology, business and (1) <u>diplomacy</u> across the world, there is a marked (2) <u>reluctance</u> amongst English speakers to learn a second language. Amongst European countries, the UK and Ireland have the lowest rates of bilingualism, with around 30 percent of people unable to hold a simple conversation in another language. In Australia and the USA, the figure is even lower. Yet research has shown that bilingualism is good for the brain. (3) <u>irrespective</u> of whether you are raised bilingual, or learn a second language at school, the process can improve (4) <u>cognitive</u> function across the board, from concentration and memory to multi-tasking. Even more (5) <u>significantly</u>, bilingualism can (6) <u>sharpen</u> the ageing mind. For example, amongst people susceptible to dementia, the (7) <u>onset</u> can be delayed by years. Clearly it's high time that those who (8) <u>bemoan</u> the neglect of language teaching in English-speaking countries were given more of a hearing.

DOMINATE

DIPLOMAT
RELUCTANT

RESPECT

COGNITION

SIGNIFY
SHARP

SET
MOAN

3 Find words or expressions in the text that mean:

1 this seems good but may bring bad consequences — mixed blessing
2 a common language used to communicate — lingua franca
3 in all ways — across the board
4 getting older — aging
5 likely to suffer from — susceptible to
6 be listened to seriously — given of a hearing

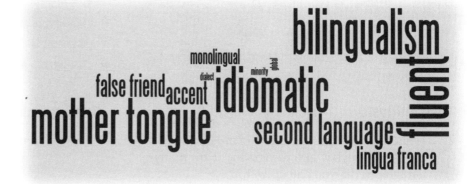

Writing: review (Paper 2 Part 2)

> **CB** pp. 78 and 84–85, **WR** pp. 198 and 201

Reorganising and correcting

EXPERT STRATEGY

Don't forget to organise your ideas into a logical progression, using paragraphs that are focused on one or two clearly-defined aspects of the topic. This is a vital skill in the production of a comprehensible and cohesive piece of writing.

Your favourite cookery writer has just opened a restaurant in your area. You decide to write a review of the restaurant for your local tourist office. You should comment on how far the restaurant reflects the standards and professionalism shown in their best-selling cookery books, referring particularly to the standard of the food, the ambiance and the service.

Write your answer in **280 – 320 words**.

A Before ordering, I produced one of Ben's cookery books at the table and everyone in our group had a good look at the fantastic illustrations!

B Fortunately, we were not disappointed: everything was cooked to perfection and of the highest quality.

C He was amused to see a copy of one of his books on our table!

D However, it was a superb evening, made even more memorable by the appearance of Ben Adams himself at the end of the meal.

E Last Saturday, we went to find out.

F Managed by the celebrated cookery writer, Ben Adams, the restaurant claims to live up to the standards of his recipes by providing fresh, locally-produced ingredients and offering its clients the highest quality dining experience.

G My only slight criticism would be that the menu was a bit over-priced: the bill for a starter, main course and dessert came to quite a lot more than I would normally be prepared to pay in a restaurant.

H Personally, I felt very relieved that a chef who could produce such wonderful books hadn't let me down.

I She escorted us to our table by the window.

J So Three Gold Spoons: thoroughly recommended – but save up your money first!

1 The model answer for this task is below. However, the sentences making up the review are in jumbled order and are not organised into paragraphs. Rewrite the review by following the instructions below.

1 There are 16 sentences (A–P) in the sample review. Put the sentences into a logical order, numbering them 1–16 and using 4–5 paragraphs. If it helps, you can write the review out in your notebook.

2 Once you have done that, identify which part of the task the student has not fully answered. Make any changes you think are necessary to the sample answer in order to incorporate the missing section, while remaining within the word limit.

3 Suggest any parts of the model which you would omit.

4 Think about any other criticism you have of the model or changes you would make.

Three Gold Spoons
Trentbridge

K The menu was impressive, not so much because of the number of dishes on it but with regard to their originality.

L The restaurant was small but the individual tables were in private alcoves, which gave a certain amount of privacy – a nice touch, I thought.

M This is a review of the Three Gold Spoons restaurant recently opened in High St, Trentbridge.

N Upon entering the restaurant, which was set in a small courtyard just off the High Street, the first thing we saw was a huge array of flowers – it was almost like going into an exotic garden!

O We all hoped that the food when it came, would be as good as the photos!

P We were welcomed by Ben's wife, Anna, who was most pleasant.

Task analysis

2 What rationale did you follow in order to split the sample review into paragraphs? How many paragraphs did you end up with?

Writing task

3 Now do the task in Exercise 1.

6A Sense of adventure

Vocabulary development 1

> **CB** pp. 90–91

Adjectives

1 Complete the text with words from the box.

> beaten   chosen   cumbersome   high-altitude
> incompatible   indispensable   lightweight
> makeshift   multi-purpose   negligible
> overcrowded   reliable

The sleeping bag dilemma

The question of whether or not you should take a sleeping bag when you go backpacking is a contentious one. A sleeping bag is rather **(1)** _____ and takes up a lot of precious space in your rucksack, making it **(2)** _____ with the idea of travelling light.

However, some experienced backpackers insist that a sleeping bag is **(3)** _____ in such **(4)** _____ places as Peru or Bolivia, or the highland areas of Vietnam or Laos, where it gets very cold at night. Another point in favour of the sleeping bag is that it is **(5)** _____ , serving as a mattress, cushion or **(6)** _____ seat on long journeys in **(7)** _____ trains. Nevertheless, thermal underwear, a fleece and a **(8)** _____ sleeping sack can also fulfil most of these functions, and are much easier to pack.

A lot depends on how far off the **(9)** _____ track you intend to go. With the wealth of information now available to travellers, it is fairly easy to find cheap accommodation that provides bedding anywhere along your **(10)** _____ route. Also, most regions now have a fairly **(11)** _____ transport infrastructure and so the need for a sleeping bag has become **(12)** _____ . All in all, it's a matter of personal preference.

Collocations: describing places of interest

2 Complete each sentence with a suitable adjective from the box.

> fertile   rugged   sprawling   sun-kissed   vibrant

1 There are some challenging walks over the _____ terrain of the Welsh coastline.
2 Singapore is a _____ city and many tourists go there to experience its amazing nightlife
3 Kerry lent on the ship's rail and gazing across the expanse of crystal blue water, caught sight of the _____ island in the distance.
4 From the observation tower, the _____ suburbs extend before you, as far as the eye can see.
5 In the _____ rice fields of Japan, farmers have created some wonderful crop art, using different coloured rice plants.

Verbs of movement: going on foot

3 Complete the text by circling the most suitable verb in italics.

When Ed Stafford set out to (1) *hike / roam / wander* across South America in an endeavour to follow the course of the Amazon river from its source to the sea, many predicted he would die in the attempt. Yet 859 days later, the former army captain proved them all wrong. To do so, he'd had to (2) *ramble / wade / march* through waters infested with piranhas, electric eels and venomous snakes, (3) *limp / traipse / amble* through dense jungle, and at one point (4) *trek / hop / stroll* 2,000 miles inland due to flooding. Together with his companion, Peruvian forester, Gadiel 'Cho' Rivera, Ed had to (5) *traverse / explore / penetrate* drug-trafficking territory, and on several occasions, (6) *trail / negotiate / navigate* the villages of hostile tribes. They were stung by wasps, bees, scorpions and mosquitoes, plagued by malnourishment and fatigue, but when they finally (7) *erupted / revealed / emerged* from the rainforest in August 2010, to be greeted by dozens of journalists and well-wishers, Ed described the feeling of elation as mind-blowing. He admits that the last day spent (8) *sprinting / trudging / skipping* towards the sea was excruciating but it was also the best day of his life.

Use of English   (Paper 1 Part 1)

Multiple-choice cloze

1   Read the title of the text and think about what you are going to read. What does the word *sightseeing* usually suggest?

2   Read the whole text quickly to get the general meaning. Then read it again carefully, choosing the best option A–D to fit each gap. Use the Help clues if necessary.

For questions **1 – 8**, read the text below and decide which answer (**A**, **B**, **C** or **D**) best fits each gap. There is an example at the beginning (**0**).

Fashions in sightseeing

The question of what (0) __A__ an entertaining sightseeing excursion is just as (1) _____ to the whims of fashion as any other leisure activity. A trip around the spectacular coastal scenery of western Scotland is now a (2) _____ attractive option but a couple of centuries ago that same landscape was (3) _____ as a wild and scary wasteland. Increasingly, in western Europe, safely decommissioned mines and other (4) _____ of the region's industrial heritage are now being reinvented as visitor attractions, whilst redundant factories and power stations get a new (5) _____ of life as shopping centres and art galleries.

This (6) _____ the question: if defunct industrial sites can attract tourists, then why not functioning ones?
The Yokohama Factory Scenery Night Cruise is just one of several industrial sightseeing tours now available in Japan. These are part of an emerging niche tourist trade, (7) _____ by a craze amongst young urbanites to reconnect with the country's industrial base. Seeing the oil refineries and steelworks at night, when lights and flares are more visible, apparently (8) _____ to the aesthetic charm of the experience.

HELP

> Q1   Which of these words is followed by the preposition *to* and a noun phrase?

> Q4   You are looking for a word that supports the idea of heritage.

> Q5   One of these words forms a common collocation with the words *of life*.

> Q7   Two of the words have a very similar meaning – but only one of them can be used in this context.

EXPERT LANGUAGE

Look back at the text. How many words can you find that have a prefix meaning *do something again*?

0	A makes	B holds	C gives	D gets
1	A determined	B subject	C dependent	D affected
2	A greatly	B strongly	C highly	D widely
3	A referred	B regarded	C reputed	D renowned
4	A legacies	B remainders	C inheritances	D leftovers
5	A term	B source	C grant	D lease
6	A begs	B leads	C rises	D brings
7	A demanded	B powered	C pushed	D fuelled
8	A boosts	B improves	C adds	D enhances

3   Find words in the text that mean:

1 sudden changes without any particular reason   _____
2 taken out of active service   _____
3 no longer used for their original purpose   _____
4 no longer in use   _____
5 with a particular focus and appeal   _____
6 a current fashion or trend   _____
7 city dwellers   _____
8 naked flames   _____

Language development 1

➤ **CB** p. 93, **GR** pp. 181–182

Present subjunctive

1 Replace the words in bold with a phrase from the box.

> *be that as it may   come what may   far be it from me to*
> *no matter what   suffice it to say   so be it*

1 **I don't care what** arguments you may have against the idea, I'm going on the Antarctic expedition!
2 Your objection to the rainforest tour project is understandable. **Nevertheless**, it stands to bring in some much needed revenue to the area.
3 If you want to spend your holiday working your fingers to the bone cleaning up beaches, then **go ahead**. Just don't expect me to go with you!
4 I'm going to cycle round the world **and nothing's going to stop me**!
5 **I don't mean to** tell you how to live your life but don't you think you should stay and try to work things out?
6 I'm not sure of the details but **put it this way**, Helen's made up her mind to leave her job and go travelling.

2 Complete each sentence by crossing out the option or options which don't fit.

1 The angry tourist demanded *he be given / being given / to be given* his deposit back immediately.
2 When booking online, it is advisable *to check / you check / to be checking* a tour operator's credentials before using them.
3 Jenny urged Mandy *that she take out / to take out / should take out* holiday insurance before travelling.
4 It is imperative *that the customer contact / for the customer to contact / to contact* the airline immediately should they wish to amend their flight details.
5 It is hotel policy *for guests being charged / to charge guests / that guests be charged* for any damage caused to their room.
6 Before Mr Banks agrees to a house exchange, it is important *to shop around / he shop around / that he would shop around* for a suitable exchange partner.
7 The company recommends that customers *would be vaccinated / be vaccinated / being vaccinated* against malaria and typhoid before travelling to certain parts of the world.
8 The hotel management respectfully requests that all guests *provide / will provide / should provide* proof of identification on arrival.

3 Complete the formal holiday complaints below in a suitable way.

1 I haven't been given the room with a view that I asked for! I insist that _____ .
2 We had booked a luxury cruise, but due to mechanical problems, the ship didn't leave port for four days. I therefore request that _____ .
3 The safaris we had been promised did not take place because the warden had been taken ill. I suggest that in future _____ is available.
4 I appreciate that you cannot be held responsible for the freak weather conditions. Be that _____ in case something like this happens.

Past subjunctive and unreal past

4 Complete each sentence by choosing the correct option.

1 You make it sound as if you thought Bangkok _____ awful!
   A were being   B were   C is
2 The cruise representative suggested the passengers _____ their luggage in their cabins, and meet in the lounge bar for cocktails at 7 o'clock.
   A had left   B to leave   C leave
3 The disgruntled holidaymaker demanded that he _____ a full refund as compensation for his ruined holiday.
   A be given   B would receive C gave them
4 Suppose he _____ you to go with him on the expedition, would you say yes?
   A asks   B were to ask   C requested
5 If only the weather were better, this _____ the perfect holiday!
   A were to be   B were   C would be
6 Imagine you _____ at the edge of a cliff, and there was a sheer drop to the sea below.
   A were standing   B will stand   C stand

5 Complete each sentence with a suitable word or phrase.

1 Pat _____ that all tour group members wear a badge with their name on for the first few days.
2 I wish you _____ taking so many photos all the time! That constant camera clicking is getting on my nerves!
3 Jamie talks as _____ easy to go backpacking round Europe for a year!
4 What if _____ robbed while sleeping in the train station, would you have been able to get home?
5 It's time people _____ more responsible in their choice of travel.
6 If only tourists _____ more respect for the local community, the island would be a much more attractive place to visit.

Use of English (Paper 1 Part 2)

Open cloze

1 Read the title of the text. What is it going to be about?

2 Read the whole text quickly to get the general meaning, then read again carefully and complete the gaps. Use the Help clues if necessary.

HELP

➤ Q1 You need a word that can be followed by *was* later in the sentence.

➤ Q2 You need a word that adds emphasis.

➤ Q3 You need a phrase that means the same as *apart from* or *except for*.

➤ Q6 Which word creates the passive form of a phrasal verb with *on*?

EXPERT LANGUAGE

Look back at the text. Find three words with negative prefixes.

For questions **1 – 8**, read the text below and think of the word that best fits each space. Use only one word in each space. There is an example at the beginning (**0**).

Snowboarding in the Himalayas

My snowboarding trip to the Himalayas was unforgettable. A helicopter set us (0) ___DOWN___ on a narrow mountain ledge at 4,800 metres, sending huge gusts of snow into the air as it departed. (1) _____ struck me was how very far we were from any sign of civilisation. (2) _____ on remote off-piste slopes in the European Alps, you're never too far away from a discarded ski pole or a chocolate wrapper borne aloft on the wind. But here, at roughly three miles up, there was nothing in sight (3) _____ than snow and rock. Rows of jagged mountain peaks stretched (4) _____ the distance, the world below invisible beneath layers of cloud. It was difficult not to feel (5) _____ similar to vertigo, a sense of disequilibrium (6) _____ on by the extremity of our isolation. Meanwhile, being stricken by altitude sickness was a real danger. (7) _____ the helicopter slowly disappeared from view, silence descended. We clipped on our boards, made our (8) _____ gingerly to the edge of the ledge and then dropped into the whiteness below.

3 Find words in the text that mean:

1 a small area of flat land   _____
2 abandoned   _____
3 carried in the air   _____
4 irregular and sharp   _____
5 fear of heights   _____
6 loss of balance   _____
7 feeling the adverse affects of   _____
8 with great caution   _____

Listening (Paper 3 Part 1)

Multiple choice

EXPERT STRATEGY

Remember that in the exam you will hear Extract One twice before you move on to Extract Two.

HELP

➤ Q1 Listen for the phrase *so what you get is ...* ; the answer follows this.

➤ Q3 Listen for an expression that means the same as *looking back.*

➤ Q5 Keith talks about feeling like he's got *jet lag.* What does that feel like?

EXPERT LANGUAGE

Look back at the questions. Find:

a three pre-modifying compound adjectives

b three strong verb and noun collocations

EXPERT WORD CHECK

adrenaline rush   sedate   glinting thrill-seeker   tucked away boundlessness   confines   set foot in oar   coffin

1 For each extract, read and listen to the opening sentence which gives you the context of the recording. Think about who is speaking, and the topic.

2 Then read the focus question and the multiple-choice options. Think about which speaker is being focused on and what you are listening for, e.g. an opinion, a feeling, an attitude, or the speaker's main point.

3 Listen to the recording and choose the correct option A, B or C. Use the Help clues if necessary.

You will hear three different extracts. For questions **1 – 6**, choose the answer (**A**, **B** or **C**) which fits best according to what you hear. There are two questions for each extract.

Extract One

You hear a radio report from a woman who is on an adventure holiday in Spain.

1 What impression has she gained of the place where she's staying?
  A It lacks some of the elements she would look for in a resort.
  B Its design reflects the needs of a particular type of visitor.
  C It offers a surprisingly wide range of outdoor pursuits.

2 When she talks about the activity she's about to try, she appears
  A reassured by her meeting with the tutor.
  B resigned to going through with the training.
  C determined to get the most out of the experience.

Extract Two

You hear two travel writers talking about their experiences.

3 Looking back, what does the woman value most about her time in India?
  A the opportunity for personal introspection
  B the chance to make a film in another language
  C the material she got for a project she was engaged with

4 They agree that travelling widely can
  A improve your understanding of your own culture.
  B increase your awareness of things different cultures have in common.
  C make you question assumptions imposed by your own cultural background.

Extract Three

You hear part of an interview with a man who's just rowed across the Atlantic Ocean.

5 What is his overriding feeling now that he's in Barbados?
  A relief at reaching his money-raising target
  B fear of having to continue with the journey
  C disorientation in an unfamiliar environment

6 What aspect of the trip has he found most challenging?
  A periods of relative inactivity
  B the physical discomfort of rowing
  C the need to interact with his companion

Reading (Paper 1 Part 6)

Gapped text

EXPERT STRATEGY

The option that fills the gap will be connected to the text coming before and after it. Always read all sections of text carefully and look for words that refer to the other sections.

HELP

➤ **Q2** Look for the option that explains why he is doing the trip.

➤ **Q3** Gandhi's name doesn't appear but there is a reference to the effect he had on Saoirse.

➤ **Q4** Look after the gap – the writer admits to being anxious. Can you find a link to this idea?

EXPERT WORD CHECK

birthplace epic pilgrimage hippy prophet saint limping blister nurture exhortation

1 Read the title and subtitle of the text.

a What type of journey do you think you are going to read about?

b What type of person would make such a journey?

2 Read the main text quickly and answer these questions:

a Where is the man going?

b Why does he want to go there?

c What preparations has he made?

3 Think about the correct answer for Gap 1.

a Read the text before the gap. What happens when the writer first meets the man? How did she know about his feet?

b Quickly scan the options. Which of them has words related to 'feet' and 'websites'? Which of them follows on logically from the first paragraph?

c Read the paragraph after the gap. Does this follow on logically from the option you have chosen?

4 Now look at Gaps 2–7 and repeat the procedure.

5 When you have finished the task, check it makes sense.

> You are going to read an article about a journey. Seven paragraphs have been removed from the extract. Choose from the paragraphs **A – H** the one which fits each gap (**1 – 7**). There is one extra paragraph which you do not need to use.

A After two weeks of solid walking from his starting point in Bristol at a rate of around twenty-five miles a day, his discomfort was readily apparent, despite the sensible footwear. 'It's all right,' he said. 'I've got blisters but bombs are falling in some places.'

B For Saoirse, both pilgrimage and this enterprise were only the first steps. His long-term vision was to nurture a money-free community where people would live and work and care for each other. Perhaps that was why when I met him that day, he struck me as an idealist who was going to come unstuck somewhere along the way.

C Was there a back-up plan if any failed to materialise? He said he didn't really have one because that would be 'contrary to the spirit of the thing'. Was he prepared to be lonely, scared, threatened? He said he had spent the previous few months trying to work through the fear, but that he 'just had to do it'.

D His mentor's exhortation to 'be the change you want to see in the world' had particular meaning for him. Then, a few years later, he was sitting with a couple of friends talking about world problems – sweatshops, war, famine etc. – when it struck him that the root of all those things was the fear, insecurity and greed that manifests itself in our quest for money. He wondered what would happen if you just got rid of it.

E Indeed, his faith in human kindness, rather worryingly, seemed to know no bounds. I convinced myself, however, that ordinary folk he'd meet along the way would mostly see that he was sincere, if a little eccentric, and would respond to that.

F I wondered if his mother at least shared some of these anxieties. All I learnt though was that she was, like his father, thoroughly supportive and was following his progress keenly through the website.

G Perhaps it is, in fact, only in the contemporary western world, the world of the selfish gene, that extreme altruism is, according to Richard Dawkins at least, 'a misfiring'. Because from all I'd heard, there it was before me on a pavement in Brighton. I felt I still hadn't got to the bottom of what drove Saoirse on, however.

H He was undertaking that extraordinary pilgrimage to promote the idea of 'freeconomy', a web-based money-free community. What's more, he'd be relying just on the kindness and generosity of strangers and contacts that he'd made through the site. I pressed him for deeper reasons.

Step this way for an alternative economy

I remember the day I met an idealistic pilgrim

Mark Boyle, or Saoirse as he preferred to be called, had set out to walk 12,000 kilometres from his home in the UK to Gandhi's birthplace in India. His mission was to prove that his dream of living in a money-free community really did have legs. I met him in Brighton soon after the start of his epic journey. Obviously, I'd no sooner caught sight of him approaching than I'd started peering downwards, because he'd obligingly stuck out a sandal-clad foot to give me a closer look. The 'boys', as he called them on his blog, had become famous in their own right.

1 _____

There was indeed plenty more in the world to worry about, yet something about this man – his gentleness, his over-active conscience, his poor feet – brought out all my maternal instincts. Saoirse, then twenty-eight, still had another two and a half years of walking ahead of him, carrying no money and very few possessions along a hair-raising route through Europe and central Asia, to his ultimate destination in India.

2 _____

It had all begun, it transpired, when Saoirse (Gaelic for 'freedom' and pronounced 'sear-shuh') was studying business and economics at Galway University. 'One day, I watched the film Gandhi, and it just changed the whole course of my life. I took the next day off lectures to start reading about him, and after that I just couldn't read enough, it made me see the whole world in a different way.'

3 _____

The idea behind the website grew out of that seemingly simple proposition. You signed up and listed all the available skills and abilities and tools you had, and donated them to others. In return, you might make use of other people's skills. For example, people might borrow power tools, have haircuts or get help with their vegetable plots.

4 _____

I asked anxiously about his planning for the journey, and he said that he was leaving it all in the hands of fate. So far, he had been in places where his friends and fellow Freeconomists could help him, so mainly he'd had arrangements for places to sleep and eat. Otherwise, he'd tried to talk to people, to explain what he was doing and hope that they would give him a hand. His T-shirt said, in big letters, 'Community Pilgrim'.

5 _____

His itinerary was certainly challenging, and he didn't even have a single visa lined up. 'They don't give visas more than about three months in advance in a lot of countries,' he'd said, 'so I thought I would just go for it.' But I had my doubts whether some of the countries involved would let a westerner – even a gentle hippy such as Saoirse – just stroll in.

6 _____

Once I had suppressed my concerns for his welfare, I found myself thinking that, actually, it is only our cynical, secular age that finds the notion of a pilgrimage odd. The idea of spiritual voyages seems to be built into almost every religion and, for most believers, Saoirse's faith that he'd be looked after, that everything would turn out OK, that what he was doing was a good thing to do for humanity – would not be odd at all. Most cultures accept the idea of a good person, a saint or a prophet.

7 _____

After nearly an hour's talking, he was starting to look tired: but made one final attempt to explain. 'Look, if I've got £100 in the bank and somebody in India dies because they needed some money, then, in a way, the responsibility of that person's death is on me. That's very extreme, I know, but I've got more than I need and that person needed it. And if you know that, then you've either got to do something about it, or you have to wake up every morning and took at yourself in the mirror.' His eyes were now red-rimmed, I think with emotion and exhaustion. We said our goodbyes. And I couldn't help noticing that he was limping. Those poor, poor feet.

Vocabulary development 2

Collocations: ethical travel

1 Complete each sentence with a word from the box.

*carbon   community-based   conscientious   informed
intrinsic   watchdog*

1 It is vital that tourism should preserve the _____ value of the local environment.
2 The travel industry needs to find more viable ways to reduce its _____ footprint in the twenty-first century.
3 Critics question the value of _____ consumerism with regard to travel, arguing that the positive impact on local communities is negligible.
4 A number of _____ organisations, such as the *Ethical Tourism Journal*, have been instrumental in bringing about stricter regulations with regard to green labelling.
5 Conscientious travellers should shop around for accredited eco-tour operators, in order to make _____ decisions about their holiday destination.
6 *Tribes* is an independent travel agency that specialises in _____ tourism which allows travellers to immerse themselves in the day-to-day lives of local people.

Collocations: food and cooking

2 Complete each sentence by using a word or phrase from Box A and a word from Box B to form culinary collocations.

A culinary	B appetite
food	buffs
local	cuisine
locally	expertise
quench your	sourced
work up an	thirst

1 The Truffle Festival in the Italian town of Alba is a must for _____ with a bit of extra cash to spare, as it's possible to sample some exotic varieties of funghi.
2 This remote little restaurant is set half a mile back from the main road, and so visitors can _____ as they walk up the track.
3 Visitors to the island have plenty of opportunity to sample the _____ in the many seaside tavernas and ouzeries which line its shores.
4 After your walk, you may like to _____ in one of the bars on the banks of the river.
5 At the food fair, local chefs demonstrate their _____ in the hope of winning one of the festival's coveted awards.
6 Buying _____ produce gives consumers the assurance of knowing where their food comes from and how it is produced.

Phrasal verbs: *go*

3 Complete each sentence with a suitable particle.

1 Although they tried to keep the guesthouse running, the business finally went _____ and they were forced to sell.
2 Jan went _____ with chicken pox while we were staying at the lodge, which wasn't much fun.
3 So, she's gone _____ to Africa as a volunteer on a community project for six months.
4 How do you go _____ finding just how green an eco-tour operator really is?
5 Having underestimated their requirements, after five days trekking, the team barely had enough food to go _____ .
6 I no longer fly as it goes _____ my principles of responsible travel.
7 Phil wants us to join the slow travel movement but I'm not sure if I go _____ with his idea or not.
8 The company director said he wanted to commit to sustainable tourism but I never believed he'd actually go _____ with it.

Words connected with travel and the environment

4 Complete the text with words from the box.

*circumnavigation   epic   globe   intercontinental
offset   power   spanning   voyage*

A solar-powered future for transport

The transport industry is making progress in its endeavours to **(1)** _____ its negative impact on the environment, largely thanks to the sun.

A two-mile-long railway tunnel near the Belgian city of Antwerp is now covered with 16,000 photo-voltaic panels, which help to **(2)** _____ both Antwerp station and trains. In London, solar panels have been installed in the roof of the new Blackfriars underground station, which stands on a bridge **(3)** _____ the River Thames. It is estimated that the power generated by the panels will be sufficient to cover 50 percent of the station's needs and reduce CO_2 emissions by approximately 511 tonnes per annum.

On the high seas, meanwhile, a solar-powered catamaran has successfully completed its **(4)** _____ of the **(5)** _____ and in the case of air travel, pilot Bertrand Piccard achieved the first **(6)** _____ solar-powered flight from Madrid in Spain to Rabat airport in Morocco. Although both **(7)** _____ journeys were incredibly slow by today's standards – the flight taking nineteen hours and the **(8)** _____ almost two years – it is believed that their success proves solar power to be a reliable source of renewable energy for transport and gives us a taste of things to come.

Language development 2

> **CB** p. 98, **GR** pp. 182–183

Emphatic statements

1 Complete each sentence in an emphatic way by choosing the correct option.

1 I asked the tour representative for help, but received none _____.
A whatever   B actually   C whatsoever
D absolutely

2 _____ way you look at it, that waitress' behaviour was out of order!
A However   B Whichever   C Whatever
D Wherever

3 _____ made you tell her Mike was leaving the country next week! You know you shouldn't have!
A However   B Whichever   C Whatever
D Whatsoever

4 _____ wanting to come to the caves tomorrow should add their name to the list.
A Anyone   B Whoever   C As
D If

5 Rich _____ she may be, she never goes anywhere or does very much.
A as   B which   C although
D if

6 _____ did you get him to agree to go? I thought he hated the tropics!
A Whenever   B However   C Whatever
D Whichever

2 Rewrite each sentence with the word in brackets so that it means the same as the first sentence.

1 I don't care what you say about solar-powered flight, I believe it's the way forward for commercial air travel.

_____ (matter)

2 Why on earth did you decide to go on holiday with them, if you don't even like them?

_____ (whatever)

3 Some people like Prague and others think it's too much of a tourist trap, but most agree that it's a magnificent city.

_____ (whether)

4 It's expensive, but a taxi ride around London is money well spent.

_____ (though)

5 I'm not worried about Carl travelling round the world any more, because I can contact him anywhere that he goes.

_____ (wherever)

6 I don't care who you are, you have no right to speak to the tour guide like that!

_____ (whoever)

3a Complete the text with suitable words.

Submerge yourself for a song

(1) _____ your opinion of the phenomenally wealthy, you've got to hand it to them; they have the means to let their imaginations run wild and then make their dreams come true, no matter (2) _____ extreme they may seem. A small number of companies cater to the whims of thrill-seeking billionaires, and the latest plaything they have come up with is the personal submarine. One company, Triton Subs, has developed several models of two- and three-seater submersibles and claims that business is good. The beauty of the subs lies in their convenience. Relatively lightweight, they can easily be hoisted on and off a yacht, enabling owners to take them for a spin (3) _____ they may be. Another point in their favour is that, (4) _____ you like diving or not, you can now experience the beauty of underwater wildlife at firsthand without having to change into a wetsuit.

Provided, that is, you can afford it. The 1000/2 model, with a capacity of two passengers and a diving range of 1,000 feet (305 metres), sells for a cool two million US dollars. Admittedly, this is a bit steep, (5) _____ way you look at it. Nevertheless, pricey (6) _____ it may be, demand is growing and submarine makers believe it will be become the billionaire's must-have plaything.

b Imagine you are an advocate of ethical travel. Write some sentences expressing your views in opposition to the personal submarine, using the prompts to help you.

1 No matter how/what …. .
2 However …
3 Innovative though they may be, …
4 Whether …
5 Whatever …
6 Whichever …

Use of English (Paper 1 Part 3)

Word formation

1 Read the title of the text. Can you predict any benefits of travel?

2 Read the whole text quickly to get the general meaning, then read it again and complete the task. Use the Help clues if necessary.

HELP

➤ **Q1** You need to add a suffix to make an adjective.

➤ **Q3** Will this adjective be positive or negative?

➤ **Q4** Be careful. One letter in this word changes when you make the noun.

➤ **Q7** Will this noun be singular or plural?

EXPERT LANGUAGE

Look back at the text. Find a phrase that refers back to a list of options.

For questions **1 – 8**, read the text below. Use the word given in capitals at the end of some of the lines to form a word that fits the space in the same line. There is an example at the beginning (**0**).

The healing properties of travel

These days, few people question the (0) _BENEFICIAL_ effects of travel. Indeed, the idea of pilgrimage as a (1) _____ activity is steeped in the history of many religions. For the medieval catholic church, for example, pilgrimages would help restore the individual to health and virtue. The problem might be a (2) _____ cough, a painful rheumatic condition or (3) _____ thoughts that ran contrary to the teachings of the church. Whatever it was, the local priest would respond with a (4) _____ drawn from the pages of an atlas rather than those of a medical dictionary. Pilgrims tended to go to places which had some (5) _____ with the history of the church itself, cures of a (6) _____ nature were not unknown . Although clinics now deal with most of the problems that motivated such pilgrimages, people still hang on to the idea that certain parts of the world possess a power to address certain (7) _____ . These are places that by virtue of their climate, haunting melancholy, (8) _____ or sheer contrast to our homelands, can salve the wounded parts of us.

BENEFIT

THERAPY

TICKLE
ACCEPT

PRESCRIBE

CONNECT
MIRACLE

AIL

REMOTE

3 Find words and expressions in the text that mean:

1 very well established _____
2 didn't follow (rules) _____
3 retain _____
4 magical _____
5 sadness _____
6 complete and utter _____
7 heal _____
8 injured _____

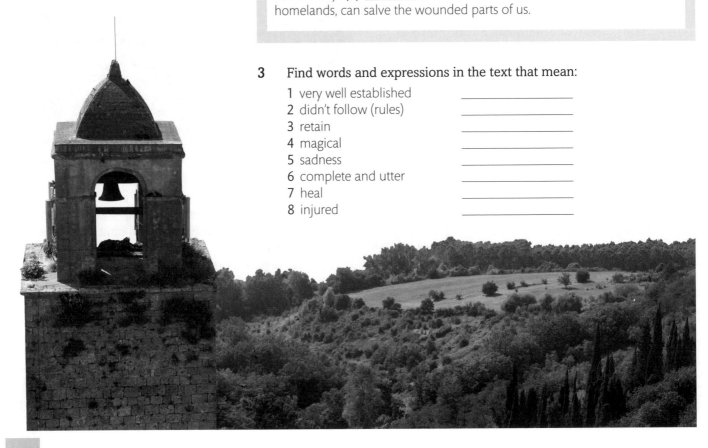

Writing: essay (Paper 2 Part 1)

➤ **CB** pp. 94 and 100–101, **WR** pp. 192–193

EXPERT STRATEGY

To evaluate the texts effectively, you should consider both the value and the limitation of the points each writer makes. Look at both texts and consider what the writer fails to mention in each case.

Analysing the task

1 Read the task and the two texts below.

Read the two texts below.
Write an essay summarising and evaluating the key points from both texts. Use your own words throughout as far as possible, and include your own ideas in your answers.

Write your answer in **240 – 280** words.

1 Maps or apps – a matter of choice

If you enjoy walking when on holiday, it is no longer necessary to slave away scrutinising a map or trying to recognise mountain peaks. You needn't bother with bulky guidebooks, or a compass, either. The latest innovations in smartphone applications have rendered such things redundant. You can now gain the information you need by simply pointing your smartphone at whichever summit, building or star may catch your eye. Of course, the diehard hikers may still choose to rely on traditional maps and a compass but a lot of us less hardy souls, who lack orienteering skills and knowledge of astronomy, will welcome these digital tools with open arms.

2 Maps as representational art

Digital mapping may be causing a cartographical revolution, but the traditional paper map is far from dead. Although sales of contemporary paper maps are declining, older renditions still arouse a great deal of interest as historical evidence of geographical detail in an ever-changing landscape. What's more, many of them are remarkable works of art, exquisite in detail and vibrant colours. The digital age may have rendered paper maps obsolete in a navigational sense but it has made people recognise their artistic and historical value and we are seeing a rise in the number of map collectors, who covet antique maps and hang them on their walls.

Write your **essay**.

Summarising

2 Using the notes you made in Exercise 1, write a paragraph summarising the two texts.

Making a critical examination of a writer's argument

3 Read Texts 1 and 2 again. Write down the following about each.

 a A valid point the writer makes about digital navigational tools.
   TEXT 1: _____   TEXT 2: _____
 b A limitation in the writer's view. What does each writer fail to mention?
   TEXT 1: _____   TEXT 2: _____

4a Read the following statements and decide which text they refer to.

 a One thing the writer fails to mention is the intrinsic reliability of the paper map. In remote, mountainous regions, both weather and the terrain can make it difficult to obtain a signal for digital tools to work.

 b While the writer makes some valid arguments in favour of digital tools, he ignores the fact that a paper map is easier to use, if you want to see the kind of terrain you'll be passing through at a glance. Screens are too small to do this effectively.

 b Make your own statements about the other text.

5 Write a paragraph evaluating the two texts. Use your answers to Exercises 3 and 4 to help you.

Writing task

6 Now do the task in Exercise 1.

Vocabulary development 1

> **CB** pp. 106–107

Collocations

1 Complete the text by using a word from Box A and a word from Box B to form collocations.

A	B
dramatic	communities
government	interest
neighbourhood	policy
tribal	shift
vested	step
unprecedented	watch

A COMMUNITY ANTI-POACHING SCHEME

In 2012, the Kenyan government took the **(1)** _____ of inviting the chiefs from different tribes to a meeting to discuss how to address the problem of ivory poaching. The aim was to bridge the gap between **(2)** _____ and get them to create a kind of **(3)** _____ scheme that would span a vast area of wilderness. The Kenyan Wildlife Service said that previously tribes had been unwilling to help but that the tide had turned.

Thanks to the efforts of organisations like the KWS and the Northern Rangelands Trust, Kenya has seen a **(4)** _____ in both local attitudes and national **(5)** _____ on poaching. As a result of various community development projects, local communities now derive income directly from tourism, running their own safari holidays. They can see that elephants and rhinos have an impact on their livelihood, giving them a **(6)** _____ in their preservation, and an incentive to help the authorities eradicate illegal hunting.

Idioms with *give* and *get*

2 Replace the words in bold with a phrase from the box.

> get me wrong get-up-and-go gets things done
> give and take give as good as you get give it a go
> I'll give you that what gets me is

Sarah: I really enjoy going to the club, but **(1) I am bothered by** the way Jan bosses everyone about.

Tim: Well, she can be a bit overbearing, **(2) I must admit** but at least she **(3) makes things happen**.

Sarah: Oh, don't **(4) misunderstand me**, she has lots of **(5) energy and enthusiasm**, and organises some great events for us but everything has to be done her way. I just think there should be more **(6) balance** in the running of the club. Other people have good ideas too.

Tim: This is all about her rejecting your idea for a sponsored marathon, isn't it? Well, you've always been able to **(7) stand up for yourself in an argument**, so why don't you argue your case? I'll back you up, if you like.

Sarah: Mm, I'm not sure she'll agree but I may **(8) try my luck**, if you're behind me. Thanks, Tim!

Bringing a touch of bling to their 'hood

Across London, **(1)** _____ are being set up to enable young people between the ages of fourteen and twenty-one to **(2)** _____ and change negative **(3)** _____ about their age group. One such **(4)** _____ , 'Bling My Hood', was started to **(5)** _____ young people in the East End of London to engage with their community after many had said they felt **(6)** _____ . The project, whose name roughly means 'shine my neighbourhood', encourages young people to take pride in their area through activities such as planting **(7)** _____ gardens, painting murals and repairing playground equipment. Areas previously affected by graffiti, vandalism and other **(8)** _____ have been improved by the **(9)** _____ sense of **(10)** _____ .

Building communities

3 Complete the text with words and phrases from the box.

> *anti-social behaviour challenge communal*
> *community projects community spirit initiative*
> *inspire marginalised perceptions stronger*

Use of English (Paper 1 Part 1)

Multiple-choice cloze

1 Read the title of the text and think about what you are going to read. What do you think is meant by *a simple life*? Why might a simple life be better?

2 Read the whole text quickly to get the general meaning. Then read it again carefully, choosing the best option A–D to fit each gap. Use the Help clues if necessary.

For questions **1 – 8**, read the text below and decide which answer (**A**, **B**, **C** or **D**) best fits each gap. There is an example at the beginning (**0**).

Is a simple life better?

What have you been up to? When (0) __A__ up with a friend, how do you tend to answer this very common enquiry? The response often (1) _____ around such big events as career developments, memorable holidays or family celebrations. I'm often struck, however, by the (2) _____ to which our real quality of life is affected more by smaller, simpler things. For me, seeing a new seedling appear from a seed I've sown never (3) _____ to bring me great pleasure. What's more, many moments of joy come unbidden – like a sudden cooling breeze on a hot day.

This (4) _____ the question of what is more relevant to our wellbeing – the big or the small? To suggest that someone should (5) _____ out happiness in simple pleasures if their career is on the (6) _____ would be absurd. Yet, we could (7) _____ have a row of ticks for all the big things and still feel miserable in our daily lives. Being overwhelmingly (8) _____ towards achievement, for instance, can make the small and the simple disappear from our awareness.

HELP

➤ Q1 Only one of these words can be followed by *around* in this context.

➤ Q3 You are looking for the word that completes a set phrase meaning 'without exception'.

➤ Q5 Which of these verbs makes a phrasal verb with *out*?

➤ Q6 You need a word that completes the idiomatic expression meaning 'in danger of going badly wrong'.

0	A catching	B making	C chatting	D keeping
1	A concentrates	B revolves	C focuses	D deals
2	A amount	B level	C extent	D quantity
3	A misses	B disappoints	C denies	D fails
4	A rears	B elicits	C evokes	D raises
5	A seek	B find	C look	D search
6	A shambles	B mess	C creek	D rocks
7	A barely	B easily	C hardly	D mostly
8	A targeted	B centred	C oriented	D determined

3 Find words and expressions in the text that mean:

1 to especially notice something _____
2 very young plant _____
3 light wind _____
4 a set of positive responses _____

EXPERT LANGUAGE

Look at the text. Find:

a an adverbial suffix added to an adjective

b a compound noun composed of an adverb and a verb.

4 Which prepositions would you use with these expressions from the options in Question 6?

1 _____ a shambles
2 _____ a mess
3 _____ the creek

Language development 1

> **CB** p. 109, **GR** pp. 183–184

Relative clauses

1 Complete each sentence with a suitable word or phrase from the box.

by which time   in which case   many of whom
that   to whom   which

1 The new cinema complex _____ is being built will boast two restaurants, a bar and a bowling alley.
2 The young people of the neighbourhood, _____ are out of work, have nowhere to go at the weekends.
3 The library is re-opening on Friday, _____ it is hoped the renovations will have been completed.
4 The wasteland, _____ has been purchased by a neighbourhood co-operative, is going to be turned into allotments for local residents to grow fruit and vegetables.
5 The street party might have to be postponed, _____ we won't be needing your help.
6 The person _____ I spoke about the problem didn't seem to know what to do.

Reduced relative clauses with participles and *to* infinitives

2 Rewrite the pairs of sentences to make one complete sentence with a reduced relative clause. Begin with the word(s) given. Make any other changes that are necessary.

1 Citizens of the Greek town of Volos set up their own local currency system. They were seeking a solution to the financial crisis of 2012.
Seeking _____ .
2 The group was called TEM Magnesias. It took its name from the points system it used to replace conventional money.
Known _____ .
3 The organisation began to trade in services and goods without using the euro. It served all individuals and businesses in the Volos region.
Serving _____ .
4 The TEM initiative was based on similar systems that were operating in Britain, Canada and Germany. It spawned local currency initiatives in other parts of the country.
Based _____ .
5 Anyone can join the group. They can visit the group's website.
Anyone wanting _____ .
6 Alternatively, they can enrol at the group's main exchange point. This is situated in the town centre.
Alternatively, the place to _____ .

Omitting the relative pronoun

3 Complete the dialogue with suitable relative pronouns. Omit the pronouns if possible.

Anita:	Will you put that camera away?
Bob:	Why? I'm not the one (1) _____ talking on the phone all the time. What you find to say to those friends of yours, I don't know.
Anita:	You can talk! You haven't stopped playing that game (2) _____ I detest since we got on the train!
Bob:	I'm not the one (3) _____ spends all her time fiddling with her BlackBerry, when she could be talking to her family.
Anita:	Huh! You were the one (4) _____ left us stranded in the middle of the museum!
Bob:	I went to find a place to eat our sandwiches! When I left, you were deep in conversation with that guide (5) _____ in charge of the Japanese group.
Anita:	Well, anyway, the rest of the time you spent filming with your camera. And I don't want the picture (6) _____ you took of me coming out of the flight simulator posted on Facebook!
Bob:	Why not? It's rather fetching.
Anita:	I was looking decidedly green! There are some things (7) _____ I'd rather our friends didn't see, thank you.
Bob:	For someone (8) _____ job involves entertaining people, you can be really miserable, you know!
Cindy:	Mum, Dad, give it a rest! Jamie and I are trying to read! I don't know. You two can be incredibly childish sometimes!

Reduced non-defining descriptive clauses

4 Rewrite the underlined sections of text as reduced clauses making any necessary changes.

Crystal Waters Permaculture Village

Crystal Waters Permaculture Village, **(1)** <u>which is situated on the subtropical east coast of Queensland</u>, Australia, is a working sustainable community project, with over 200 permanent residents. Permaculture, **(2)** <u>which is a term that was coined by the Australian designer and environmentalist</u>, Bill Mollison, is a form of ecological design **(3)** <u>that aims to develop sustainable human communities</u>, by integrating ecological engineering with housing and sustainable agriculture.
(4) <u>Crystal Waters, which was founded in 1985 on six hundred and forty acres of land</u>, was the world's first permaculture settlement. Designers collaborated to produce sustainable homes **(5)** <u>which were made from natural materials</u> such as straw bale, rammed earth and mud. The village received a UN World Habitat Award for its pioneering work in 1996, **(6)** <u>which gained it worldwide interest</u>.

Use of English   (Paper 1 Part 2)

Open cloze

1   Read the title of the text. What do you think *social fitworking* could be?

2   Read the whole text quickly to get the general meaning, then read again carefully and complete the gaps. Use the Help clues if necessary.

HELP

➤ Q1   Here you need a word which makes a contrast.
➤ Q2   Together with *anything* this phrase is another way of saying 'almost nothing'.
➤ Q4   Which time marker will make sense in this gap?
➤ Q8   Which verb followed by *for* means 'explains'?

EXPERT LANGUAGE

Look back at the text. Find two compound adjective and noun combinations.

For questions **1 – 8**, read the text below and think of the word that best fits each space. Use only one word in each space. There is an example at the beginning (**0**).

Social fitworking

In common (**0**) __WITH__ many of life's self-imposed hardships, fitness training is more fun if there's a chance to share the experience with others. For anyone (**1**) _____ the most ardent fitness fans, however, there's (**2**) _____ anything to be said in favour of a lonely workout at the gym on a cold winter's night. (**3**) _____ wonder, therefore, that what are known as 'social fitworking' events are taking off in a big way across London. (**4**) _____ the domain of the serious athlete, group fitness competitions have been redesigned for general use, and young Londoners have been signing up (**5**) _____ their droves. With names like 'Warrior Dash' and 'Tough Mudder', the events involve teams of runners racing over obstacles in rough terrain. Quite (**6**) _____ from the physical benefits, being part of a team is a motivating experience, (**7**) _____ it involves actually competing together, chatting in the bar or sharing photos online afterwards. The fact that the events attract men and women in roughly equal proportions could also (**8**) _____ for some of the appeal.

3   Find words and expressions in the text that mean:

1   something difficult to bear   _____
2   very keen   _____
3   becoming popular   _____
4   once restricted to   _____
5   in large numbers   _____
6   about the same number   _____

Listening (Paper 3 Part 2)

Sentence completion

EXPERT STRATEGY

Read the information before and after the gap in each sentence. Remember that you will probably hear a number of different words or phrases that could possibly fit the gap. You must listen for the information that completes the sentence with the correct meaning.

HELP

➤ **Q1** Two types of people are mentioned. Which type of person goes in first? Check that you've spelled this word correctly.

➤ **Q2** Listen out for the phrase *overriding concern* as this refers to the answer.

➤ **Q4** Be careful – three methods are mentioned – which does *CycleAware* recommend?

➤ **Q8** You hear the words *clean* and *secure* on the recording. Jerome also says that the racks should be under cover – but this is not what he *stresses*.

EXPERT WORD CHECK

hands-on assistance   drawn up
potential hazard   kit   subsidy
infrastructure   overlooked   perk
remuneration package   claim

1 Read the instructions for the task below and answer the questions.

a Who are you going to hear?

b What will that person be talking about?

2 Read the sentences in the task. How much do you find out about *CycleAware* from them?

3 Try and predict the type of information you will be listening for. Which answers are likely to be words specific to cycling?

4 Listen to the recording and complete the sentences. Use the Help clues if necessary.

You will hear a man called Jerome Wilby giving a talk about *CycleAware*, an organisation that promotes cycling as a way of commuting to work. For questions **1 – 9**, complete the sentences with a word or short phrase.

CycleAware

CycleAware initially sends people called (1) _____ into companies to discuss how to encourage cycling to work.

Jerome sees concerns about (2) _____ as the greatest barrier in convincing people to cycle to work.

CycleAware mentors take on the role of (3) _____ for people cycling to work for the first time.

CycleAware recommends that cyclists use a (4) _____ to attract the attention of other road users.

Adjustments to (5) _____ is the commonest maintenance issue dealt with by *CycleAware* teams.

Jerome uses the term (6) _____ to stress the comprehensiveness of the service *CycleAware* provides.

Jerome sees the provision of (7) _____ as a crucial first step for a company wishing to promote cycling to work.

Jerome stresses the need for cycle racks to be (8) _____ as well as clean and secure.

A firm which gave additional (9) _____ to employees cycling to work is given as a example of good practice.

Vocabulary development 2

Compound words: *life* and *home*

1   Complete each sentence with a compound word formed by combining *life* or *home* with a suitable word from the box. The words may be one word, two words or hyphenated.

coach   made   school   style   time   town

1   Alan's was a very solitary _____ , as he rarely socialised with anyone.
2   Barnie's mum decided to _____ him, as she felt he would benefit from a more flexible timetable, and it transformed her relationship with him.
3   Some people are content to stay put all their lives and never leave their _____ , but I'm a bit of a nomad.
4   Darren's mum's _____ bread is the best I've ever tasted! I wonder what she puts in it!
5   For Tim, winning that scholarship to study in Paris was the chance of a _____ .
6   Nothing seemed to be going right, so I went to see a _____ , and she really helped me turn my life around!

Word formation: adjectives and adverbs

2   Complete each sentence with a suitable form of a word from the box. You will need to add both a prefix and a suffix to each word.

compare   convention   guide   practice   resist   respect   sustain

1   The urge to dive into the crystal clear water and swim to the other side was _____ tempting for Sam.
2   It's time households using _____ energy sources searched for alternative ways to heat and light their homes.
3   The tenants in the flat upstairs behave extremely _____ towards their neighbours, playing loud music every night until the early hours.
4   Peter's got some pretty _____ ideas about living in an eco-commune, but he's having trouble persuading the rest of his family to go.
5   Eric was under the _____ notion that money would bring him happiness, yet despite working hard he never seemed to enjoy himself.
6   Kate exchanged her life in the urban jungle for the _____ beauty of the views surrounding the remote village in Tuscany.
7   Kevin reckons we should go and live on a houseboat, but it's totally _____ (practice) for me because I'm asthmatic.

Describing a way of life

3   Complete the text with words and phrases from the box.

*ambience   artificial   awe-inspiring   concerned
invigorating   manner   self-sufficient   simple
strapped   undeterred*

Alternative lifestyles: build your own island

Do you crave an island paradise of your own but are (1) _____ for cash? Well, you could always follow Richie Sowa's example.
This innovative British carpenter went to Mexico in search of the (2) _____ life. (3) _____ about the environment, he began collecting plastic bottles from the beach and came up with the incredible idea of building his own island home. Using thousands of recycled plastic bottles packed into mesh bags and fishing nets to form the floating base, Richie laid a structure of plywood and bamboo on top. Then he transported sand from local beaches and planted mangrove trees to create shade and keep the island cool. Spiral Island was eventually destroyed by a hurricane. Yet (4) _____ , Richie built another one. He claims he finds his way of life (5) _____ , if sometimes hard work. He is largely (6) _____ , with a solar oven and self-composting toilet and his own fruit trees and vegetables.
Spiral Island II's peaceful (7) _____ welcomes all (8) _____ of visitors, human or otherwise; Richie shares his home with a dog, cats, ducks and chickens. Aesthetically, the island may not be as (9) _____ as Dubai's (10) _____ Palm island but it is definitely a home in paradise.

Prepositions

4   Complete each sentence with a suitable preposition.

1   The actress has worked tirelessly to raise global awareness _____ the problem of HIV facing African countries.
2   We assure you that the Government is committed _____ finding way to combat climate change.
3   Karen's research involves studying the health issues associated _____ Vitamin B deficiency.
4   The benefits _____ the local community in adopting this policy are obvious.
5   The organisation makes it their business to keep abreast _____ all the latest news and information regarding the government's policy on whaling.
6   At present, more than two thousand hunters are engaged _____ illegal poaching in the country.
7   Jane Goodall has dedicated her life _____ studying apes.
8   The group is involved _____ various community projects designed to help the local youth learn useful skills in order to find employment.

Reading (Paper 1 Part 7)

Multiple matching

EXPERT STRATEGY

When you think you have found a match for the question in the text, write the question number in the margin next to the relevant piece of text – you can then go back and check it later.

HELP

➤ Q1 *Pull his weight* means to contribute effectively to a joint effort.

➤ Q2 *Misgivings* means to have doubts.

➤ Q5 An *analogy* is a comparison with another situation.

➤ Q10 Be careful, three terms are quoted, two in Section A and one in Section B.

EXPERT LANGUAGE

Daycare is a compound noun. Look back at the text. Find twelve more compound nouns.

EXPERT WORD CHECK

reversal brain-mashingly bosom child-rearing nursery swore by striker whinge inflict blissfully

1   Read the title and subtitle of the text. What issues do you think will be raised?

2   Read the rubric for the exam task. Then read all the questions and underline the key words in each question.

3   Underline the parts of the text which deal with the ideas mentioned in the questions.

4   Complete the exam task. Use the Help clues if necessary.

You are going to read an article by a man who took a year off work to look after his young daughter. For questions **1 – 10**, choose from the sections (**A – D**). The sections may be chosen more than once.

In which sections does the writer

accept his failure to pull his weight as a parent?	1
admit to his own underlying misgivings about a decision?	2
attempt to justify his failure to fulfil his intention?	3
cast doubts on the true motives of those having recourse to an alternative solution?	4
give an analogy to underline his disappointment?	5
insist that he'd thought through the implications of a decision seriously?	6
recall a momentary feeling of regret borne out of frustration?	7
remember feeling relieved when a problem was successfully addressed?	8
report a misinterpretation of his motives by others?	9
supply a term to help us understand a role he performed?	10

5   Find words and expressions in the text that mean:

1 open-minded (Section A)   _____
2 a feeling of superiority (Section A)   _____
3 competitive environment at work (Section A) _____
4 made anxious or worried (Section A)   _____
5 unfairness (Section B)   _____
6 get by without a plan (Section C)   _____
7 agreed to a request (Section D)   _____

6   For each of your answers to Question 5, say why you think the writer chose to use that particular word or expression.

DADDY DAYCARE

What's it like to be a stay-at-home father?

A When I'd first told people that I was taking a year off work to look after my daughter, they reacted in one of three ways. Women, and the more enlightened men, were genuinely supportive and interested to know how I'd approach it. Other
5 men were divided into two groups; those who tried to conceal their smugness and pleasure that I was dropping out of the rat race and those who looked jealous because they thought this meant I'd be taking it easy. This doesn't reflect well on the male population. But men are complicated beings and I can't claim to
10 be totally comfortable with what is, however you dress it up, a reversal of traditional gender roles. My own father was very positive about everything but, in offering kind words, described me as a 'house husband'. Is there any bloke so unconcerned with his sense of self that he wouldn't be disquieted by this job
15 description? The alternative, 'stay-at-home dad' didn't sound great to me either. Because, I reasoned, the last thing I'd be doing was that. Taking care of a child, however lovely she is, can be brain-mashingly tedious. I decided that if we didn't get out and find interesting things to do, I'd quickly wish I was back
20 in the relaxing bosom of the office.

B Don't get me wrong, I completely adore my daughter and value every minute we spend together. But up till now, my wife had usually been around and, if I'm honest, did more than her fair share. For the first year of my daughter's life I'd mainly
25 provided moral support and heavy lifting – a sort of child-rearing assistant. Yet I hadn't gone into this lightly. When my wife had to go back to work full-time and could no longer be constantly in control, we looked at other options. We decided against nursery because we thought our daughter was too
30 young to spend all day fighting over toys. We knew a few people with nannies and they swore by them. Some of them will continue to employ these essential members of domestic staff as long as the inequities of the global labour market make it relatively affordable, possibly even when their children have
35 grown up. It wasn't for us. And that left me.

C Before starting my new life, I set myself a number of rules so that we'd make the most of our time together. First of these was: no television. I was determined that we'd do something different each day. We wouldn't just muddle through our
40 weeks. We'd learn and grow together as we treated every day as a new adventure where anything was possible. And so four months before my daughter's second birthday, I took charge. On day one of our new life together, my wife was working from home. My daughter made it clear who her preferred
45 choice of carer was. At every opportunity I was reminded I was a mere reserve player, brought off the bench because the star striker was needed elsewhere. So we headed for the playground, or at least tried to. When I picked the child up,
she wanted to walk. When I put her down, she wanted to
50 be carried. After fifteen minutes, we'd travelled about fifteen metres and I thought, 'What on earth am I doing here when I should be at work?'

D Finally reaching the park, however, we relaxed and began the serious business of playing. I pushed her high on the swings,
55 fast on the roundabout and taught her how to scale the netting to reach the high slide. Mother may know best about almost everything but nobody teaches climbing like daddy. Then on day two she was ill; nothing serious but enough to change her character. Normally she chatters away happily but that day she
60 was giving off that awful whinge-cry-shout noise that other people's children inflict upon you in supermarkets. I needed to stop this quickly, so put a laptop in front of her and clicked on the first children's programme offered by the BBC iPlayer. A cartoon with trains seemed promising. The child fell instantly,
65 blissfully silent. Each time a ten-minute episode ended, I'd hear an insistent request for more and I readily complied. I'm sure I wasn't the first to fall into the trap of thinking, 'What harm can it do? She can learn just as much from a talking train as from me.'

Language development 2

> **CB** p. 114, **GR** pp. 184–185

Time and reason clauses

1 Replace the underlined time reference in each sentence where necessary by using a word or phrase from the box.

as soon as	before	ever since	no sooner	now that
the moment	until	while		

1 <u>Once</u> he no longer eats takeaways every day, Carl has more energy.
2 <u>As soon</u> as she set up the Freecycle site, fifty people joined.
3 Rachel stayed <u>before</u> the residents' meeting had finished and then left without a word.
4 <u>After</u> he was a young boy, Richie has always enjoyed making things.
5 <u>The moment</u> they were living in Peru, they learnt to build houses out of bamboo.
6 <u>While</u> going to university, Gina had taken a gap year to work as a volunteer on an African community project.
7 <u>As soon</u> had he finished university than he went to live with indigenous tribes in Central America.
8 <u>The moment </u>they had finished work on the school building, the youth group went on to paint the local library.

2 Match the beginning of the sentences (1–8) with their endings (A–H).

1 Ian bought the farm
2 The Residents Association is
3 I'll support the project,
4 Ryan and his friends are doing up the old van,
5 Fiona has handed in her notice
6 Volunteering is not like other work experience
7 We don't need to discuss the catering further,
8 Alice has brought the building proposal with her,

A in that the benefit of your work is often far-reaching.
B hoping to convert it into a mobile library.
C in case the mayor wants to discuss it.
D in order to travel the world.
E with a view to creating an eco-community there.
F seeing that it will benefit local youth groups.
G planning on taking up the matter with the local council.
H since that has already been decided upon.

Result clauses

3 Complete each sentence by circling the correct word or phrase in italics.

1 The town council should construct a bypass, *in which case / otherwise / so that* the town centre will become even more congested.
2 She set up an online business, and *consequently / so that / in such a way* she is able to work from home.
3 The mayor arranged the agenda for the meeting *in so far as / in such a way as to / in which to* make his proposal for the Film Festival take precedence.
4 The residents were not informed of the plans to develop the industrial park, *in which case / therefore / hence* their outrage.
5 I may volunteer on an eco-project next year, *so that / as a result / in which case* you can live in my house.
6 The government has cut our funding by 30 percent. *That being the case / Resulting in / In such a case,* we've been forced to abandon the parks project.

Concession clauses

4 Complete the text by circling the most suitable word or phrase in italics.

Life coach Polly Applebee tells you how to change your life around in four easy steps

A Alter your perspective

Your home environment has no doubt instilled certain expectations in you about how your life should develop. **(1)** *Nevertheless / As a result*, these may be restrictive or misleading, depending on your background. To change your life around, start by shaking off such expectations, and setting yourself some new targets.

B Focus your efforts

Ask yourself what you really want out of life. Make a list of ideas about your career, money, people you love, things you'd like to do, etc. Study it **(2)** *so as / in such a way* to decide which three items are the most important to you. **(3)** *In case / Much as* you'd like to achieve everything on your list, it's unrealistic to imagine doing so. **(4)** *Furthermore / However*, by consciously choosing three specific goals, you will be amazed at how much more focused and determined you feel.

C Overcome your doubts

Confidence is everything. **(5)** *All the same / That being the case*, a certain amount of fear and uncertainty is natural. Practise hiding it, and remain focused on your goal. **(6)** *Despite / Although* you may be shaking on the inside, show outward confidence and believe in yourself. Learn to view every obstacle as an opportunity.

D If at first you don't succeed ...

We are all afraid of failing. **(7)** *In such a case / Be that as it may*, failure is an essential part of success and you need to embrace that fact and see setbacks as stepping stones towards your ultimate goal. Difficult **(8)** *though / so* it may seem at the time, you should use your mistakes as learning tools and move on.

Use of English   (Paper 1 Part 4)

Key word transformations

1   Look at the key word in each question. How can this word be used to express the idea missing from the second sentence?

2   Answer Questions 1–10, using the Help clues if necessary.

HELP

➤ Q1   The last word in your answer will be a form of the verb *to be*.

➤ Q2   You are looking for an idiomatic expression with *keep*.

➤ Q3   The key word is the second element of a phrasal verb.

➤ Q7   You need to use the word *should* in your answer.

For questions **1 – 10**, complete the second sentence so that it has a similar meaning to the first sentence, using the word given. **Do not change the word given.** You must use between **three** and **eight** words, including the word given.

1   If anyone wants to file a complaint, they should do so before the end of the month.
wishing
The deadline _____ the end of the month.

2   Paul didn't want to commit himself to a long-term career path.
options
Paul wanted _____ his long-term career path was concerned.

3   The day was made extra-special by the contribution of a prominent local celebrity.
apart
What _____ the contribution of a prominent local celebrity.

4   Closing the factory would affect the local economy badly.
repercussions
The closure _____ the local economy.

5   This window should be kept closed at all times.
account
On _____ opened.

6   Grace wouldn't allow anything to stop her fulfilling her dream.
stand
When it came to fulfilling her dream, Grace would let _____ way.

7   In my opinion, Henry was wrong to put Mandy in such an embarrassing situation.
never
To my _____ Mandy in such an embarrassing situation.

8   In practice, Tim has handed the business over to his daughter.
intents
To all _____ in the hands of his daughter.

9   Damian did everything possible to make his new neighbours feel welcome.
lengths
Damian _____ sure that his new neighbours felt welcome.

10 Linda was about to serve lunch, when Boris rang the doorbell.
point
Linda _____ when Boris rang the doorbell.

Writing: letter of opinion (Paper 2 Part 2)

➤ **CB** pp. 110 and 116–117, **WR** pp. 198–199 and 202–204

> **EXPERT STRATEGY**
>
> Whenever possible, relate your answer to your personal knowledge or experience, as you will have more ideas to write about.

Analysing the task

1 Read the exam task below and make notes on the following:

a the person you are writing to

b your reason for writing

c the situation you must describe

Developing ideas

> Following public concern about the increasing levels of litter being dropped on the streets in some urban areas, a popular English-speaking magazine has invited readers to send in letters expressing their own opinion about the situation in their home town. You decide to send in a letter, assessing the current situation in your area and suggesting ways in which it could be improved in the future.
>
> Write your letter in **280 – 320** words.

2 Consider the following questions about your town or neighbourhood, and make notes on what you could include in your answer to the task in Exercise 1.

a How clean is it?

b Is litter picked up regularly?

c Are there a sufficient number of litter bins on the streets? Are they emptied regularly?

d Are there any laws against dropping litter in the street? If there are, do people respect them?

e Do local volunteer groups ever clean up the streets, beaches, etc.?

f What can be done to improve the situation? *(e.g. Hold community clean-up activities, raise people's awareness by distributing leaflets, have a community award scheme for the cleanest street, etc.)*

Planning your letter

3a Organise your notes into two main paragraphs. Look at the questions in Exercise 2 and decide where the second paragraph should start.

b Write an introductory paragraph and a brief concluding paragraph.

Varying sentence structure

4 Rewrite each sentence with the word or phrase in brackets. Make any other changes that are necessary.

1 Our neighbourhood is fairly clean but we do get quite a lot of litter in the High Street, particularly on Saturdays. (Be that as it may)

2 The litter bins are emptied every Tuesday and Friday. I don't think this is sufficient. (which)

3 A group of teenagers hang out in the park. They vandalise the children's playground and leave bottles lying around. This is one problem that is ignored. (being ignored + reduced relative clause)

4 A neighbourhood volunteer group cleans up the park once a month. This helps to reduce the problem . (in this way)

5 A park keeper looks after the park during the day, but at night patrols are needed to prevent damage being caused. (Nevertheless)

6 If the teenagers are not provided with their own meeting place, they will continue to damage the park area. (otherwise)

Writing task

5 Now do the task in Exercise 1. Try to use structures like those in Exercise 4 and others from the Language Development sections in this module.

Vocabulary development 1

➤ **CB** pp. 122–123

Prepositions

1 Complete the text with suitable prepositions.

Writers' homes

The homes of many writers and historical figures are turned (1) _____ museums for interested members of the public to visit. Sometimes the homes are fascinating because they are exactly what might be expected, sometimes because they are not.

Of enormous interest when we visit the homes of authors (2) _____ particular is how they ensured privacy. Goethe, the great German writer and scientist who lived in Weimar, had the luxury (3) _____ surrounding his study (4) _____ antechambers and corridors, so that he would always know when he was about to be disturbed. Jane Austen at her house in Chawton, now a museum, made sure that the door (5) _____ the drawing room was never oiled – (6) _____ its squeak, she could conceal her manuscript (7) _____ the table. Dostoevsky's house in St Petersburg has a very overcrowded and cramped feel, but he evidently made sure that his workroom was the farthest (8) _____ the front door, giving him plenty (9) _____ time to put his work (10) _____ when visitors were approaching.

We seem to be irresistibly drawn to such houses. To know that you are in the place where the first lines (11) _____ a great novel were written, gives us the feeling, however illusory it may be, that we might be (12) _____ touch with the source of their inspiration and their thought.

Different structures/buildings

2 Match the different types of structures or buildings to their definitions.

aqueduct   dungeon   edifice   fortress   landmark monument

1 a building or large structure that is built to remind people of an important person or event _____
2 a large strong building, used for defending an important place _____
3 a place or building that is easy to recognise and helps you know where you are _____
4 a structure like a bridge that carries water across a river or valley _____
5 a dark underground prison, especially under a castle, that was used in the past _____
6 (a formal word for) a building, especially a large one _____

Expressions and phrasal verbs: *draw* and *drop*

3 Complete each sentence with *draw* or *drop*.

1 We could argue until the cows come home about the meaning of art but can we _____ the subject for the time being?
2 Can we stop at the bank on the way? I need to _____ some money out.
3 I don't mind trying some brighter colours but I _____ the line at red walls and a black ceiling!
4 Many great artists _____ on the colours and beauty of nature for inspiration.
5 We _____ a hint that the building was in a bad state of repair but the landlord conveniently _____ our attention to the wonderful view.
6 From the current debate, it would be difficult to _____ the conclusion that modern architecture is as impressive as more traditional architecture.

Art: personality types

4 Complete the text with words from the box.

boxes   handwriting   images   letters   patterns rounded   shading   signs   sketchy   straight

What your doodles say about you

Have you ever spent a whole phone call listening to your friend and all the while scribbling away aimlessly on a piece of paper? You'd be surprised how much those doodles say about your character. According to **(1)** _____ experts (or 'graphologists'), because we doodle without thinking, the **(2)** _____ we choose can reveal our underlying preoccupations as well as aspects of our character. The following are some of their conclusions.

• Emotional people who crave harmony tend to go for **(3)** _____ shapes and symbols such as circles, suns, flowers, hearts, lips and balloons. More down-to-earth, practical people who desire order draw square shapes, **(4)** _____ lines and things that represent material security, such as **(5)** _____ , doors, forts, towers, block **(6)** _____ and numbers. And determined people with a lot of mental and physical energy draw pointed **(7)** _____ , from stars to arrows, zigzags, spires, stick figures and lightning. People who are sensitive or hesitant tend to draw with short, light or **(8)** _____ lines.
• Digging into the paper or going over and over something are **(9)** _____ that someone is frustrated, obsessed or stuck with a problem. Heavy **(10)** _____ or criss-crossing of strokes suggest depression or worry.

Use of English (Paper 1 Part 1)

Multiple-choice cloze

1 Read the title of the text and think about what you are going to read. What does *on approval* mean? How might it apply to works of art?

2 Read the whole text quickly to get the general meaning. Then read it again carefully, choosing the best option A–D to fit each gap. Use the Help clues if necessary.

For questions **1 – 8**, read the text below and decide which answer (**A**, **B**, **C** or **D**) best fits each gap. There is an example at the beginning (**0**).

Art on approval

For inexperienced collectors, the idea of (0) __A__ over a large sum of cash for a piece of contemporary art is a daunting prospect. It's quite (1) _____ that the work will look out of place in a domestic setting, or that the buyer might simply (2) _____ of it. In an ideal world, it would be possible to spot a piece with potential, size it up, (3) _____ a deposit and take it home on approval. Only after living with it for a while would you (4) _____ into a formal commitment to buy.

But many dealers are reluctant to allow this arrangement because there is always the possibility that such a (5) _____ of trust will backfire drastically. In the late 1990s, for example, some of the world's leading dealers were (6) _____ in by confidence tricksters. A bogus count asked to view some pieces in situ in various lavishly (7) _____ apartments he owned. The generous hospitality he offered the dealers hoodwinked them into leaving the works of art with him on extended loan. Both the count and the works of art (8) _____ disappeared without trace.

HELP

➤ Q1 Which of these words means 'possible to imagine'?

➤ Q2 You are looking for a verb that means 'get fed up with'.

➤ Q4 Only one of these verbs can be followed by the preposition *into*.

➤ Q7 You are looking for the word which collocates with *lavishly*.

EXPERT LANGUAGE
Look back at the text. Find a sentence with negative head inversion.

0	A handing	B paying	C giving	D passing
1	A reasonable	B understandable	C acceptable	D conceivable
2	A bore	B fatigue	C tire	D loathe
3	A put down	B leave off	C offer up	D make over
4	A accept	B enter	C agree	D engage
5	A matter	B gesture	C motion	D token
6	A ripped	B fooled	C taken	D tricked
7	A appointed	B realised	C arranged	D organised
8	A imminently	B punctually	C accordingly	D promptly

3 Find words and phrases in the text that mean:

1 off-putting _____

2 not fitting in with its surroundings _____

3 check the measurements _____

4 in order to try out _____

5 go badly wrong _____

6 criminals who get people's trust _____

7 fake _____

8 in place _____

9 fooled _____

10 were never seen again _____

4 Which prepositions follow these options from Question 6?

1 ripped _____

2 fooled _____

3 tricked _____

Language development 1

➤ **CB** p. 125, **GR** p. 185–186

Common words and expressions: verb phrases + -ing

1 Complete each sentence by circling the correct word from each pair in italics.

1 It's no *worth / good* leaving it until the last minute to ask him to design the interior – he'll be busy with other projects.

2 They were planning a trip to Scotland, with a *sight / view* to visiting some of the castles.

3 We are totally *concerned / committed* to supporting up-and-coming young artists.

4 Are you considering the *possibility / potential* of acquiring one of her watercolours?

5 Let's take *benefit / advantage* of having a few days off and visit some of the local sights.

6 I'm a bit *likely / prone* to catching colds so shall we paint indoors today?

7 We didn't visit the final museum on our list for *fear / worry* of missing the coach back to our hotel.

8 Unfortunately, there's no *intention / prospect* of the new opera house being finished this year.

2 Complete each gap with ONE word.

Roz and Max are doing some DIY in their house.

Roz: Max, I really don't feel (1) _____ to hanging wallpaper right now. I'm sick and (2) _____ of going up and down ladders.

Max: OK. (3) _____ of doing that, why don't you go and paint the porch? That's quite a nice job and there's no (4) _____ in wasting the rest of the daylight.

Roz: Hmm, OK.

Max: I hope you're not having any (5) _____ about our having decided to do up the house ourselves, Roz? It's going to save us a lot of money, you know.

Roz: No, I'm fine. It's just that I'm (6) _____ at making the soft furnishings than I am at painting and I just seem to make such a mess everywhere! And (7) _____ knowing how nice it's going to look in the end, I can't (8) _____ thinking about how long it's going to take us to get finished.

Max: Look, I don't (9) _____ calling it a day, if you're a bit fed up. Let's go for a walk and we can make up (10) _____ not painting the porch by discussing our interior decorating plans over supper!

Roz: Absolutely, Max! I'll be ready in five minutes!

---

3 Rewrite each sentence with the word in brackets so that it means the same as the first sentence.

1 The art tutor at my evening class said my first sketch was pretty well executed. (executing)
The art tutor at my evening class complimented me _____ .

2 Jack maintains that he never does anything less than a really good job. (prides)
Jack _____ .

3 I hear that the lovely old building in the centre is going to be knocked down – that's awful! (being)
I hate the thought _____ .

4 I certainly would never buy a brand new car. (intention)
I have _____ .

5 Yvonne bought a sculpting kit as well as painting materials. (buying)
In addition _____ .

6 I'm afraid it was my fault that the plate got broken. (responsibility)
I have to take _____ .

4 Choose the correct preposition, then complete the sentences with the correct form of a verb from the box.

---

*forge   get away   look after   maintain   miss   own
plan   renovate   spend   study*

---

1 There's no likelihood *for / of* _____ from the art exhibition early – we've been invited to meet some important art dealers later.

2 I'm stuck *with / to* _____ my six-year-old nephew today – perhaps I'll take him to the Teddy Bear museum!

3 Trish has no objection *for / to* people _____ those fantastic yachts but she just wishes she could have a look around one of them!

4 I hear they're planning *on / about* _____ that whole inner-city area, which will be great.

5 A lot of effort has gone *into / for* _____ the highest standards of customer care.

6 The council is responsible *to / for* _____ and implementing schemes aimed at improving conditions for motorists, public transport users, cyclists and pedestrians.

7 Tom is really excited *for / about* _____ civil engineering – roads and bridges have always fascinated him.

8 Did you hear about the case in Holland where some crooks were found guilty *by / of* _____ well-known paintings by Picasso?

9 Despite all the tourists, we have no regrets *about / with* _____ all day at the Louvre Museum.

10 There's no excuse *in / for* _____ his lecture – he's one of the greatest living art historians of current times.

Use of English (Paper 1 Part 3)

Word formation

1 Look at the title and the first paragraph of the text. What does the word *squeeze* suggest there is a lack of? How might architecture need to change in the future?

2 Read the whole text quickly to get the general meaning, then read it again and complete the task. Use the Help clues if necessary.

HELP

➤ Q2 Make an adjective and then an adverb out of this word.
➤ Q3 Add a word to make a compound meaning 'equivalent'.
➤ Q6 How can you form a verb from this adjective?
➤ Q8 Add a prefix to this word and then create the past participle to act as an adjective.

EXPERT LANGUAGE

Look back at the text. Find two nouns which are followed by an infinitive form.

For questions **1 – 8**, read the text below. Use the word given in capitals at the end of some of the lines to form a word that fits the space in the same line. There is an example at the beginning (**0**).

The big squeeze

The past few years have been a period of innovation and adjustment in architecture, with many of the
(0) ASSUMPTIONS of the twentieth century now being   ASSUME
called into question.
For example, in the struggle to accommodate ever-expanding populations, architects are
(1) _____ turning their attention to space-saving   INCREASE
designs. The average house built in Britain today
(2) _____ provides 30 percent less space than   TYPE
was provided by its (3) _____ of a century ago.   COUNTER
Much of that change has taken place in recent years
and there is every (4) _____ that the trend will   LIKELY
continue.
Many architects welcome the challenge of designing
homes which use space with greater (5) _____ ,   EFFICIENT
without compromising aesthetic and environmental
aims. To avoid a small living space appearing cramped,
for example, there is a need to (6) _____ clutter.   MINIMAL
That's why the provision of (7) _____ space is a   STORE
crucial element in any design.
One country that can teach us a great deal about
space-saving interiors is Japan. Architects there
have a knack of squeezing extra space out of easily
(8) _____ voids, which are often tucked away   LOOK
deep within buildings.

3 Find words and phrases in the text that mean:

1 reconsidered   _____
2 crowded   _____
3 too many things in a place   _____
4 a special ability   _____
5 empty spaces   _____
6 hidden   _____

Listening (Paper 3 Part 4)

Multiple matching

EXPERT STRATEGY

Each of the two tasks has a different focus. Think about the task focuses carefully. You are listening for words and phrases that relate to the idea in the focus, not only for vocabulary that matches the words in the options.

1   Read Task One carefully. Think about the vocabulary and expressions you would expect to hear when people are talking about a work of art.

2   Then read Task Two carefully. What is the main idea you are listening for? What kind of things do people appreciate in a work of art?

3   Now listen and do the tasks. Use the Help clues if necessary. You can do one task at a time, or both tasks at once – the choice is yours.

You will hear five short extracts in which people are talking about a work of art.

Task One

For questions **1 – 5**, choose from the list (**A – H**) what first brought the work of art to the speaker's attention.

Task Two

For questions **6 – 10**, choose from the list (**A – H**) what each speaker appreciates most about the work of art.

While you listen, you must complete both tasks.

Task One		Task Two	
A being invited to an exhibition		A the memories it evokes	
B reading a review of it		B its air of mystery	
C a friend's recommendation	Speaker 1 [1]	C the skill of the artist	Speaker 1 [6]
D a course of study	Speaker 2 [2]	D the fascinating detail	Speaker 2 [7]
E a family gathering	Speaker 3 [3]	E the overall effect	Speaker 3 [8]
F a chance encounter	Speaker 4 [4]	F its monetary value	Speaker 4 [9]
G seeing the artist at work	Speaker 5 [5]	G the reactions it provokes	Speaker 5 [10]
H receiving it as a gift		H the message it conveys	

HELP

➤ Q2 Listen for who told the speaker about it.
➤ Q3 Listen for how the speaker first heard about this particular work of art by the artist.
➤ Q7 Why does the speaker keep looking at the painting?
➤ Q8 Listen for the phrase *I love it to bits*; the answer follows this.

4   Match the expressions from the recordings (1–10) with their definitions (A–J).

1 large as life (Speaker 1)
2 highly thought of (Speaker 1)
3 bumped into (Speaker 2)
4 slammed (Speaker 2)
5 executed (Speaker 3)
6 sat (Speaker 3)
7 draws me to it (Speaker 4)
8 intricacy (Speaker 5)
9 getting out of hand (Speaker 5)
10 in tune with (Speaker 5)

A complicated design
B having an instinctive understanding
C in person
D becoming unreasonable
E reviewed negatively
F well regarded
G met by chance
H was the artist's model
I carried out
J attracts

EXPERT WORD CHECK

*ceramics   art pottery   on an impulse
stand up to   aesthetically   corridor
a giveaway price   critical appraisal
enhanced   craftsmanship*

Reading (Paper 1 Part 6)

Gapped text

EXPERT STRATEGY
Remember to keep reading all the options, even if you think you've fitted one into an earlier gap. You may want to go back and change your mind. Underline the links as you choose an answer, so that you can go back and double check.

EXPERT LANGUAGE
Look back at the base text and options. Find sentences that begin with an adverb or phrase that is related to time.

EXPERT WORD CHECK
defining moment   meld   covetable idiosyncratic   referral   leveraging high-end   sift through   their undoing iteration

1 Read the title and subtitle of the text. What is it going to be about?

2 Read the main text quickly and answer these questions:
a Why was the striped dress important?
b What irony about brands marketing through blogs is exposed?
c What are hippies and punks an example of?

3 Look at Gap 1.
a Read the text above the gap.
b Read Extract C. It mentions *the garment*. What is this a reference to?
c Read the text below Gap 1. What are the words *the former* a reference to?

4 Now look at Gaps 2–7 and repeat the procedure.

5 When you have finished the task, check it makes sense

> You are going to read a newspaper article about the fashion industry. Seven paragraphs have been removed from the extract. Choose from the paragraphs **A – H** the one which fits each gap (**1 – 7**). There is one extra paragraph which you do not need to use.

A And it didn't stop at incentives either. One high-end retailer reportedly even started holding workshops to give its key bloggers tips on how to make their blogs more shoppable, thereby ensuring that potential clients need look no further.

B Celebrity weeklies were increasingly taking their cues from hot blogger stories and this one was picked up everywhere. What's more, it was not only blogs about celebrities that were having an impact. People writing about everything from watches to their own lives were becoming more influential.

C In other words, the garment had gone viral. But the question remained: Did this occur because A-listers were shown wearing the item and consumers wanted to be just like them, or was it because key fashion bloggers picked, from the thousands of images they sift through each day, those particular pictures to feature?

D Paradoxically, therefore, it became quite possible that their very success could ultimately be their undoing. In this, they were simply the latest iteration of a recurring theme: fashion's ability to identify, and co-opt, an influential minority.

E Some from this earlier generation subsequently parlayed their fame into paid consultancies or jobs with brands. Unsurprisingly, given their many thousand followers, the brands loved them, and were keen to bring them into the fold.

F Some retailers, many of them also etailers, started doing exactly that, zooming in on blogs in an attempt to facilitate sales at the point of inspiration. Potential customers were online every single moment of the day, and wherever they were, they were also shopping. Brands were trying to close the gap between seeing an item and buying it.

G The emergence of such pseudo-blogs underlines a shift that was happening across the blogosphere at that time. There were still people doing it solo, but there were now many other blogs, owned by media companies and set up as digital platforms. In the world of celebrity fashion blogs, these included collective blogs reviewing celebrity style and directing viewers to retailer sites.

H What's more, one prominent blogger believes commercial tie-ups are an inevitable result of blogging becoming, for some, a business. She says, 'As more and more of the most influential bloggers moved from blogging part-time to making it the main focus of their professional activity, they are necessarily looking for ways to monetise their influence in order to make a living.'

The Online Tastemakers
How bloggers changed the face of fashion marketing

How you quantify real online influence remains a subject of much debate in the fashion industry. For many, however, the defining moment came back in 2011. The story began when a major US fashion chain store, known for colourful, funky pieces, sent a dress with navy and red stripes to a few celebrity friends. Coincidentally, and in the space of four weeks, all wore the dress in public. Before you could say, 'What a cute outfit', various blog sites had written about this sartorial mind meld. Within a week, the store had nearly sold out of the $49.90 item, which means that, according to the estimates of one industry expert, they had moved in excess of ten thousand dresses.

1 _____

In the past, the correct interpretation would probably have been the former; it is received wisdom in the fashion industry that celebrities sell clothes. Yet some people are in no doubt that this was the moment when things changed. For these commentators, it was the bloggers who were behind that striped dress becoming so covetable.

2 _____

These were not, however, necessarily the same bloggers who had first gained the fashion industry's attention a few years previously. Those were primarily fashion fans with laptops, embraced for their idiosyncratic take on fashion and invited to sit in the front row at catwalk events, the seats traditionally reserved for the powerful editors of glossy magazines.

3 _____

The newer breed of bloggers was different. Focusing on red-carpet events and celebrities, they played into several contemporary trends: a fascination with famous people, especially reality TV stars; our desire to cut through large amounts of information quickly; and the ability of online sites to drive sales. For the most part, these blogs are distinguishable from the earlier wave because they've been conceived from the outset as commercial enterprises, albeit presented in the format of a blog.

4 _____

The kind of business such referrals started to generate caused a shift in thinking at some fashion brands about the best way to reach consumers. When they blogged about people wearing things, they were adding another level of endorsement. Brands soon realised that rather than spend a huge amount on advertising and marketing, they'd be better off targeting the bloggers.

5 _____

But with all this going on, how was an independent blogger to work more closely with a brand whilst simultaneously retaining what, for many, made them worth reading in the first place? That sense that bloggers are just like me, only more obsessive; that we respond to them as readers because we assume a purity in their approach; they are, we imagine, doing it for fun, not leveraging for profit?

6 _____

Looking back, it is possible to see a familiar pattern emerging. It had happened with those who rejected fashion's rules (hippies, punks), just as it happened with those who wanted to be ironic and distant from fashion (Tom Ford's early Gucci) and it had already happened with the first wave of bloggers. At the end of the day, the fashion industry absorbed the trends and made them mainstream. For independent bloggers, the process started with that striped dress.

7 _____

And this makes sense and it is something that blog followers, who are not so easily manipulated as might be supposed, can appreciate – in the same way that they can see when something is branded. At the end of the day, they could ask themselves the questions, 'Do you really want that dress because a particular blogger showed it to you and you liked the blog?' and 'Did the blogger show you that dress because the brand asked them to?'

Vocabulary development 2

Phrasal verbs

1   Complete the text with a phrasal verb in the correct form. Use the verb given plus a particle from the box. You will need to use some particles more than once.

away   into   off   out   to   up   with

HANGING ON TO OLD TREASURES

Be careful what you **(1)** _____ (part) when you move away from the family home. It's very easy to fall into the trap of thinking that childhood books and toys are valueless and that they **(2)** _____ (take) too much room. What happens later on in life, when you suddenly wonder what happened to that lovely boxed set of children's books or that collection of china animals? Gone forever.

Of course, if you really **(3)** _____ (get) collecting any such items and if you're lucky, you might be able to **(4)** _____ (pick / them) cheaply at bazaars or second-hand shops. You might also be able to **(5)** _____ (root / them) on eBay. You'll never find the exact replacements, however.

If you do manage to **(6)** _____ (build) a decent collection, you have two options: either you keep them or you sell them. It all depends how emotionally attached you become to them!

There was a case recently of an American football player who'd **(7)** _____ (stash) a two-million-pound collection of rare Winnie-the-Pooh items over the years. Since he was **(8)** _____ (look) sell them, his agent suggested they **(9)** _____ (put / them) for auction. The player of course made a huge profit on his original investment and that for him was the fun of the game.

Collecting can be both fun and a challenge – but remember that some of those childhood treasures can be a good way of **(10)** _____ (kick) your very first collection.

Word formation: adjectives ending in *-less* and their adverb forms

2a   Form adjectives ending in *-less* from the following words and categorise them under the headings below. Check you understand their meanings.

character   clue   effort   end   hope   meaning
speech   spot   stain   time   use   worth

Positive	Negative	Neutral / Could be either

b   Complete each sentence with an adjective or adverb formed from the words in Exercise 2a.

1   Needless to say, all the kitchen and bathroom appliances are made of _____ steel.
2   The long avenue of trees seemed to stretch _____ into the distance.
3   His office was in a _____ concrete building, typical of buildings built in the 1970s.
4   We were left _____ when confronted by his rather avant-garde paintings.
5   Most of these items are _____ in monetary terms but they have a lot of sentimental value.
6   The furniture removals man _____ picked up two huge boxes of books.

Expressions and phrasal verbs with *wear* and *keep*

3   Where necessary, combine words from the box with the words *wear* or *keep* and complete the sentences.

appearances   casual   tear   tidy   word

1   Emily's situation was pretty desperate but for the children's sake, she tried to _____ up _____ .
2   Most household items will need to be replaced sooner or later due to general _____ and _____ .
3   He said he'd come and help me throw out some old furniture so I hope he's going to _____ his _____ and not let me down.
4   If you want to _____ your house _____ , then you should follow the old adage, 'A place for everything and everything in its place.'
5   The market for smart _____ _____ is still doing pretty well.
6   Did they really need that new car or did they simply want to _____ up with the Joneses?

Language development 2

> **CB** p. 130, **GR** p. 186

-ing form or infinitive

1   Complete each sentence by circling the correct verb form from each pair in italics.

1   Do you think you'll end up *be able / being able* to make a living out of your sculptures?

2   I don't really know how *to portray / portraying* perspective in this type of painting.

3   According to Feng Shui principles, we'd be better off *to have / having* the mirror on this wall.

4   I'm in no mood *to fork out / forking out* a lot of money on designer clothes at the moment.

5   Karen took the trouble *to make / making* me a home-made card for my birthday.

6   I didn't like my mother *to display / displaying* so many valuable items in her home – especially with small children around!

2   Complete each sentence with a preposition and the correct form of a verb from the box. Sometimes there may be more than one possibility.

change   come up with   convince   pull down
succeed   understand

1   When are you going to make up your mind _____ _____ the colour scheme in your flat? It's about time, isn't it?

2   If they haven't got a justifiable reason _____ _____ that old building, then I think we should put in a complaint.

3   The best way _____ _____ good fashion ideas is by looking at fashion magazines.

4   I have difficulty _____ _____ what she wants to convey through this particular sculpture.

5   My friends went to great lengths _____ _____ me to enter the competition.

6   I really feel that Maria has little chance _____ _____ as an artist – it's such a competitive world.

3   Circle all the adjectives in italics that are correct in each sentence.

1   Jason is *bound / due / enthusiastic* to go to the vintage car rally because he wants to show off his 1926 Bentley!

2   Junior seamstresses are *apt / liable / accustomed* to make mistakes in the beginning.

3   Even those people who were not *reluctant / inclined / accustomed* to buying vintage clothing found some good bargains.

4   We are *ready / willing / anxious* to help the fair trade companies in any way we can.

5   I had grave doubts as to whether Simon was *prepared / capable / inclined* of fulfilling his commitments to the design company.

6   The two men are *worried / guilty / accused* of stealing a valuable masterpiece.

4   Complete the text with the correct form of the verb given in brackets.

Manolo Blahnik, shoe designer

Manolo Blahnik, born in 1942 to a Czech father and a Spanish mother, is a world-famous shoe designer, who has dominated shoe design since **(1)** _____ (set up) in business in London in the early 1970s. Manolo was brought up in the Canary Islands where an early influence on him was his mother. As well as **(2)** _____ (be) interested in the world of haute couture, she was also willing **(3)** _____ (try) her hand at **(4)** _____ (make) things herself; at one time, she persuaded the local cobbler **(5)** _____ (teach) her how **(6)** _____ (make) Catalan espadrilles from ribbons and laces. Manolo loved to watch her **(7)** _____ (make) them and he remembers the feel of the shoe as it was slowly taking shape.

After **(8)** _____ (have) a home education, Manolo studied in Geneva and eventually moved to Paris **(9)** _____ (study) Art. There, he made ends meet by **(10)** _____ (work) at a vintage clothes store. He then moved to London, ostensibly to study English but he ended up **(11)** _____ (spend) most of his time **(12)** _____ (watch) films at the cinema! In the meantime, Manolo was starting **(13)** _____ (get) into design and toyed with the idea of **(14)** _____ (become) a stage set designer. On a trip to New York where he went in the hope of **(15)** _____ (drum up) some design work, he was fortunate enough **(16)** _____ (introduce) to the editor of US Vogue, who suggested that he move into the design of accessories, in particular shoes.

From that moment on, he never looked back although it took him many years **(17)** _____ (learn) the craft of shoe-making and produce shoes that were both technically perfect and a work of art. Like all truly talented designers, he had the ability **(18)** _____ (stamp) all his work with a distinctive signature style, while at the same time **(19)** _____ (show) his innovative skill. Manolo Blahnik designs each shoe he produces himself: he does the sketch and he then creates the mould for the shoe, **(20)** _____ (carve) the heel and perfecting the design. So when you buy Manolo Blahnik shoes (or 'Manolos'), at least you know that is truly what you are buying – if you can afford it, that is!

Use of English (Paper 1 Part 4)

Key word transformations

1 Look at the key word in each question. How can this word be used to express the idea missing from the second sentence?

2 Answer Questions 1–10, using the Help clues if necessary.

HELP

➤ Q1 You need to use a passive form here.
➤ Q2 Use a phrase that includes the word *line*.
➤ Q3 Make a noun out of *reluctant*.
➤ Q5 Use the key word as part of a phrasal verb.
➤ Q9 You need to use the noun that corresponds to 'obligatory'.

For questions **1 – 10**, complete the second sentence so that it has a similar meaning to the first sentence, using the word given. **Do not change the word given.** You must use between **three** and **eight** words, including the word given.

1 There was no sign of Gareth when they arrived at the rendezvous point.
nowhere
Gareth _____ when they arrived at the rendezvous point.

2 Although Carol's dad liked teenage fashions, he didn't approve of her having a tattoo.
drew
Much as Carol's dad liked teenage fashion,_____ having a tattoo.

3 Sandra thought her son was reluctant to go dancing because he was shy.
down
Sandra put her _____ to shyness.

4 The new stadium is unlikely to be finished in time for the start of the season.
prospect
There is _____ finished in time for the start of the season.

5 Although she was very enthusiastic about singing, Gwenda lacked the necessary talent.
make
Gwenda's enthusiasm _____ for her lack of talent.

6 Lots of people believe that Harry intends to stand for election, but he is not.
popular
Contrary _____ standing for election.

7 Only supporters' club members are entitled to enter the family enclosure.
restricted
Entrance _____ members of the supporters' club.

8 'I don't think you'll regret visiting the museum,' said Monica.
worth
Monica said that _____ visit.

9 'Attendance at extra lectures is not obligatory,' said our tutor.
under
Our tutor said that _____ extra lectures.

10 Obviously, the company takes all complaints very seriously.
saying
It _____ very seriously by the company.

Writing: essay (Paper 2 Part 1)

> **CB** pp. 126 and 132–133, **WR** pp. 189–190

> **CB** pp. 126 and 132–133, **WR** pp. 189–190

EXPERT STRATEGY

When expressing your opinion in the task, avoid making sweeping statements in order to sound impressive.
It is best to remain fairly tentative in your opinions through the use of modal verbs and perhaps a rhetorical question.

Analysing and understanding the input texts

1   Read the task and the two texts below. Do the texts express similar or opposing points of view? Underline actual phrases that tell you.

Read the two texts below.
Write an essay summarising and evaluating the key points from both texts. Use your own words throughout as far as possible, and include your own ideas in your answers.
Write your answer in **240 – 280 words.**

1 Freedom in art

Fashions in art over the centuries have evolved in many different ways, but the fundamental difference between art nowadays and what it was in previous centuries is the complete freedom of expression that modern-day artists enjoy. Through their use of colour, they can portray their particular representation of reality, without having to conform to outdated rules about perspective. It is up to the person viewing that painting or work of art to interpret the artist's message as they see fit; in previous times, there was no ambiguity about what was being represented and therefore art represented no sense of challenge. It simply reflected the real world.

2 Art – a satisfying portrayal of reality

Any comparison between the great artists of earlier centuries and those of today cannot fail to come down on the side of the past masters. Their mastery of perspective, their attention to detail and the evocation of atmosphere within a recognisable scene give the person viewing that art a sense of satisfaction and a sense that they are viewing the world through the enhanced eye of the artist. What, in contrast, do these contemporary splashes of colour thrown across a canvas give us other than a feeling of mild amusement? I hardly think they inspire in us respect or a feeling of reverence for the creative artist's skill.

Write your **essay.**

2   Which of the sentences below correctly summarise the ideas in Text 1? Which correctly summarise Text 2? There are two extra sentences that do not summarise either text.

A The writer argues in favour of an art form where the subject matter is clearly depicted.

B The writer claims that the rules that governed art in earlier years were based on false assumptions.

C The writer makes the point that abstract art may inspire ridicule.

D The writer outlines the importance of a type of art that is not rule-bound.

E The writer refers to the skill required by modern-day artists.

F The writer supports the idea of art as being something that requires a certain amount of thought.

Using discourse markers

3   Complete the discourse markers in the sentences below with a suitable missing word. Choose the four sentences you think might be relevant to an essay based on the texts in Exercise 1.

1 _____ I see it, modern art has a particular attraction simply because of the freedom of interpretation that it offers each individual.

2 It is _____ accepted that modern art is far superior to any previous art form.

3 It may be _____ that much of modern art does not depict reality in a way that is easily comprehensible.

4 Just _____ fashions in clothing belong to different periods of time, so styles of art go in and out of fashion.

5 To _____ with, it must be pointed out that art has nothing at all to do with reality.

6 With _____ to earlier art forms, the focus then was very much on a realistic portrayal of what artists saw around them.

Writing task

4   Now do the task in Exercise 1.

9 Fitness and nutrition

9A How far can you go?

Vocabulary development 1

> **CB** pp. 138–139

Idioms: sport

1a Match each idiom (1–6) with its definition (a–f) and the sport it originated from (i–vi).

1 back the wrong horse
2 be below the belt
3 below par
4 in the same league as
5 time out
6 go off the deep end

a (take) a break from sth
b as good as
c overreact (in anger)
d make the wrong choice
e not performing as well as one can
f unfair comment, criticism

i basketball
ii boxing
iii golf
iv horse racing
v swimming
vi football, rugby

b Complete the dialogue with a suitable form of the idioms in Exercise 1a.

Sharon: Hey, Greg! What's this I hear about Mark Lynes?
Greg: Yeah, well ... Apparently the manager kicked him off the first team, saying his performance had been **(1)** _____ all season, and Lynes walked out.
Sharon: So? The manager's right, isn't he?
Greg: Maybe, but replacing him with Farmer! I mean, the man's a born loser!
Sharon: Now that's a bit **(2)** _____ , Greg! Farmer's not such a bad player. But I agree, he's not **(3)** _____ Lynes.
Greg: Well, I think they're **(4)** _____ in Farmer. Ian Coles would have been a better choice.
Sharon: Personally, I think Lynes was wrong to **(5)** _____ like that. A little bit of **(6)** _____ might have done him some good and then he could have made a comeback. There's no way they'll let him back in now.

Word formation

2 Complete each sentence with the correct form of the words in brackets. You will need to make more than one change to each word.

1 The tennis ace wept _____ (console) after her defeat against the number 10 seed.
2 Danielle _____ (shine) her rivals in the gymnastics tournament, walking away with the gold medal.
3 The manager totally _____ (estimate) Shelley's determination to overcome her injury, and was amazed by the speed of her recovery.
4 14-year-old Lucy Palmer's _____ (stand) performance on her pony, Rusty, gained her the cup for most promising young rider.
5 Warner has been playing _____ (consist) for the past few games and so we've decided to drop him from the team.
6 The match between John Isner and Nicolas Mahut at Wimbledon lasted an incredible 11 hours over three days, a feat _____ (parallel) in the history of tennis.

3 Complete the text with the correct form of words from the box.

*challenge   circumnavigate   controversial   ensue
epic   isolate   resource   undertake*

Heroine of the high seas

In January, 2012, 16-year-old Laura Dekker from the Netherlands arrived in the Caribbean island of St. Maarten in her 38-foot yacht, Guppy, successfully completing her single-handed **(1)** _____ of the globe. She is the youngest person to do so to date, yet she won't be entering the Guinness Book of World Records, due to the **(2)** _____ caused by her trip.

Laura originally hoped to set sail on her **(3)** _____ voyage aged 13, having sailed from the Netherlands to Britain and back the year before. However, the Dutch child welfare authorities took legal action to try and stop her from **(4)** _____ the trip, and a court battle **(5)** _____ which divided the country and resulted in a stalemate lasting over 10 months. Eventually, an agreement was reached, but Laura was 15 by the time she set off. She faced several **(6)** _____ during the voyage, not least of which was the attempt to keep up with her schoolwork. Nevertheless, this **(7)** _____ young woman managed to overcome storms, prolonged **(8)** _____ and the threat of pirates in order to achieve her goal, and amazingly enough, didn't fall behind with her studies.

Use of English   (Paper 1 Part 1)

Multiple-choice cloze

1   Read the title of the text and think about what you are going to read. Do you think the skills needed for athletics can be taught?

2   Read the whole text quickly to get the general meaning. Then read again carefully, choosing the best option A–D to fit each gap. Use the Help clues if necessary.

For questions **1 – 8**, read the text below and decide which answer (**A, B, C** or **D**) best fits each gap. There is an example at the beginning (**0**).

Improving athletics teaching in schools

The Elevating Athletics Fund is an (**0**) __A__ sponsored by AVIVA, a major UK financial institution. It aims to ensure that all children have a positive first experience of athletics, and hopes to make participation in a range of sports both attractive and rewarding to all children. The fund was launched against the (**1**) _____ of research that revealed that 52 percent of teachers felt inadequately prepared to teach basic athletics skills. The (**2**) _____ on which the work of the fund is based is that the fundamental skills of athletics, (**3**) _____ running, jumping and throwing, (**4**) _____ a good performance in many other sports and so should be taught as enabling skills before a child goes on to sport-specific training. The fund is designed to make an (**5**) _____ at grassroots level and so was set up with a (**6**) _____ to providing practical training and support for every single sports teacher in the UK. In doing so, it hopes to raise the (**7**) _____ of athletics teaching in schools, and thereby bring sporting success within the (**8**) _____ of a much wider cross-section of the population.

HELP

➤ Q1   Only one of the options completes the phrase *against the … of*.

➤ Q3   Choose the option that means 'that is to say' when introducing specific examples.

➤ Q4   Choose the option that means 'provides a foundation for'.

➤ Q7   All the options have a similar meaning, but only one collocates with *raise*.

EXPERT LANGUAGE

Look back at the text. Find:
a three verbs followed by the infinitive
b one adjective followed by the infinitive

0	A initiative	B exercise	C operation	D association
1	A backdrop	B upshot	C outcome	D downside
2	A essence	B reason	C premise	D substance
3	A exactly	B namely	C precisely	D clearly
4	A underpin	B subsidise	C uphold	D forecast
5	A influence	B result	C effect	D impact
6	A mind	B view	C goal	D wish
7	A prestige	B image	C profile	D standing
8	A scope	B range	C reach	D dream

3   Find words and expressions in the text that mean:
1 gave financial backing   _____
2 with ordinary people   _____
3 basic abilities that facilitate more specific training   _____
4 in this way   _____
5 representative sample   _____

4   Look at Question 1.
1 What type of words are these?
2 Which of these words has an antonym formed in the same way?
3 Can you find other examples of this type of word amongst the options?

5   Look through all the questions.
1 Which word in the options is a verb made using a noun + suffix?
2 What is the noun?

Language development 1

➤ **CB** p. 141, **GR** pp. 186–187

Sentence adverbials

1   Complete each sentence with a word from the box.

Believe   Funnily   Generally   Incredible

1 _____ as it may sound, there were times during the ordeal when I was incredibly happy. I think it was simply because I was still alive.
2 _____ enough, I sometimes miss the feeling of suspense and not knowing whether I would survive another day.
3 _____ speaking, the local people were very friendly and helped us with supplies.
4 _____ it or not, Peter just won the archery tournament! Amazing, isn't it?

Gradable and ungradable adjectives

2   *Quite* can be used to both modify and intensify words in certain contexts. Decide whether *quite* in the statements below means a) fairly or b) totally/completely.

1 You're quite right. I couldn't agree with you more.
2 It looks quite rough out there. I wouldn't go sailing today if I were you.
3 What a journey! I feel quite exhausted.
4 The route for the car rally this year is quite challenging, and will certainly test the drivers.

3   Complete each sentence by using an adverb from Box A and an adjective from Box B to form collocations.

> A highly   meticulously   perfectly   purely
>   ridiculously   stunningly

> B beautiful   capable   coincidental   expensive
>   tidy   unlikely

1 Laura argued that she was _____ of taking care of herself in the ocean.
2 After his tenth defeat in a row yesterday, it now seems _____ that Jim will continue playing professionally.
3 The early-morning view from the top of the Grand Canyon was _____ .
4 During her voyage, Ellen kept the boat's cabin _____ so that she could find things easily in an emergency.
5 Steve coming to my rescue like that was _____ . He didn't even know I was taking part in the race.
6 That new GPS system was _____ to install. I'm going to be on a tight budget from now on!

Adverb-adjective collocations

4   Complete each sentence by crossing out the adverb in italics which does not commonly collocate with the adjective.

1 The sea looked *deceptively / genuinely / perfectly* calm, but Laura knew there was a storm coming.
2 It was *stupidly / tremendously / perceptibly* naïve of you to think you could go windsurfing in this weather! You almost drowned!
3 Sharon was *patently / genuinely / understandably* surprised to have won that award.
4 The spectators became *perceptibly / decidedly / unbearably* quieter as the chess game got under way.
5 After his outburst on the pitch, the player was *conspicuously / deceptively / reassuringly* absent from the press conference.
6 It was becoming *decidedly / patently / stupidly* obvious to the crew that they would have to radio for help.

Collocations

5   Complete the text with words from the box.

*painfully   reluctantly   seriously   sheer
somewhat   truly   utterly   widely*

Fulfilling the dream of a lifetime

On June 15th 2012, in a **(1)** _____ publicised event, 33-year-old Nik Wallenda realised his lifetime dream of becoming the first man to walk across Niagara Falls on a tightrope. An accomplished stuntman, Wallenda already held several world records for tightrope walking, but found this experience totally different from any other, due to the **(2)** _____ power of the water thundering just below him, shooting up spray that **(3)** _____ hindered visibility. Afterwards he recalled feeling, while not exactly frightened, **(4)** _____ unnerved by not being able to focus on the movement of the cable, since all he could see was cascading water and this mist all around him. He was also **(5)** _____ aware of the safety rope he had **(6)** _____ agreed to wear dragging along the wire behind him. At some point just after the halfway mark, he admitted to feeling **(7)** _____ drained, both mentally and physically, but his concentration and training kept him going. As Wallenda ran the last 15 feet with the crowd cheering him on, one young onlooker described the spectacle as **(8)** '_____ awesome'.

Use of English   (Paper 1 Part 3)

Word formation

1 Read the title of the text. What makes tennis such a popular spectator sport? Why do some people dislike it?

2 Read the whole text quickly to get the general meaning, then read it again and complete the task. Use the Help clues if necessary.

HELP

➤ Q2 This noun needs to become a verb. It follows the same pattern as 'sympathy'.
➤ Q3 You must add another word to make a compound here – it is the opposite of 'triumphs'.
➤ Q6 You need to add a prefix here.
➤ Q7 You should turn this verb into an adjective.

For questions **1 – 8**, read the text below. Use the word given in capitals at the end of some of the lines to form a word that fits the space in the same line. There is an example at the beginning (**0**).

The fascination of tennis

People who are unfamiliar with tennis often find its appeal (0) _PUZZLING_ . What is so gripping about watching two people (1) _____ hit a fluffy pressurised ball across a net, they wonder. Yet tennis is a major spectator sport, that catches the imagination of millions. This is partly because when we watch a match, we (2) _____ with the players, sharing their triumphs and (3) _____ as, like them, we focus intently on every shot. The tension is palpable and the spectator is (4) _____ drawn into the duel being played out on court. But some of the fascination also comes from the (5) _____ of the game itself. David Foster Wallace, who wrote *Infinite Jest*, a work of fiction about the sport, provides a valuable (6) _____ into the technical background when he describes tennis as 'chess on the run.' According to Wallace, professional players are making (7) _____ calculations every moment the ball is in play, as they seek to anticipate how their (8) _____ will return a shot and what their own response needs to be.

PUZZLE
REPEAT

EMPATHY
SET

ESCAPE

INTRICATE

SIGHT

MULTIPLY

OPPOSE

3 Find words in the text that mean:

1 that holds your attention _____
2 victories _____
3 that you can feel _____
4 interpersonal battle _____

4 Make verbs from these adjectives.

1 popular _____
2 mechanical _____
3 neutral _____
4 critical _____
5 legitimate _____
6 emphatic _____
7 analytical _____
8 hypothetical _____
9 digital _____
10 energetic _____

Listening (Paper 3 Part 2)

Sentence completion

EXPERT STRATEGY

Remember that although you won't hear exactly the same sentences, the information comes in the same order as the sentences on the page.

1 Read the instructions for the task.

a Who are you going to hear?

b What will that person be talking about?

2 Read the sentences. How much do you find out about *Sports Psychology* from them?

3 Try and predict the type of information you will be listening for.

4 Listen to the recording and complete the sentences. Use the Help clues if necessary.

HELP

➤ Q1 You are listening for a field of study – listen for the word *field* because the answer comes soon afterwards.

➤ Q2 Be careful. Three types of concentration are mentioned. Listen for the names of winter sports.

➤ Q3 Listen for a word that indicates that Graeme is surprised.

➤ Q5 You are listening for a part of the body.

➤ Q8 Be careful – is the answer singular or plural?

➤ Q9 The speaker lists three emotions, but only one of them is linked to poor performance.

EXPERT LANGUAGE

Look back through the sentences. What type of verbs are used after Graeme's name? Do you expect to hear these words in the recording?

EXPERT WORD CHECK

*optimise   short burst   bobsleigh
get under the skin of   do wonders for
tightening   adversity   shed tears
pent-up emotion   downward cycle*

You will hear a sports psychologist talking about how he helps athletes prepare for major sporting events. For questions **1 – 9**, complete the sentences with a word or short phrase.

Sports Psychology

Graeme identifies research into (1) _____ as the most relevant aspect of psychology for sports coaches.

Graeme points out that certain winter sports require what is called (2) _____ concentration.

Graeme is surprised at how often (3) _____ are a cause of distraction for experienced athletes.

Graeme recommends that athletes set themselves (4) _____ goals as a way of maintaining focus.

Graeme gives the example of (5) _____ as a 'trigger' word that might help a sprinter.

Graeme feels that making use of (6) _____ is the best way to improve self-confidence.

Graeme thinks an athlete who wasn't nervous before an important event might lack (7) _____ .

Graeme has found that athletes use the word (8) _____ for the various symptoms of stress.

Graeme mentions that feelings of (9) _____ can lead to a deterioration in an athlete's performance.

Vocabulary development 2

Verbs connected with eating and diet

1   Complete the text with verbs from the box.

*acquire   chew   crave   eliminate   incorporate
savour   water   whet*

Tips for balancing your diet

✓ Rather than calories and quantity, think of food in terms of colour, variety and freshness. Try to **(1)** _____ different-coloured fruits and vegetables into your daily menu.

✓ Make gradual changes to your diet. There's no need to completely **(2)** _____ those sweets that make your mouth **(3)** _____ but try and reduce the frequency with which you eat them.

✓ **(4)** _____ a taste for salads by experimenting with flavours. Adding olive oil and balsamic vinegar, or nuts and honey to leafy green salads makes them incredibly tasty, and is also healthy.

✓ Add naturally sweet vegetables, such as corn, carrots, sweet potatoes, yams and squash to your salads to make them more interesting and **(5)** _____ your appetite for fresh food. In doing so, you will find that you **(6)** _____ other sweets less.

✓ Finally, learn to slow down the pace at which you eat. **(7)** _____ your food properly before swallowing it, and **(8)** _____ every mouthful. Eating with other people will help you to achieve this, as it makes the mealtime experience more enjoyable.

A matter of taste

2   Complete each sentence by choosing the correct option.

1 Don't eat that bread! It's three days old, so it'll be _____ .
   A crumbly   B stale   C crusty

2 I love eating _____ raw carrots as a snack.
   A crispy   B crusty   C crunchy

3 Why not try our _____ 5oz sirloin steak, chargrilled to perfection?
   A succulent   B crispy   C tangy

4 If the water is too hot, the coffee will taste _____ .
   A tangy   B sour   C bitter

Collocations to do with food

3   Match the beginnings of the sentences (1–8) with their endings (A–H).

1 Every Saturday a market selling only organic
2 Rice is the staple
3 A diet rich in complex
4 You're anaemic, so take this course of dietary
5 Treat your taste
6 For the best results, use only natural
7 To maintain a balanced
8 Salmon and tuna are good sources of essential

A ingredients rather than processed ones.
B buds to this tangy fruit smoothie.
C fatty acids such as Omega 3.
D food of many Japanese people.
E produce is held in the town square.
F diet, eat a variety of fruit and vegetables.
G supplements to re-establish a balance.
H carbohydrates like pulses gives you energy.

More food idioms

4   Rewrite the story below, replacing the underlined phrases with your own words.

A Good Egg

When fourteen-year-old Jason Walker sat his parents down and, **(1)** <u>cool as a cucumber</u>, told them he was going to cycle round the UK to raise money for Cancer Research, his dad initially **(2)** <u>went bananas</u>. He told Jason that he was **(3)** <u>as nutty as a fruitcake</u> and that he **(4)** <u>had too much on his plate</u> to go galavanting off for six months on some **(5)** <u>half-baked</u> whim. Jason calmly replied that, seeing as he was the **(6)** <u>cream of the crop</u> in his class and had little difficulty with his lessons, it would be a **(7)** <u>piece of cake</u> for him to catch up with his schoolwork when he got home. His dad finally relented and Jason set off on his grand adventure. Apart from once finding himself **(8)** <u>in a pickle</u> when he was chased through a village by a pack of dogs, he achieved his goal. So, his father was forced to **(9)** <u>eat his words</u> and finally admit that in fact he was immensely proud of what his son had done!

Reading (Paper 1 Part 7)

Multiple matching

1 Read the title of the text. What issues do you think will be raised about football supporters and how their attitudes may have changed in recent years?

2 Read quickly to check your predictions and find out what the following are given as an example of: Den Haag, Carlisle United, Arsenal, Chelsea, the Calciopoli scandal.

3 Read the instructions for the exam task. Then read all the questions and underline the key words in each question. Then complete the exam task. Use the Help clues if necessary.

HELP
➤ Q2 A *parallel* is a type of comparison.
➤ Q3 A common misconception is mentioned in Sections A and B – which person conforms to it?
➤ Q6 *Allegiance* means 'loyalty'.

EXPERT LANGUAGE

Look back at Section B of the text. Find four examples of a quantifier used as a pronoun.

EXPERT WORD CHECK

lifelong   lapse   glory hunter hooliganism   bribery   gambler pervade   immune   match-fixing wrongdoing

You are going to read an article about footballer supporters. For questions **1 – 10**, choose from the sections **(A – D)**. The sections may be chosen more than once.

In which section does the writer

seek to account for a mismatch between level of support and achievement? `1`

find evidence of a parallel in a related activity? `2`

give the example of an individual who appears to conform to a common misconception? `3`

mention an individual who became disillusioned with football following a disclosure? `4`

outline evidence that contradicts a widely held assertion? `5`

point to likely explanations for changes of allegiance amongst football fans? `6`

provide an example of the broadening appeal of football generally? `7`

refer to some research that confirms the extent of one factor affecting fan loyalty? `8`

report a reluctance within football to confront certain issues? `9`

suggest that there has been relatively little research into a phenomenon he outlines? `10`

4 Find words in the text that mean:
   1 addicted (Section A) _____
   2 committed supporters (Section B) _____
   3 spectator numbers (Section B) _____
   4 fall into disuse (Section B) _____
   5 puts (people) off (Section C) _____
   6 dishonest (Section C) _____
   7 sudden fall in number (Section C) _____
   8 may have negative future implications (Section D) _____
   9 profitable (Section D) _____
   10 withdraw (Section D) _____

Why we still follow football

A Like a lot of people, I still remember the first football match I ever saw. It was in The Hague in 1979, and Den Haag beat Utrecht 3–1. That day we discovered my brother needed glasses, because he couldn't read the scoreboard. Going to watch football is one of the comforting rituals that carry you through life. It's also one of the few pleasures that parents and children can share: in the stadium, everyone becomes nine years old again. To quote a poem by the Dutchman Henk Spaan, 'A stadium is a monument to the common man.' Nowadays, the common woman goes too. Yet this ritual is poorly understood. The sports economist Stefan Szymanski and I have just published a new version of our book *Soccernomics* and two questions we ask are: why exactly do people go to watch football? And what makes them stop? The great myth is that most spectators simply have to go; that they are helpless, lifelong fans of one club, bound to it by blood and soil. This myth was nicely worded by Charles Burgess, journalist and Carlisle United fan, 'There never was any choice. My dad took me ... to watch the derby match against Workington Town just after Christmas 41 years ago. I was hooked and have been ever since. My support has been about who we are and where we are from.'

B British fans, in particular, like to present themselves as lifelong diehards, and some are. However, as Szymanski and I found, while studying 61 years of English football attendances, most aren't. Indeed very few take their seats year after year at the same club. Many people change clubs. For instance, according to surveys carried out by the Sport+Markt consultancy, 90 percent of English fans of Chelsea in 2006 had not supported the club in 2003. Some fans move to another town and start watching their new local club, or start following the team their children like, or abandon football because they're too busy. The marketing expert Alan Tapp, studying a club in the English Midlands, found that fans who let their season-tickets lapse often had small children. Older people, with less complicated lives, tended to keep their seats. In other words, showing up year in, year out isn't a great marker of loyalty; rather, it's a good marker of age. Few English fans are lifelong diehards. But nor are most glory hunters, who only watch winning teams.

C Rather, we found that most spectators go to watch a plausible team playing locally in a comfortable, safe stadium – winning matters less to them than having a pleasant experience. Arsenal is the perfect example: when the club moved from Highbury to the Emirates, the larger new stadium filled, even though the team had stopped winning trophies. We know that hooliganism deters fans from going to football. But one thing deters them even more: match-fixing. If people think that crooked players or referees have fixed results in advance, they will stop going. After Italy's Calciopoli bribery scandal broke in 2006, a Roman friend emailed me to say he was 'in a strange mood. It was all fake!' He'd always thought he was watching reality, but it had just been a show. The economists Babatunde Buraimo, Giuseppe Migali and Rob Simmons showed in a recent paper that the five top-division clubs found guilty in Calciopoli subsequently saw their attendances slump. These teams lost perhaps a fifth more fans than 'innocent' clubs.

D That is ominous, because match-fixing is going global. The rise in online betting, especially in Asia, has made it more lucrative for gamblers to fix matches. Sometimes clubs secretly bet on themselves to lose. The economist Romesh Vaitilingam found a similar phenomenon in tennis, where players often bet on themselves to lose first-round matches, and then pull out, claiming to be injured. Match-fixing has pervaded football from Asia to Italy. Perhaps only a handful of leagues on earth remain immune, for now. Steven de Lil, the policeman in charge of fighting 'football fraud' in Belgium, told me it's very hard to catch match-fixers. Football is a closed world, and clubs rarely report wrongdoing, he said. What de Lil has seen influences the way he now watches football as a fan, 'I always have my suspicions. I go to see a good match, but pretty soon I'm thinking, "How can that be happening?"' Once most of us watch football like that, we'll stop watching.

Language development 2

➤ **CB** p. 146, **GR** pp. 187–188

Adjectives, nouns, verbs and prepositions

1 Replace one incorrect preposition in each sentence.
1 The Olympic gold medallist attributes her improved performance in her recent change to a raw food diet.
2 Selection for the team will be subject from your performance in the trials next week.
3 The trainer imposed a strict diet and training programme for all the athletes in the Olympic team.
4 Leafy green vegetables contribute with the healthy development of memory.
5 I am often confused on all the mixed messages we receive about which foods are good for our health and which aren't.
6 Any athlete who fails to comply by the rules of the tournament will be disqualified.

Same word, but which preposition?

2 Some words can be followed by more than one preposition. Complete each sentence with the correct preposition.
1 Claire's going to become a nursery school teacher because she's very **good** _____ young children.
Jodie's exceptionally **good** _____ diving, and has won several medals.
Raw fish is extremely **good** _____ you, as it contains a number of minerals which are difficult to find in other foods.
2 Did you **apply** _____ that job at the sports centre?
I've just **applied** _____ study Sports Nutrition at Teeside University.
3 Water **counts** _____ 61.8 percent of a person's body weight
I know I can **count** _____ you to help me stick to this low-fat diet.
I managed to get the day off after all, so if you still have tickets left for the final, you can **count** me _____ !
4 He had a massive row with both the umpire and his opponent, **resulting** _____ his being disqualified.
Her obesity **resulted** _____ a largely sedentary lifestyle and a diet consisting mainly of junk food.
5 The management **blamed** the coach _____ the team's poor performance record.
The athlete **blamed** his failure to win _____ poor diet and insufficient training.
6 At the press conference this morning, there was no **hint** _____ a possible reconciliation between the boxer and his trainer.
Paula **hinted** _____ the possibility of her taking part in the badminton tournament.

Prepositional phrases

3 Complete each sentence by circling the correct word or phrase from each pair in italics.
1 She won the Sportsperson of the Year award *by / in* recognition of her achievements both on and off the tennis court.
2 Alice, *on / in* behalf of all of the team, I'd like to present you with this small gift as a token of our appreciation for all your hard work.
3 All members of the squad, *beyond / without* exception, are expected to be on the pitch at 7.30 a.m., ready for training.
4 Taking a day off just before an important competition is *out of / beyond* the question. So, forget it!
5 Simon made some drastic changes to his diet *for / from* fear of getting heart disease.
6 *With / In* all likelihood, the team will be relegated at the end of the season, as they have failed to win a match so far.

Mixed prepositions

4 Complete the text with suitable prepositions.

Eat raw meat?

There is an abundance **(1)** _____ cookbooks on the market which advocate changing to a raw-food lifestyle. Since the switch to raw food was endorsed by celebrity chefs like Gordon Ramsay, raw-food restaurants have started sprouting up around the country. And opting **(2)** _____ uncooked food does not mean abstaining **(3)** _____ eating meat. Ramsay says, 'a lot of people are a little bit intimidated **(4)** _____ the idea of eating raw meat and fish, which is a great shame, because I think they are really missing out – it is a very healthy and natural way **(5)** _____ doing things.' A number of nutritionists and food experts committed **(6)** _____ the raw-food diet now offer courses **(7)** _____ how to make the switch, claiming that the health benefits **(8)** _____ going raw are many. Raw foods are packed **(9)** _____ valuable enzymes, which are a wonderful source **(10)** _____ energy and also play a role **(11)** _____ maintaining a healthy digestive system. Cooking destroys these enzymes.

Some nutritionists question the justification **(12)** _____ eating raw meat, however, expressing concern **(13)** _____ whether it is safe. They argue that eating raw mass-produced beef, pork and lamb that are full of hormones is not conducive **(14)** _____ a healthy diet. People prone **(15)** _____ allergies should therefore be wary **(16)** _____ choosing to eat raw food, and care should be taken in the preparation **(17)** _____ raw meat **(18)** _____ general.

There is no doubt that eating a certain amount of raw food **(19)** _____ a regular basis is good for you but if you're planning on eating raw meat and fish, make sure you get advice **(20)** _____ how to prepare it safely.

Use of English (Paper 1 Part 2)

Open cloze

1 Read the title of the text. What advantages of exercise do you expect to be praised?

2 Read the whole text quickly to get the general meaning, then read again carefully and complete the gaps. Use the Help clues if necessary.

HELP

➤ **Q1** Look forward in the sentence – you need a word that complements *that*.

➤ **Q3** You need a word that makes a phrase with *to whether* to provide a link.

➤ **Q5** You need a preposition to complete an idiomatic expression with *their own steam*.

➤ **Q7** Which verb makes the phrasal verb meaning 'to tolerate'?

➤ **Q8** You need a preposition here that means 'further than.'

EXPERT LANGUAGE

Look back at the text. Find:

a an auxiliary verb used for emphasis
b a verb followed by a participle

For questions **1 – 8**, read the text below and think of the word that best fits each space. Use only one word in each space. There is an example at the beginning **(0)**.

In praise of exercise

Few people would question the assertion that taking exercise is a good thing. Exercise is reputed to tackle a wide range of health issues head on, (0) ___NOT___ least obesity, depression and poor circulation. Indeed, (1) _____ extensive is the list of ailments for (2) _____ exercise is potentially beneficial that you'd think doctors would start prescribing it instead of drugs. It's rather a neat idea. Apparently, however, doubts exist (3) _____ to whether such a policy could ever work in practice. Doctors do, of course, sometimes prescribe exercise programmes, often of six weeks' duration and under the supervision of a fitness instructor, and the short-term benefits are generally evident. But (4) _____ it comes to the longer term, with patients having to carry on with the programme (5) _____ their own steam, the situation is less (6) _____ cut. In short, it only works if you can get people to do it. Whilst people can (7) _____ up with anything for six weeks, a long-term commitment involves a lifestyle change, and that seems to go (8) _____ many people's capabilities.

3 Find words in the text that mean:

1 a clearly stated opinion _____
2 directly _____
3 movement of the blood around the body _____
4 to deal with _____
5 illnesses _____
6 to summarise _____

Writing: essay (Paper 2 Part 2)

➤ **CB** pp. 142, 148-149, **WR** p. 194

EXPERT STRATEGY

Remember there is a word limit for your answer, so focus on two or three main points in favour of the statement, and two or three points against it. Build the main body of your answer around this, with examples to support the points you make.

Choosing what to include in your answer

1   Read the task, and the list of points one candidate has made. Which points would you include in an answer to this question? Which points could become irrelevant to the topic?

Following a class discussion on success and failure, your English tutor has asked you to write an essay in response to the following quote, saying whether you agree with the statement or not, and giving examples to support your views.
'People's best successes come after their disappointments.'
Write your answer in **280 – 320** words.

    1 making mistakes – part of learning process, in both sport and working life
    2 defeat can lead to loss of confidence, despair
    3 often difficult to overcome defeat
    4 sport like other areas of life – learn to respect opponents
    5 sometimes necessary to recognise lack of ability in a particular sport
    6 failure – reflect on your mistakes, correct them
    7 someone always successful – complacent
    8 failure teaches a person humility
    9 media ridicule of defeated sportspeople – hard to deal with
    10 success always greater if result of hard effort

Planning your answer

2   Organise your points into two main paragraphs, as shown below.

Points supporting the statement	Points against the statement
1 _____	1 _____
2 _____	2 _____
3 _____	3 _____

3a Read the following extract from a candidate's answer. Underline the point she makes, and the example she gives to support her point.

> Nevertheless, it takes a great deal of courage and determination to recover from defeat and not everyone succeeds. There are many stories of athletes abandoning professional competition as a result of being unable to cope with defeat. This is particularly hard for champions, who may find it psychologically hard to come to terms with defeat after having experienced the glory of success.

b   Think of a suitable example to support each point you intend to make in your answer. Use these prompts to help you.

There are several examples of ...
This is particularly true for ...
This can be seen in ...
For instance, ...
You often hear of ...

Writing task

4   Now do the task in Exercise 1.

Vocabulary development 1

➤ **CB** pp. 154–155

Collocations

1 Complete each sentence by using a word from Box A and a word from Box B to form collocations.

> **A** business career comfort consumer
>   financial learning target
>
> **B** acumen backing behaviour curve ladder
>   market zone

1 Have you got any _____ for your new venture? I assume it would be difficult to move forward without that.
2 The last few months have been a steep _____ for everyone involved in the project.
3 What's the _____ for your new clothing range – is it young adults or over-35s?
4 Sometimes, if you have to work in an area that takes you outside your _____ , it can push you towards greater personal development.
5 A certain amount of _____ and know-how will certainly help you to make your way up the _____ within the company.
6 When a new product is launched, _____ is quite difficult to predict accurately, although certain sales forecasts can be made.

Idioms: success at work

2 Complete the idiom in each sentence with words from the box.

> box ceiling door ground scratch trumps

1 I think Jackie really came up _____ when she made that new deal.
2 Annie had got quite high up in the company but then she started to feel that she had hit a glass _____ .
3 During the brainstorming session, we were told to use our imagination and think outside the _____ .
4 Getting an internship means that you've got a foot in the _____ at last.
5 Once this training course has finished, I'll be able to hit the _____ running and really make an impact.
6 Jake's work hasn't been up to _____ lately, so try to find out what's affecting his performance.

Verb phrases

3 Complete the dialogues with the correct form of verbs from the box. There is one verb you do not need.

> bring carve out come drive get have (x2)
> launch strike

> A **Emily:** Well Adam, I'm really glad we were able to **(1)** _____ a deal this morning.
>   **Adam:** You certainly **(2)** _____ a hard bargain, Emily but I feel that our companies will work very well together.
> B **Sally:** I've heard that Eve is **(3)** _____ a career for herself in that law firm she works for.
>   **Angie:** Good for her, I say! She must **(4)** _____ nerves of steel, though – I couldn't deal with all those tricky situations on a daily basis.
> C **Sophie:** Hey Frank, you know I'm **(5)** _____ a new online business very soon and I think it could be right up your street. You **(6)** _____ a really good track record in that area so how about **(7)** _____ on board? My partner and I are keen to collaborate with you.
>   **Frank:** That sounds a great idea, Sophie! You know I'm always ready to **(8)** _____ my teeth into new projects!

Word formation: adjectives and adverbs with *in-* or *un-*

4 Complete each sentence with an adjective or adverb formed from one of the verbs in the box.

> achieve conceive decide deter explain signify

1 I wish I didn't act so _____ sometimes. It gives other people a bad impression when you can't make up your mind what to do!
2 It was _____ that a sales manager as experienced as Ben wouldn't pull off that deal.
3 _____ by her early failures, Cherry decided to persevere with her writing.
4 Really, I think the errors were _____ when taken in the overall context of an excellent piece of work.
5 Her parents had taught her that no goal was _____ if she set her mind to it.
6 Rod _____ took early retirement last year, despite having been promoted to a senior management role shortly before.

Use of English (Paper 1 Part 1)

Multiple-choice cloze

1 Read the title of the text and think about what you are going to read. How do small companies usually expand?

2 Read the whole text quickly to get the general meaning. Then read again carefully, choosing the best option A–D to fit each gap. Use the Help clues if necessary.

For questions **1 – 8**, read the text below and decide which answer (**A, B, C** or **D**) best fits each gap. There is an example at the beginning (**0**).

How a small company grows

Although Gecko Headgear is a company that now (0) __A__ in the design and manufacture of marine safety helmets, the company started out making surfboards. Feeling a need to (1) _____ their product offering, they identified a (2) _____ in the niche watersports market, for an innovative heat-retaining helmet. The idea soon (3) _____ a winner amongst surfers, but wanting to expand its customer (4) _____ the company approached other potential users, including the Royal National Lifeboat Institution (RNLI), quite a bold (5) _____ for a small company. The RNLI wanted its own version of the helmet, but Gecko found working with such a big organisation a whole new ballgame. The RNLI helmet had to be adapted, tested and certified before it could go on the market, so there was a need to (6) _____ investment capital by means of a bank loan. This paid off in the long run, however, as the RNLI helmet was a big success. And since then, Gecko haven't (7) _____ on their laurels, as ten subsequent versions of the helmet have been further refined in (8) _____ with customer feedback.

HELP

➤ Q1 You are looking for a verb that means 'increase the range of things'.

➤ Q6 Which of these words forms a common collocation with *capital*?

➤ Q7 A verb is needed that completes the common expression which means 'became complacent'.

➤ Q8 The word is part of a three-word phrase that includes the preposition *with*.

EXPERT LANGUAGE

Look back at the text. Find three nouns preceded by several different adjectives. Why are the adjectives hyphenated in one of the examples?

0	A specialises	B concentrates	C focuses	D targets
1	A multiply	B variegate	C diversify	D heighten
2	A space	B gap	C blank	D hole
3	A resulted	B showed	C achieved	D proved
4	A base	B foundation	C structure	D net
5	A stroke	B turn	C move	D bid
6	A earn	B gain	C build	D raise
7	A rested	B stayed	C reclined	D stuck
8	A accord	B line	C response	D theme

3 Find words and expressions in the text that mean:
1 items for sale _____
2 a new experience _____
3 turned out to be a good move _____
4 at a later time _____

4 Look at the options for the example question. The three incorrect options cannot be followed by *in*. Can another preposition follow each of them, and if so, which preposition?

Language development 1

➤ **CB** p. 157, **GR** pp. 188–190

Direct to reported speech

1 Rewrite these quotes from a top business person by using reported speech.

1 'I've never spent a minute of my life regretting things I could have bought.'
He claimed that _____ .

2 'If you happen to see something that looks like a good bargain, it's only natural you're going to try and buy it.'
He explained that _____ .

3 'My latest deal will probably go down in history as one of the best that has ever been done.'
He emphasised that _____ .

4 'My biggest battle was won in this boardroom last year.'
He admitted that _____ .

5 'I won't ever make a bid for a company unless I'm sure of its worth.'
He assured me that _____ .

6 'I was lucky and received some really good training and advice in the early years.'
He acknowledged that _____ .

Phrasal verbs for reporting and rephrasing

2 Rewrite the sentences by using a verb from Box A and a particle or group of particles from Box B to form phrasal verbs in the correct form.

A blurt   dwell   fill   get   speak   touch
B in on   on (x2)   out   out against   through to

1 'I'm really not at all satisfied with company policy regarding small businesses,' Jack said.
Jack _____ the company policy regarding small businesses.

2 'In the meeting, I shall only mention the possibility of redundancies briefly,' the manager said.
The manager said that, in the meeting, he _____ the possibility of redundancies.

3 'Don't think too much about the mistakes you made – it's best to move on,' George told Will.
George told Will not _____ the mistakes _____ .

4 'I'm not very happy in my job,' Kay said without thinking.
Kay _____ that she _____ job.

5 'Sorry, but the lines were busy yesterday when I tried to phone your office,' Stella said.
Stella said that she _____ their office the day before.

6 'So Ben, this is what's been happening while you've been away,' Polly explained.
Polly _____ what _____ .

Verbs for reporting and summarising

3 Complete each sentence by crossing out the options that are not correct. In some sentences all the options may be correct.

1 Our accountant recommended *that we set up / our setting up / to set up* a second company.

2 We were warned *we shouldn't take / about taking / not to take* too many risks.

3 My parents persuaded *I should take / my taking / me to take* some more qualifications before going into business.

4 Toby suggested *going / to go / I go* into partnership with him!

5 Rick blamed himself *he didn't act / for not acting / his not acting* soon enough.

6 I'm afraid that I refuse absolutely *to agree / that I agree / agreeing* to these terms.

Rephrasing and summarising: impersonal report structures

4 Rewrite the underlined parts of the sentences in an appropriate manner, using a verb or a noun from the box in the correct form. Add any other words that are necessary. Use the passive where required.

Verbs	Nouns
allege	comment
confirm	criticism
deny	recollection
rumour	statement

1 Tim <u>said something</u> about the conference but I didn't quite hear.
Tim _____ .

2 <u>They say that she was involved</u> in some newspaper scandal but <u>no one has said officially</u> whether this is true.
She _____ .

3 The Minister of Education will <u>issue a public announcement</u> at the weekend.
The Minister _____ .

4 I feel that the <u>way she was verbally attacked about her conduct was</u> quite unjustified.
I feel that _____ .

5 <u>People have been saying</u> that some cheating has been going on. If this is true, there could be serious consequences.
It _____ .

6 I'm afraid I <u>don't remember</u> writing down the topic of the essay for next week – could you give it to me, please?
I'm afraid _____ .

7 His <u>said he didn't have</u> any involvement in match-fixing.
He _____ .

Use of English (Paper 1 Part 2)

Open cloze

1 Read the title of the text. What are *logos*? Why are they important to brands?

2 Read the whole text quickly to get the general meaning, then read again carefully and complete the gaps. Use the Help clues if necessary.

HELP

➤ Q2 Which word forms a linking expression with *if*?
➤ Q3 You need a verb here.
➤ Q4 Add a preposition to make a common phrasal verb.

EXPERT LANGUAGE

Look back at the text. Find three phrases that express the absence of something.

For questions **1 – 8**, read the text below and think of the word that best fits each space. Use only one word in each space. There is an example at the beginning (**0**).

No logo

In the luxury goods market, the prominent logos once associated (0) ___WITH___ lavish lifestyles may soon be a thing of the past. Amongst all sorts of brands, there is a growing consensus that 'anonymity' is the key to being recognised. In (1) _____ words, we recognise the brand from its quality and style (2) _____ if the logo is nowhere to be seen. (3) _____ the example of one well-established luxury brand, known for the timeless elegance of its handbags rather than for bringing (4) _____ a new style every season. During the last economic recession, (5) _____ the fact that the only logo is discreetly stamped inside, it seemed to thrive. The explanation for this might of course lie in the fact that, facing tighter budgets, customers wanted a bag that would (6) _____ the test of time. But it could also be that in a world devoid of logos, it is the product itself (7) _____ accentuates personality. What's more, the bags still tapped (8) _____ a desire for admiration, albeit from informed insiders.

3 Find words and expressions in the text that mean:

1 luxurious   _____
2 no longer exist   _____
3 agreement   _____
4 not becoming old-fashioned   _____
5 do well   _____
6 less money to spend than before   _____
7 last well   _____
8 makes stronger   _____

Listening (Paper 3 Part 3)

Multiple choice

1 Read the instructions for the task, and think about what you are going to hear. Then read through the questions. How much do you find out about the topic and speakers.

a from the rubric?

b from the questions?

2 Listen to the recording and choose the correct option A, B, C or D. Use the Help clues if necessary.

HELP

➤ Q1 Listen to the beginning of Lois' first turn. What is she agreeing with John about?

➤ Q2 Lois says, *I'd go along with that* to show agreement – listen for that phrase.

➤ Q5 Be careful, the first quote is not actually from Freud.

EXPERT LANGUAGE

Look back at the questions. Find six strong verb and noun collocations

EXPERT WORD CHECK

*a necessary evil   overstated
traumatic   soured   chronic
trade-off   slacker   social standing
social mobility   cornerstone*

You will hear two academics called John Farrendale and Lois Granger, taking part in a discussion on the subject of attitudes to work. For questions **1 – 5**, choose the answer **A**, **B**, **C** or **D** which fits best according to what you hear.

1 Lois agrees with John's point that
   A most people dread the prospect of unemployment
   B the psychological effects of unemployment can be overstated.
   C some people are better equipped to deal with unemployment than others.
   D problems arise when unemployment coincides with other traumatic events.

2 Lois agrees with the listener who suggested that
   A work is only one aspect of a fulfilling life.
   B voluntary work may be more rewarding than paid work.
   C not everybody can expect a high level of job satisfaction.
   D people should prepare for redundancy as they would for retirement.

3 What is John's attitude towards people who see work as a 'means to an end'?
   A He doubts their level of commitment to the job.
   B He accepts that they have made a valid choice.
   C He fears it will lead to difficulties for them later.
   D He feels they may be missing out on something important.

4 When asked about so-called 'slackers' at work, John points out that
   A they accept the notion that work is a necessary evil.
   B people often jump to unfair conclusions about them.
   C their views are unacceptable in a free labour market.
   D such an attitude has become increasingly unacceptable.

5 Lois quotes the psychologist Freud in order to
   A show how intellectual ideas have shifted over time.
   B provide a contrast to the ideas of Bertrand Russell.
   C question the idea that a desire to work is a natural thing.
   D lend weight to John's ideas about increased social mobility.

3 Match the expressions from the recording (1–8) with their definitions (A–H).

1 the be all and end all	A unchanging
2 come as a blow	B do the required amount of work
3 tying too close a knot	C socially unacceptable
4 perilous	D the most important thing
5 intrinsic	E dangerous
6 pull their weight	F be a shock
7 taboo	G with inherent qualities
8 immutable	H making a close link

Reading   (Paper 1 Part 5)

Multiple choice

1   Read the title and subtitle of the text. Why do you think that people might easily be cheated on the internet?

2   Read the text quickly to see whether your predictions were correct.

3   Look through the multiple-choice questions and then read the text carefully to complete the task. Use the Help clues if necessary.

HELP

> **Q2** *Such* usually refers to something that has just been mentioned. What is the writer sceptical about at the end of the previous paragraph?

> **Q3** Read the section about vertical and horizontal trust carefully. What has changed?

> **Q6** The writer uses the word *cheering* – which option does this suggest?

EXPERT LANGUAGE

Look back at the first paragraph of the text. Find two negative adjectives being used with a qualifying phrase to express a positive idea. Why has the writer used them?

EXPERT WORD CHECK

*perpetrated   caught off-guard
fraudster   regaled with
leap of faith   swindled   shattered
disabused   lick their wounds
ensconced*

You are going to read an article about internet fraud. For questions **1 – 6**, choose the answer (**A**, **B**, **C** or **D**) which you think fits best according to the text.

1   In the first paragraph, the writer reveals feelings of
   A   shock that her friends were so gullible when booking online.
   B   guilt for having suggested a fraudulent website to her friends.
   C   regret that she hadn't heeded various warnings about internet fraud.
   D   concern that she was unaware of certain risks in making online bookings.

2   In her use of the phrase 'such scepticism' (line 23) the writer is referring to her
   A   dislike of making purchases online.
   B   distrust of certain stories she's heard.
   C   frustration at aspects of life in New York.
   D   realisation of why certain crimes are prevalent.

3   In the second paragraph, the writer suggests that
   A   people's faith in their peers may be misguided.
   B   people's distrust of institutions makes them vulnerable.
   C   people have tended to lose faith in those they once trusted.
   D   people have more faith in officials if they interact over the internet.

4   When discussing the statistics about internet crime, the writer points out that
   A   some people are more at risk than others.
   B   the problem is now being tackled effectively.
   C   it's not easy to predict who will fall victim to it.
   D   certain types are growing at the expense of others.

5   What does the writer imply about her friends in the penultimate paragraph?
   A   They are resigned to the loss of their money.
   B   They are already hot on the trail of the fraudster.
   C   They are unimpressed by the attitude of the police.
   D   They are hoping to pursue their case through the banks.

6   From the final paragraph, we understand that the writer
   A   finds people's reliance on technology puzzling.
   B   remains optimistic about the future of internet business.
   C   believes that regulation of online booking sites is needed.
   D   has reservations about a new type of website that has emerged.

The technology of trust

Why do people fall victim to internet fraud?

A few weeks ago, some British friends told me that they would be coming to New York for a holiday and needed a place to stay. Since my own apartment was already full with extended family, I suggested they look on the internet – and they duly booked one of their own. It seemed ideal, at least in cyberspace: a mid-town address, a reasonable rental price and spacious rooms. I guess I should have checked it out, being on the spot, but these friends are by no means uninitiated first-time travellers and it never occurred to me to intervene. Anyway, the booking turned out to be an internet fraud perpetrated by a man named Lester Gold. It's a sobering tale on several levels, not least in that we'd all been caught off-guard. Indeed, since this particular fraudster struck, I've been regaled with a host of similar tales: such scams, it seems, are far from uncommon here. No surprise, perhaps, given the city's sky-high hotel prices, tourist influx – and the presence of platforms which have no liability for what is advertised or posted there.

But amid such scepticism, what is notable is the extent to which our faith in technology remains so high. According to one recent 18-country survey, public confidence in banks, government and most business has tumbled in recent years, whilst faith in technology has remained entirely steady. And whereas financial analysts, CEOs and government officials used to be considered reliable sources of information, these days 'a person like yourself' or 'a regular employee' commands more trust. Vertical trust, it seems, has been replaced by a horizontal slant, as the public turns to their peer group for advice, via social-networking sites. To put it another way, while we no longer have faith in bankers, bureaucrats or estate agents, we are taking leaps of faith with our tablets and smart phones. This horizontal trust does not, in itself, cause people to be swindled. For every gullible internet user out there, there are also dozens of others who are profoundly savvy.

Nevertheless, the numbers are thought-provoking, even in hard-nosed, cynical New York. According to data compiled by the Internet Crime Complaint Center, in 2010 there were 14,689 cases of reported cyber fraud in the state of New York, which created $26.5111 worth of losses, with an average swindle of $700. This was a fraction lower than the previous year, but more than double the level five years previously. Just over 20 percent of these frauds were for 'non-delivery of merchandise' (such as paying for a flat that never existed), while 18 percent of the losses were linked to identity theft, 13 percent to auction fraud and 8 percent to credit-card fraud. And while some of those duped were tourists, particularly from Canada, the UK, Australia and India, the majority were Americans, often New Yorkers themselves. It seems we're all prone to let down our guard online – probably because the sheer intimacy of the medium makes it feel seductively familiar, there is an implicit temptation to trust. Of course, for my friends who suffered at the hands of Lester Gold, that trust is now shattered. The New York Police Department has disabused them of the idea that contacting the bank that handled the fraudster's account would be a fruitful avenue to pursue, suggesting that their best bet is to analyse the geographical source of the original internet postings (in this case Wisconsin), file a report with the police – and then lick their wounds.

In the meantime, however, this particular family has made an intriguing discovery. Precisely because these rental frauds keep happening, a class of companies is now springing up that try to offer a new form of security. Groups have emerged in the past few years to match online renters and landlords – but via a central platform that forces everyone to post a set of videos, pictures and details online. The idea appears to be that if humans can connect face-to-face, via cyberspace, this will create new forms of trust. It's a fascinating example of the way that seemingly impersonal, dehumanising technology keeps dancing with 'the social'; and, of course, it is also a very cheering sign of the adaptive capabilities of free-market capitalism and entrepreneurs. Better still, I am pleased to say that these new systems work. My friends are now happily ensconced in a Brooklyn rental, after Skyping with the landlady – even as 'Lester Gold' is probably hunting for his next victims.

Vocabulary development 2

Prepositional phrases

1a Choose ONE preposition that completes all three phrases in italics in each sentence. Then circle the phrase that fits the context.

1 There were five thousand applications _____ *response to* / _____ *place of* / _____ *proportion to* the job advertisement.
2 I went back to my old school _____ *the strength* / _____ *no account* / _____ *the off-chance* that I'd bump into one of my former teachers.
3 I'm _____ *a disadvantage* / _____ *a loose end* / _____ *a stretch* this weekend – how about a trip to the university museum?
4 Is it my imagination or does Greg feel _____ *of character* / _____ *of work* / _____ *of his depth* in that very academic environment?
5 The poetry reading wasn't really _____ *my liking* / _____ *a fault* / _____ *no purpose*: we should have gone to the theatre instead.
6 Liz will be so glad when she's finally got those qualifications _____ *discussion* / _____ *control* / _____ *her belt*.

b Now complete each sentence with a prepositional phrase from Exercise 1a.

1 To be honest, she got the job _____ of her qualifications and her experience.
2 And to think that I read those books over the holidays _____ – they've changed the curriculum this year!
3 I believe the creation of a new university Chair is currently _____ .
4 When Ludovic embarked upon his degree course, he was _____ because his English was not as good as his fellow students'.
5 _____ the proposed lecture, there was a screening of an Italian film!
6 _____ should students choose fewer than five compulsory subjects. There are also two optional courses.
7 For Jeff to get angry like that over an academic issue was extremely _____ – he must have felt very strongly about it.
8 How can you manage to study for ten hours _____ ? I'd be exhausted!
9 Sophie will be able to work anywhere once she has enough experience _____ .

Words connected with education

2 Complete each sentence with a word from the box, making the word plural if necessary. There are two words you do not need.

*bachelor's   disciplines   dissertation   faculty
fieldwork   graduate   pedagogical   scholarship
tertiary   tuition*

1 Undergraduates in the French department will need to write a final _____ of 20,000 to 30,000 words.
2 I'm afraid that university _____ fees have gone up a lot in recent years.
3 Most of our courses lead to a _____ degree after three, four or five years of study.
4 The level of private investment in _____ education in the UK is already far above the EU averages.
5 Did Henry win a _____ to Oxford? That's great news!
6 Applied Mathematics uses the principles of mathematics within other _____ , such as physics, chemistry, biology and finance.
7 Despite having first-class degrees from top institutions, many _____ are finding it hard to land their first job.
8 The Dean of the _____ will be making a speech at the degree ceremony and presenting the awards.

Collocations

A easy   foregone   last   loaded   plain   sandwich
B conclusion   degree   option   questions   sailing   straw

3 Complete each sentence by using a word from Box A and a word from Box B to form collocations.

1 The successful applicant will follow a suitable _____ course requiring a year in industry.
2 It was a _____ that Steffie would be good at French since her mother was a French teacher!
3 After spending so much time on the application, hearing that I hadn't been accepted for the Erasmus scholarship was the _____ .
4 Trish's excellent results this year mean that the rest of the course will be reasonably _____ from now on.
5 The survey has been criticised for using _____ to ensure a positive response from the public.
6 Contrary to popular belief, studying English at university is certainly no _____ .

Language development 2

> **CB** p. 162, **GR** p. 190

Collocations with *come, go, make* and *take*

1 Complete the text with suitable words to form collocations.

How you can sometimes turn things around – by never giving up!

Sam Williams set up his own business when he was a teenager, buying and selling online. He quickly made quite a lot of money so he left school at eighteen and focused on building up his business. Unfortunately, after a couple of years, it became obvious that the economy was **going from bad (1)** _____ and it therefore **came as (2)** _____ when Sam started to feel the effects. He had **taken (3)** _____ of his parents' advice to go and study at university and as a result, all their hopes of their son getting a decent education had **gone by (4)** _____ . To be honest, he had always **taken it (5)** _____ that the business would continue to flourish and he wouldn't need any further academic qualifications. Within another six months, the market for his goods had collapsed and it didn't look like there was any chance of the business **making a (6)** _____ in the near future. Indeed, by the following summer, he had **gone out (7)** _____ . He was back to square one.

However, Sam was not one to give up – he always believed in **making the (8)** _____ difficult situations. So – better late than never – he **took (9)** _____ his parents' advice and he **came to (10)** _____ ; he would go to college, get a degree in Business Studies, and **take (11)** _____ to start all over again. And this is exactly what he did. While at college, he made some really good contacts and also **came (12)** _____ with the fact that he'd made some serious mistakes in the past. Valuable lessons were learnt!

Now, five years later, Sam has gone into partnership with two colleagues and their business is doing well, **taking (13)** _____ all the challenges they have had to face. It's not easy but it **goes (14)** _____ that Sam now feels that his house is built on a rock, rather than shifting sand!

Collocations

2 Complete each sentence by circling the correct word or phrase in italics.

1 Mr Jenkins confirmed that he would be at our *disposal / discretion* every Wednesday afternoon.
2 There was absolutely no *contrast / comparison* between the two students' output.
3 I was taken *aback / apart* by the amount of reading that needed to be done for the course.
4 You are under no *obligation / requirement* to pay all the fees by September.
5 Students have *allowance / access* to the labs between the hours of eight and ten in the evening.
6 I'm afraid her problems are all of her own *make / making*.
7 It's really no *concern / worry* of mine whether you come to the meeting or not – it's entirely up to you.
8 Jenni knew that Zoe was making *an attempt / a try* to win her friendship but she just wasn't interested.
9 If you want to study for a PhD at the London School of Economics, you'll have to meet their very strict entry *requests / requirements*.
10 As soon as I entered the room, the interviewer put me at my *ease / comfort* by asking me about my family.
11 Ryan's initial enthusiasm for the project is fortunately showing no *symptoms / signs* of waning.
12 I fully intend to take *use / advantage* of the resources of the library while I am here.

Word formation: nouns formed with particles

3 Complete each sentence by combining the word in brackets with a suitable particle to form a noun.

1 One of the _____ (draw) of doing a distance learning course is that you can't enjoy student life as much as if you were on campus.
2 I've had excellent _____ (feed) on my research project so far.
3 I hope to see a long-awaited _____ (turn) in my personal finances fairly soon.
4 The latest research findings promise a real _____ (break) in the study of Alzheimer's disease.
5 Having to miss the first term due to illness was an unfortunate _____ (set), but James is catching up now.
6 The _____ (turn) for the lecture by a visiting professor was quite impressive.
7 The _____ (take) of overseas students has been going up steadily in recent years.
8 For a relatively small _____ (lay), you can start an online business.

Use of English (Paper 1 Part 4)

Key word transformations

1 Look at the key word in each question. How can this word be used to express the idea missing from the second sentence?

2 Answer Questions 1–10, using the Help clues if necessary.

HELP
➤ Q1 Use an infinitive form after *failure*.
➤ Q3 You will need to use the word *charity* as an adjective.
➤ Q7 The verb *have* collocates with *intention*.
➤ Q8 *Likelihood* takes the definite article.
➤ Q10 This is an ironic idiomatic phrase that indicates great surprise.

For questions **1 – 10**, complete the second sentence so that it has a similar meaning to the first sentence, using the word given. **Do not change the word given.** You must use between **three** and **eight** words, including the word given.

1 Unless you pay your bill, your electricity supply may be disconnected.
result
Failure _____ electricity supply being disconnected.

2 Geraint drove his car into a stationary vehicle.
collision
Geraint's car was _____ a stationary vehicle.

3 As a way of recognising all the work she does for charity, Sam was given a medal.
in
Sam received a medal _____ work she does.

4 Fiona's boss rejected her request for a raise without giving a reason.
hand
Fiona's request for a raise _____ her boss.

5 Once he'd moved to the seaside, Ralph came to like seafood better.
taste
Ralph _____ moving to the seaside

6 Simona pays no attention to the rules when she plays tennis.
disregard
Simona plays tennis _____ the rules.

7 As long as sales hold up, the shop intends to stock paperback novels.
decline
Providing there's _____ every intention of stocking paperback books.

8 How likely is the company to make a profit this year?
likelihood
What _____ a profit this year?

9 It is completely forbidden for employees to give interviews to the press.
circumstances
Under _____ give interviews to the press.

10 Bruce was taken completely by surprise when news of his promotion came through.
feather
You _____ when news of his promotion came through.

Writing: essay (Paper 2 Part 1)

➤ **CB** pp. 158 and 164–165, **WR** pp.192–193

EXPERT STRATEGY

Clarity is vital in this type of essay. Use appropriate discourse markers to show the points where you are expressing your opinion as opposed to summarising the writer's point of view. Express yourself as concisely as possible, without getting yourself tangled up in over-complicated sentences.

Formulating ideas and opinions

1 Read the task and the two texts below and make brief notes about:

a the writer's ideas as expressed in the two texts.

b your opinion of these ideas.

Read the two texts below.
Write an essay summarising and evaluating the key points from both texts. Use your own words throughout as far as possible, and include your own ideas in your answers.
Write your answer in **240–280 words**.

1 An education for life?

It cannot be denied that the most important years which should be spent acquiring academic qualifications are a person's teens and early 20s. These are the years when the brain is most receptive to new ideas and also when there is the maximum time for learning to take place. Young people are eager to explore new concepts, new ideas that will help them to make sense of the world they live in. If that opportunity to learn is lacking or is not exploited, then there is little likelihood of it occurring again. In later years, other matters tend to become more important, such as a job and a family.

2 Lifelong learning

The learning process shouldn't be seen as a finite phenomenon, something that can only last for a particular period of time in a person's life and then stops. How many adults go on courses in their 30s and 40s in order to acquire new knowledge? And how many examples are there of many people in their 50s who seem to be at the height of their intellectual powers? Since the human brain matures over time, developing ever more complex capabilities, learning should surely be seen as a lifelong process. Our motto therefore should always be: 'It's never too late to learn'.

Write your **essay**.

Expressing yourself: using collocations in your writing

2a Match the beginnings of the collocations (1–10) with their endings (A–J).

1 come	A a negative effect
2 develop	B down
3 devote	C formal education
4 express	D one's capabilities
5 have	E priority
6 lay	F the foundations
7 put	G the view
8 settle	H time
9 take	I to an end
10 undertake	J to good use

b Complete the sentences, which have been taken at random from a sample essay, with the collocations from Exercise 2a. Notice the different ways of expressing similar ideas.

1 In later years, other matters can sometimes _____ _____ , such as finding a job or _____ _____ and starting a family

2 It is true that children and young people _____ a lot of _____ to learning and education.

3 It would be sad to think that learning _____ _____ when formal education stops

4 The writer _____ _____ that lifelong learning should be encouraged.

5 Their years of schooling _____ _____ for the rest of their lives.

6 The most important years for the learning process are those during which young people _____ their _____ at school and college.

7 It is therefore vitally important that these years are _____ and are not wasted.

8 One of the goals of life should be to _____ _____ as far as it is possible

9 Some young people resent the fact that they are forced to learn certain subjects that they are not interested in. This can _____ _____ .

Writing task

3 Now do the task in Exercise 1, using some of the material and ideas on this page to help you.

Practice exam

Reading and Use of English

Part 1

For questions **1 – 8**, read the text below and decide which answer (**A**, **B**, **C** or **D**) best fits each gap. Mark your answers **on the separate answer sheet**. There is an example at the beginning (**0**).

0 A way   **B** orientation   **C** direction   **D** route

0	A	B	C	D
	▬	▭	▭	▭

The International Space Station

If you look to the heavens between sunset and moonrise in London, the brightest object you're likely to see will be a white spark racing the wrong **(0)** ____A____ across the sky from west to east. **(1)** _____ it's not cloudy, the International Space Station (ISS), humanity's toehold on the edge of the vast reaches of the cosmos, is easier to spot with the **(2)** _____ eye than Venus.

Unlike the cramped Apollo capsules, the ISS is like an artificial island in space; its 14 modules have more elbow **(3)** _____ than a typical family house. Together with its 20 solar panels, it could **(4)** _____ the length of a football pitch. Since the year 2000, nearly two hundred astronauts and mission specialists from 15 countries have **(5)** _____ the ISS home.

Its success is encouraging since it emerged as a compromise when the USA, Russia, Europe and Japan found they could not afford separate space stations, and supporters love to **(6)** _____ it up as an example of international co-operation. But it has not been without its technical **(7)** _____ , the final components only being put into place in 2008, eight years **(8)** _____ schedule.

1 A Understanding	**B** Assuming	**C** Allowing	**D** Supposing
2 A bare	**B** single	**C** naked	**D** normal
3 A space	**B** range	**C** room	**D** scope
4 A expand	**B** spread	**C** reach	**D** stretch
5 A known	**B** regarded	**C** referred	**D** called
6 A make	**B** put	**C** hold	**D** stand
7 A hitches	**B** catches	**C** hindrances	**D** checks
8 A outside	**B** behind	**C** beyond	**D** without

Part 2

For questions **9 – 16**, read the text below and think of the word which best fits each space. Use only **one** word in each space. There is an example at the beginning (**0**). Write your answers **IN CAPITAL LETTERS on the separate answer sheet**.

0	S	E	T														

Row to the pole

In August 2011, six adventurers (**0**) __SET__ out from Resolution Bay in northern Canada in a rowing boat, on (**9**) _____ was to become an epic journey. Their aim was to try to do (**10**) _____ never attempted before; rowing the 450 miles to the North Pole.

Although many people still regarded the feat (**11**) _____ an impossible dream, the ongoing retreat of the Arctic ice sheet (**12**) _____ to climate change had turned it (**13**) _____ a distinct possibility. In the summer months, the break-up of the ice in the immediate vicinity of the pole was opening up the area to oil and gas exploration. Meanwhile, scientists were predicting that the impact of global warming was becoming so extreme that the Arctic (**14**) _____ well be free of ice by the year 2030.

The time seemed ripe for Jock Wishaw and his team to go (**15**) _____ a new record by attempting to row to the pole in an open boat. (**16**) _____ facing a sea congested with broken ice over the final few miles, the team eventually made it – exhausted but jubilant after their 28-day journey.

Part 3

For questions **17 – 24**, read the text below. Use the word given in capitals at the end of some of the lines to form a word that fits in the space in the same line. There is an example at the beginning (**0**). Write your answers **IN CAPITAL LETTERS on the separate answer sheet**.

0	I	N	T	R	O	D	U	C	T	I	O	N			

The birth of the barcode

Alan Haberman will be remembered as the man responsible for the (**0**) __INTRODUCTION__ and standardising of the barcode: the black-and-white stripes and numbers symbol that forms the basis of modern product (**17**) _____ systems. — INTRODUCE / IDENTIFY

(**18**) _____, however, Haberman's motivation came not so much from a desire to make a profit for the supermarket chain which employed him, as from his own sense of frustration at standing in supermarket queues. — APPEAR

Haberman, a retail executive, spearheaded the development of the first barcode and (**19**) _____ scanner device, which was first used in 1974. As well as speeding up the process of collecting payments at the store's (**20**) _____, the new electronic system could also (**21**) _____ managers on the movement and current status of the shop's stock, thereby allowing (**22**) _____ reorders and deliveries, and saving hours of unnecessary and (**23**) _____ inventory work by staff. — ACCOMPANY / CHECK / DATE / TIME / PAINS

The barcode system also later helped protect stores against the scourge of shoplifting, when a tag was added that would bleep as (**24**) _____ made their way through the store exit. — OFFEND

Part 4

For questions **25 – 30**, complete the second sentence so that it has a similar meaning to the first sentence, using the word given. **Do not change the word given**. You must use between **three** and **eight** words, including the word given. Here is an example (**0**).

Example:

0 Would you have any objection to my bringing a friend to your party?

mind

Would **you mind if I** brought a friend to your party?

0	You mind if I

Write **only** the missing words **on the separate answer sheet**.

---

25 No matter what happens, I am never going to stay in that hotel again.

ever

Under _____ stay in that hotel again.

26 Simon has to get used to the idea that he won't be able to play football anymore.

terms

Simon has to _____ the idea that he won't be able to play football anymore.

27 Darius completely ignored his teacher's advice when it came to choosing an essay title.

notice

When choosing an essay title, Darius _____ advice his teacher had given him.

28 The travel agent had given John the impression that the hotel would provide all meals.

believe

The travel agent _____ that the hotel would provide all meals.

29 Unless the weather suddenly gets worse, the match will be played on Saturday.

deterioration

As _____ in the weather, the match will be played on Saturday.

30 Many people wrongly believe that the island was discovered by chance.

popular

Contrary _____ discovered by chance.

Part 5

You are going to read an article about road transport. For questions **31 – 36**, choose the answer (**A**, **B**, **C** or **D**) which you think fits best according to the text. Mark your answers **on the separate answer sheet**.

Goodbye to traffic jams?

Does technology hold the key to getting road transport moving again?

No exhibit was more popular at the 1939 World's Fair in New York than General Motors (GM) 'Futurama', the Norman Bel Geddes-designed fantasia of vast, modern and largely empty superhighways swooping past tall towers. More than thirty thousand visitors a day were captivated by what was described as 'a prophecy of cities, towns and countryside served by a comprehensive road system'. The US may have got that road network – the vast Interstate Highway System knitting together a nation – but little else of Bel Geddes' automotive utopia came to fruition. Nor could the designer's dream of smoothly speeding traffic survive its own internal contradiction: that those great empty roads would, inevitably, fill and then grind to a halt.

At Expo 2010, the World Exposition held in Shanghai, GM was once more envisioning the future of transport, but the changed tenor of the times was evident. Instead of big cars with tailfins soaring down an ever-expanding highway network, GM's pavilion featured small, whimsical vehicles plugged into electric – and wireless – networks. But the spirit of Bel Geddes endures. Jean Liu-Barnocki, the pavilion's deputy director, predicted that in future 'people will be relieved from the stress of driving and have more free time behind the wheel.' And that's not all: 'Information sharing between cars will eliminate accidents and traffic jams,' he says. To hear Liu-Barnocki talk, GM could well be taking a page from Bel Geddes, circa 1940, in his prescient book *Magic Motorways*, in which he envisioned drivers receiving messages from highways, traffic signals talking to cars, and automated highways that maintained the 'control of speed and spacing of cars in the same traffic lane'.

The future of driving always seems to be further away than it appears. But the onset of increasingly sophisticated and inexpensive technologies – everything from GPS to WiFi to Lidar (think radar, but with light waves) – along with the sheer necessity of managing our limited transport networks more efficiently, means we are drawing closer to a radical re-imagining of the driving experience. Crucially, we are possibly coming to grips with a problem that has plagued society since the days of Caesar's Rome: traffic. *line 21*

Technologically, the roads of tomorrow are drawing into view. The idea of traffic signals communicating with cars, for example, is becoming a reality, and intersections warning drivers that another vehicle is approaching are being tested in a European Union-funded research project. And as for the speed of cars, and distance between them being controlled in a designated traffic lane, this is coming to fruition under the EU's Safe Road Trains for the Environment or Sartre, programme. This creates highway 'platoons' in which groups of wirelessly connected vehicles move automatically in the wake of a human-controlled lead vehicle. As project director Tom Robinson of the British transport company Ricardo explains, as well as regularising how fast traffic flows, the platoons will also be more efficient in terms of fuel use and arguably safer. They could even help reduce so-called 'ghost jams', those shockwaves of clogged traffic caused by variations in driver speed or braking that can bloom into full-blown jams. German researchers have already successfully tested the concept with trucks.

The road to smarter traffic does have a potential fork. There are two schools of thought, says Kevin Borras, *line 32* editor of the publication *Thinking Highways*. One of them argues that 'the future of traffic technology is in co-operative systems, cars that communicate with other cars or with the infrastructure'; the second says that 'the future is going to be hand-held, that personal and personalised information is going to be the way forward'. Borras expects it to be a combination of the two. Because it's one thing to sort out the best routes for the traffic network as a whole, it's another to entice individual drivers into taking them – sometimes the social hurdles are greater than the technological ones. Then there are the questions of assigning legal liability when driver-assist technology fails. It is also unclear how drivers themselves will respond to surrendering their autonomy. At Honda's research centre in Ohio, I was told that some drivers were uncomfortable with the safe following distance set by engineers in adaptive cruise control systems – they felt there was too much space. As Henry Barnes, New York traffic commissioner in the 1960s, once noted, 'As time goes on the technical problems become more automatic, while the people problems become more surrealistic.'

31 What is suggested about Bel Geddes' 'Futurama' in the first paragraph?

A Its principal prediction has become a reality.

B Its visual impact outweighed its practical contribution.

C It failed to take into account existing advances in technology.

D It placed too much emphasis on the speed at which traffic would move.

32 What point does the writer make about the exposition in Shanghai?

A It picked up on ideas from Bel Geddes' exhibit.

B It reflected changed priorities since Bel Geddes' day.

C It appeared far less imaginative than Bel Geddes' model.

D It tended to focus more on drivers and vehicles than Bel Geddes did.

33 The writer mentions 'Caesar's Rome' in line 21 to emphasise his point that

A attempts to alleviate traffic congestion often lack foresight.

B technology alone cannot solve problems of traffic congestion.

C traffic congestion has always presented an intractable problem.

D the management of traffic congestion has hardly developed since then.

34 What is the main advantage of the 'platoons' mentioned in the fourth paragraph?

A The possibility of human error is removed from driving.

B Certain types of traffic congestion would be avoided.

C One driver would control the speed of all vehicles.

D The environmental benefits that would result.

35 The phrase 'potential fork' in line 32 suggests that advances in traffic technology

A are likely to be delayed by disagreements.

B may be too ambitious to work in practice.

C seem to be heading in conflicting directions.

D are coming about as a result of a compromise.

36 What does the writer conclude about 'smarter traffic' in the final paragraph?

A Legal issues provide the greatest barrier to its implementation.

B It will only succeed if there is a centralised infrastructure in place.

C It may be a disadvantage if drivers can communicate with each other.

D Individual drivers may not be ready to give up control of their vehicles.

Part 6

You are going to read a newspaper article about the naturalist Jane Goodall. Seven paragraphs have been removed from the article. Choose from the paragraphs **A – H** the one which fits each gap (**37 – 43**). There is one extra paragraph which you do not need to use. Mark your answers **on the separate answer sheet**.

A meeting with Jane Goodall

The celebrated naturalist shares her views on the role of zoos and importance of dogs for human contentment

It's a crisp winter's afternoon in Sydney. The sky is blue, and a frosty wind is blowing down Middle Harbour and across the grassy expanse of The Spit Reserve, a dog-friendly park, where I often take my shaggy, excitable four-legged friend Sam. Wrapped up in a long cream coat, Dame Jane Goodall emerges into the squall from a black four-by-four. 'Oh, it's cold here!' she gasps, perhaps hinting that she hopes our meeting won't go on too long.

37

For more than fifty years, Jane's been famous as the woman who taught the world about chimpanzees. As a young woman with little more than secretarial training, she was chosen by the anthropologist Louis Leakey to live among a group of chimpanzees in the Gombe wildlife park in East Africa and study their behaviour. She found a vantage point, high up above a lake from which to do this unobserved.

38

Although she continues to be closely involved with chimpanzee research, since the 1980s Jane's focus has been on the wider issues of conservation, particularly through a youth programme called Roots & Shoots. This is now active in over a hundred countries and encourages young people to take on projects to help other animals and the environment. Jane's philosophy – that each of us can make a difference every day – clearly chimes with the growing numbers of people taking part.

39

Now nearing eighty, Jane is slight, but not frail, and seems to thrive on the hectic schedule. Her white hair is pulled back in a ponytail, and her unlined face exudes calm. There's also a mischievous twitch at the corner of her mouth, and a twinkle in her eye. As she and Sam wrestle with sticks, she tells me how important dogs were as an inspiration for her early work.

40

The then scientific establishment dismissed the idea out of hand. 'University professors told me that I was mistaken. But observing the animals themselves had taught me that it was true.' Things have come a long way, she notes. 'These days you can study the animal mind at universities, and even animal personality.'

41

Her lifestyle means that Jane is fortunate enough to meet plenty of folk she does warm too, however, from inner-city kids to heads of state. At a conference a couple of days earlier, she'd talked about how important dogs are for contentment. We clamber up from the beach and walk towards the house she's staying at. Sam trots between us, Jane keeping an eye on him with gentle but firm commands.

42

'We have this glorified idea of freedom,' she explains. 'For chimps, living somewhere like Gombe is certainly the ideal – but if you're a chimp in the wild elsewhere in Africa, there's always a tension from destruction of their habitats, poachers and so on. Or there's a risk of being captured for medical research or circuses or pets.

43

Once we're at the house, we continue talking while Sam dashes around the garden. But after a few minutes, someone brings him back on the leash, explaining that he had nearly eaten one of the neighbour's pair of free-roaming rabbits. I start to give him a stern talking-to, but Jane quickly comes to Sam's defence. 'He's not naughty, he's just being a dog.' As we make our farewells – Jane has another appointment to get to – she gives Sam a final pat. 'He'll sleep well tonight,' she says. 'And he'll be dreaming of rabbits.'

A That's why a well-designed captive environment, with a good amount of space, safety and people around who care for them and look after them, is also good. 'Most people don't bother to put themselves in the position of a chimp,' she says. 'They assume they know best.'

B So it was that she came to spot one doing something of tremendous significance – using a stem of grass as a tool to extract termites from a nest. It was an enormous discovery. Until that point, tool use was considered the defining characteristic of humanity, the thing that set us apart from the animals.

C Jane has noted that, on the contrary, chimps seem to get along rather well with dogs. 'It's fascinating,' she says. 'I'd love to study it. I've seen many examples of dogs and chimps that form close bonds. I even wrote a children's book about one.'

D It's a fundamental shift of perspective for which Jane can take much of the credit. 'People think that my favourite animals must be chimps, whereas actually it's dogs, because of the deep relationship they have with us. There's something about having a dog in a room full of people that just illustrates that so well. It opens the heart. And if it doesn't, they're not the sort of people I want to know.'

E Indeed, an intelligent – 'quite opinionated' – mutt called Rusty was her childhood companion in fact, teaching her that animals other than humans do have emotions. When she emerged from the jungle, she reported that chimps, too, were emotional beings.

F 'I get so upset by the way people think that in order to train a dog you've got to have dominance and that you've got to have instant obedience,' she says. When I first thought of suggesting that we take Sam for a walk, I had been worried she'd be opposed to the whole idea of having pets, or keeping animals in zoos, but her views are more nuanced than that.

G Delivering that message has turned her into a kind of Ancient Mariner of the environmental movement. She's never in the same place for more than three weeks. For years now, she's been on the road more than three-hundred days a year, working fifteen-hour days, seven days a week.

H Any briskness is put aside, however, when I introduce her to our companion for the afternoon. 'Hello, boy,' she calls, and suggests I let him off the leash. Sam promptly sprints for the beach, where other dogs are running and swimming. 'That's better,' she says, and follows him down to the sand.

Part 7

You are going to read an article about people who follow several careers at the same time. For questions **44 – 53**, choose from the sections (**A – D**). The sections may be chosen more than once.

Mark your answers **on the separate answer sheet**.

Which section mentions someone who

admits to finding satisfaction in an increased workload? | 44 |

can be regarded as farsighted in anticipating developments of this kind? | 45 |

has diversified without straying far from an original career path? | 46 |

identifies personality traits needed to cope with downsides of this way of working? | 47 |

has studied the reasons behind the development of the phenomenon? | 48 |

mentions having no regrets about giving up a single career in favour of new challenges? | 49 |

pinpoints the sector of the workforce most likely to benefit from this type of working? | 50 |

predicts fluctuations in demand for some of the skills offered in a portfolio? | 51 |

has coined an alternative term for someone who works in this way? | 52 |

realises that pursuing certain types of career strand can be counter-productive? | 53 |

The portfolio career

A new generation of workers is discovering that maintaining a 'portfolio' of different careers can pay off in terms of time, money and quality of life.

A If you ever get home late from the office and collapse onto the sofa, wondering what happened to your social life, or sit in meetings dreaming about more flexible working hours, you might need an extra job or two. On the face of it, that sounds like the last way to redress your work-life balance, but you shouldn't necessarily reject the idea out of hand, according to Matt Pearsen of recruitment group APOS. Here's how it works. Scaling back time spent on a 'main' career gives freedom to develop other strings to your bow, as you spread your well-honed skills across different part-time roles. As Matt says: 'Because you're at the helm of your own bespoke career, you can structure your work around your lifestyle, taking time out when you need it.' On those terms, a compilation career suddenly sounds pretty appealing. It's certainly worked for Sarah Dillon, 30. 'Traditional careers all seemed to be about specialising yourself into a silo until you could do your job with your eyes closed,' says the translator/teacher/event manager/web designer, who swapped office life in London for a laptop in Brisbane. 'I couldn't get excited about that. There were so many things I was interested in pursuing, and they were all important.' For Sarah, taking control of her own day-to-day career direction has been both challenging and rewarding. 'I definitely work harder now, and the hours can be longer, but I have the best possible balance between paying my bills and being fulfilled. I'm glad I didn't wait until I burnt out or retired to make the change.'

B This shift is no surprise to management experts. As early as 1982, management guru Charles Handy was suggesting that in the 21st century, more than fifty percent of all jobs would be conducted on a part-time, freelance or self-employed basis as people develop a more pick-and-choose attitude to work. It turns out he was spot on. So what's behind this rise? Marci Alboher, bestselling author of *One Person/ Multiple Careers: A New Model for Work/Life Success* describes herself as a 'slash careerist – as in lawyer/ journalist/author/writing coach'. Her research reveals that, while recession-proofing and maternity planning can play a part, the most common trigger for adopting a portfolio career is personal fulfilment. 'They allow people a certain amount of stability while giving them the freedom to follow something they feel close to,' she says. 'I've met computer programmer/theatre directors, lawyer/ministers and longshoreman/filmmakers. All of these combined careers are ultimately about figuring out ways to make room for everything we want to be in our lives.'

C For some, it's less of a conscious decision. Thirty-three-year-old Anita Westmorland's portfolio career built itself. The professional actor is now also a director/event manager/set stylist/interior designer. 'All these different careers came from the same root,' she explains. 'I started out acting, but it was hard to support myself. As I was working for small theatre companies with no budget for a stylist, I took the opportunity to learn new skills that would give me the chance to earn extra income elsewhere. Before long I knew how to manage lots of aspects of staging, so events management evolved as a natural fourth strand. Now all four careers pay quite well – and they're all things I love.' Your choice of second and third careers is as crucial as your first, says Anita. 'Some actor friends have gone for 'steady' second careers in law or accounting,' she says. 'Slowly and surely, that's taken over, and they don't act much now, or enjoy their day jobs. I wanted to avoid that.' 'You do need to keep your eye on the ball,' agrees advertising planner/wedding photographer/honey producer Ben Bowles, 46. 'There'll be times when you're staring at a gap in one or more of your careers, calling around and hoping something comes up.'

D Some are more suited to a portfolio career than others, suggests Jenny Ungless, a life coach for Monster. co.uk. 'Portfolio careers are great if you're adept at multi-tasking and communicating. And for many, a portfolio career can be the solution to balancing work and home life. Working mums can set up an office at home and work on a wide variety of jobs when the children are at school or after they've gone to sleep.' The experts agree, though, that a portfolio career isn't for everybody. 'People who are optimistic by nature seem to be better protected against the strains of a portfolio-working lifestyle,' claims Peter Totterdell, senior research fellow at the Institute of Work Psychology. He identifies 'autonomy, uncertainty and social isolation' as the big impacts on any portfolio careerist's lifestyle. 'Organisation is the key,' agrees Ungless, 'It's a challenge. But if you can keep control of your schedule, and have skills that can be transferred to a variety of jobs, a portfolio career really can offer the best of all worlds'.

Writing

Part 1

Read the two texts below.

Write an essay summarising and evaluating the key points from both texts. Use your own words throughout as far as possible, and include your own ideas in your answers.

Write your answer in **240 – 280 words on the separate answer sheet**.

1

What is art?

Basically, anything that was created by the human mind or body has the potential for being defined as a work of art. Generally speaking, however, we draw a distinction between that which is designed, and then mass produced and that which is the original artefact created by a talented individual. That's why the designer of a stylish coffee pot may be recognised as a true artist, but on purchasing the pot from a chain store one does not take possession of a work of art. By the same token, a simple line drawing by an eminent artist could assume great artistic value and meaning and become a sought-after work of art.

Has art lost its way?

If you ask me, a lot of the stuff on show in art galleries these days is worthless rubbish that anyone could have produced – even me! Why people pay ridiculous sums for the stuff is a mystery to me, and I'm pretty sure in a few years time when these so-called artists have been forgotten, the people buying this stuff will realise they have been taken for a ride. 'What about Picasso?' I can hear you saying, 'people said that about his innovative work at first.' Well, I may not like the pictures, but even I can see that the man could paint, which is more than can be said for today's lot.

Write your **essay**.

Part 2

Write an answer to **one** of the questions **2 – 5** in this part. Write your answer in **280 – 320** words in an appropriate style **on the separate answer sheet**. Put the question number in the box at the top of the answer sheet.

---

2 An English-language magazine has invited readers to send in articles in which they share their experience of doing research on the Internet. You decide to send in an article in which you describe both successful and unsuccessful Internet searches you have attempted, giving advice to other readers based on your experience.

Write your **article**.

3 You regularly use a website which you find particularly interesting or useful. The website has invited users to write a report explaining why they prefer it to other similar sites. They are also interested in hearing any criticisms of the website, and suggestions for how it might be improved.

Write your **report**.

4 A travel magazine is running a series of restaurant reviews in English for visitors to your local area. You have been asked to write a review of a restaurant you have visited recently, commenting on all aspects of the experience and saying how suitable the restaurant would be for visitors from other countries.

Write your **review**.

5 Write an answer to one of the following two questions based on a book you have read. Write (5a) or (5b) at the beginning of your answer.

(a) A local school wants to select a short novel in English for advanced level students to read and discuss in class. You have been asked to recommend a suitable novel. The school has asked you to write a report saying why you think the book you recommend is suitable for this purpose.

Write your **report**.

(b) You have read a novel in English which you bought from an online bookshop, which offered a discount to English language students. The bookshop has asked you to write a reader review in which you say whether you would recommend the book to other English language students and why.

Write your **review**.

Listening

Part 1

You will hear three different extracts.

For questions **1 – 6**, choose the answer (**A**, **B** or **C**) which fits best according to what you hear.

There are two questions for each extract.

Extract One

You hear part of a radio programme on which a woman is talking about keeping bees.

1 She puts her recent beekeeping disaster down to
  A her own lack of experience.
  B the effects of a disease.
  C simply being unlucky.

2 What does she regard as the main advantage of her new 'beehaus'?
  A the amount of honey it can hold
  B the material from which it is made
  C the ease with which it can be handled

Extract Two

You hear a famous rock guitarist talking about his recent work.

3 What is he doing?
  A justifying a bad decision
  B explaining the background to a decision
  C responding to criticism of an unpopular decision

4 How did playing with the band called *The Ashes* make him feel?
  A nostalgic for the early days of his career
  B reluctant to commit himself to going on tour with them
  C determined to take charge of their musical development

Extract Three

You hear an academic talking about a computer program she has experimented with.

5 What is the usual purpose of the computer program?
  A It reports the main ideas in texts.
  B It indicates how clearly a text is written.
  C It comments on the use of language in texts.

6 When she used the program with a novel, she found that
  A it was unable to identify where the story was set.
  B it tended to interpret meaning very literally.
  C it failed to recognise spoken dialogue.

Part 2

You will hear a naturalist called Phil Asterton giving a lecture about a species of bird called the Common European Starling. For questions **7 – 15**, complete the sentences with a word or short phrase.

Phil says that in the Americas and Australasia, starlings are in the category known as **(7)** _____ species.

Phil mentions **(8)** _____ as a type of landscape where starlings are not found.

A female starling is most easily identified by the **(9)** _____ colouring around its beak.

Phil uses the term **(10)** _____ to describe the starlings' nesting behaviour.

Phil was surprised to learn that young starlings are fed almost exclusively on **(11)** _____ .

Phil says that the flight patterns of flocks of starlings have been studied by **(12)** _____ as well as by biologists and engineers.

Researchers point to the starlings' fast **(13)** _____ to explain how the birds manage to fly in such close formation.

Phil gives the example of **(14)** _____ as sounds which starlings now commonly imitate.

Researchers have suggested a link between the local variations in starling song and **(15)** _____ in human languages.

Part 3

You will hear a philosopher called Marc Jerome and a psychologist called Elena Berensen taking part in a discussion on the subject of identity and the labels that identify groups of people in society.

For questions **16 – 20**, choose the answer (**A**, **B**, **C** or **D**) which fits best according to what you hear.

16 What does Marc suggest about being labelled as 'a philosopher'?

    A It's the label he uses most often.

    B It's not a label he could use in other contexts.

    C It's the label that best describes what he does.

    D It's only one of various labels he sometimes uses.

17 Elena suggests that the term 'pigeonholed' is used by people who

    A prefer not to use labels.

    B dislike the labels they've chosen.

    C resent having labels applied to them.

    D feel that they don't fit under any labels.

18 Marc and Elena agree that a very strong sense of identity can

    A leave people unprepared for changing circumstances.

    B have adverse effects on relationships at work.

    C make people too quick to categorise others.

    D lead to tensions in aspects of family life.

19 When asked about labelling by the media, Elena reveals

    A a determination to make it more sensitive.

    B a concern about the social consequences.

    C a feeling that it isn't greatly significant.

    D an acceptance that it has a part to play.

20 In his concluding comments, Marc suggests that labels of identity

    A allow the individual to fit into society.

    B help the individual to prioritise things in life.

    C prevent the individual from being truly unique.

    D stop the individual from becoming too self-obsessed.

Part 4

You will hear five short extracts in which people are talking about job interviews they attended. While you listen, you must complete both tasks.

Task One

For questions **21 – 25**, choose from the list (**A – H**) what made each speaker apply for the job.

A being approached by a recruiter

B an online advertisement

C feeling obliged to do so

D wanting more responsibility

E wishing to make a point

F a need to gain experience

G the prospect of a better salary package

H the reputation of the employer

Speaker 1	21	
Speaker 2	22	
Speaker 3	23	
Speaker 4	24	
Speaker 5	25	

Task Two

For questions **26 – 30**, choose from the list (**A – H**) how each speaker felt after the interview.

A aware of an error of judgement

B unsettled by one aspect of it

C surprised at how challenging it was

D disappointed with the outcome

E less keen on the job itself

F unimpressed by the interview panel

G amused at the way it was set up

H intimidated by the other applicants

Speaker 1	26	
Speaker 2	27	
Speaker 3	28	
Speaker 4	29	
Speaker 5	30	

Speaking

Part 1 (2 minutes / 3 minutes for groups of three)

Interlocutor Good morning / afternoon / evening. My name is _____ and this is my colleague
_____ . And your names are _____ ? Could I have your mark sheets, please?

Thank you.

First of all, we'd like to know something about you.

Where are you from *(Candidate A)*? And you *(Candidate B)*?

(Address Candidate B) Are you working or studying at the moment?

(Address Candidate A) And you?

Select a further question for each candidate.

- How easy is it to find work in … ?
- Do you think you'll use English in your future work? (Why? / Why not?)
- Do you think other languages could become more important than English? (Why? / Why not?)
- How important are your friends to you? (Why? / Why not?)
- Is it important to have hobbies as well as a career? (Why? / Why not?)
- What would be your idea place to live? (Why?)

Candidates _____

Interlocutor Thank you.

Part 2   (4 minutes / 6 minutes for groups of three)

Interlocutor Now in this part of the test you're going to do something together. Here are some pictures of people with cars in different situations.

First I'd like you to look at pictures * and * and talk together about the different image of driving each of them presents.

You have about a minute for this, so don't worry if I interrupt you. *(2 minutes for groups of three)*

Candidates _____

Interlocutor Thank you. Now look at all the pictures.

I'd like you to imagine that a motoring organisation is putting on an exhibition entitled 'Driving Today' as part of a recruitment drive to attract new members. These are some of the images that will be used in the exhibition. The organisers want to use one of them on a poster to advertise the exhibition.

Talk together about the different issues related to driving these pictures show. Then decide which one would be best to use on the poster advertising the event.

You have around three minutes to talk about this. *(4 minutes for groups of three)*

Candidates _____

Interlocutor Thank you.

Publicity poster – Driving today exhibition

Part 3 (10 minutes / 15 minutes for groups of three)

Leisure

Interlocutor Now, in this part of the test, you're each going to talk on your own for about two minutes. You need to listen while your partner is speaking because you'll be asked to comment afterwards.

So *(Candidate A)*, I'm going to give you a card with a question written on it and I'd like you to tell us what you think. There are some ideas on the card for you to use if you like.

All right? Here is your card.

Please let *(Candidate B)* see your card. Remember *(Candidate A)* you have about two minutes to talk before we join in.

Candidate A _____

🕑 *2 minutes*

Interlocutor Thank you.

Task 1(a)

Why is sport such an important part of many people's lives?

- the need for exercise
- the competitive element
- the social functions of sport

Interlocutor *Ask one of the following questions to Candidate B:*

- Are you generally a sporty person?
- Do you think children should be encouraged to play team sports?
- Why are some sports more successful on TV than others?

Interlocutor *Invite Candidate A to join in by selecting one of the following prompts:*

- How about you?   • What do you think?   • Do you agree?

Candidates _____

🕑 *1 minute*

Interlocutor Thank you.

Interlocutor Now *(Candidate B)* it's your turn to be given a question. Here is your card.

Please let *(Candidate A)* see your card. Remember *(Candidate B)* you have about two minutes to tell us what you think, and there are some ideas for you to use on the card if you like. All right?

Candidate B _____

🕐 *2 minutes*

Interlocutor Thank you.

Task 1(b)

Why have social networking sites become so important in recent years?

- the development of technology
- how sites influence people and events
- changing social habits

Interlocutor *Ask one of the following questions to Candidate A:*

- Are you a big user of social networking sites?
- Do you think these sites have changed people's attitudes?
- How do you think these sites might develop in the future?

Interlocutor *Invite Candidate B to join in by selecting one of the following prompts:*

- How about you?   • What do you think?   • Do you agree?

Candidates _____

🕐 *1 minute*

Interlocutor Thank you.

Interlocutor Now, to finish the test, we're going to talk about leisure in general.

Address a selection of the following questions to both candidates:

- What is the right balance between work and leisure time?
- Do you think that some people have too much leisure time?
- Should schools and colleges organise leisure activities for their students?
- Do you think leisure pursuits help children to develop into good citizens?
- Do you think some people become too passionate about their leisure pursuits?
- Why do some retired people find it hard to fill their time at first?

Candidates _____

Interlocutor Thank you. That is the end of the test.

UNIVERSITY *of* **CAMBRIDGE**
ESOL Examinations

Do not write in this box

Candidate Name
If not already printed, write name in CAPITALS and complete the Candidate No. grid (in pencil).

Candidate Signature

Examination Title

Centre

Supervisor:
If the candidate is ABSENT or has WITHDRAWN shade here ▭

Centre No.

Candidate No.

Examination Details

0	0	0	0
1	1	1	1
2	2	2	2
3	3	3	3
4	4	4	4
5	5	5	5
6	6	6	6
7	7	7	7
8	8	8	8
9	9	9	9

Candidate Answer Sheet 1

Instructions

Use a PENCIL (B or HB). Rub out any answer you wish to change using an eraser.

Part 1: Mark ONE letter for each question.

For example, if you think **B** is the right answer to the question, mark your answer sheet like this:

Parts 2, 3 and **4:** Write your answer clearly in CAPITAL LETTERS.

For Parts 2 and 3 write one letter in each box. For example:

Part 1

1	A	B	C	D
2	A	B	C	D
3	A	B	C	D
4	A	B	C	D
5	A	B	C	D
6	A	B	C	D
7	A	B	C	D
8	A	B	C	D

Part 2

Do not write below here

9		9 1 0 u
10		10 1 0 u
11		11 1 0 u
12		12 1 0 u
13		13 1 0 u
14		14 1 0 u
15		15 1 0 u
16		16 1 0 u

Continues over ➡

CPE R1

DP690/190

137

Part 3

		Do not write below here
17		17 1 0 u
18		18 1 0 u
19		19 1 0 u
20		20 1 0 u
21		21 1 0 u
22		22 1 0 u
23		23 1 0 u
24		24 1 0 u

Part 4

		Do not write below here
25		25 2 1 0 u
26		26 2 1 0 u
27		27 2 1 0 u
28		28 2 1 0 u
29		29 2 1 0 u
30		30 2 1 0 u

denote Print Limited 0121 520 5100

UNIVERSITY *of* CAMBRIDGE
ESOL Examinations

Do not write in this box

Candidate Name
If not already printed, write name
in CAPITALS and complete the
Candidate No. grid (in pencil).

Candidate Signature

Examination Title

Centre

Supervisor:
If the candidate is ABSENT or has WITHDRAWN shade here ▭

SAMPLE

Centre No.

Candidate No.

Examination Details

0	0	0	0
1	1	1	1
2	2	2	2
3	3	3	3
4	4	4	4
5	5	5	5
6	6	6	6
7	7	7	7
8	8	8	8
9	9	9	9

Candidate Answer Sheet 2

Instructions
Use a PENCIL (B or HB). Rub out any answer you wish to change using an eraser.

Parts 5, 6 and 7: Mark ONE letter for each question. For example, if you think **B** is the right answer to the question, mark your answer sheet like this:

0 A B C D

Part 5

31	A	B	C	D
32	A	B	C	D
33	A	B	C	D
34	A	B	C	D
35	A	B	C	D
36	A	B	C	D

Part 6

37	A	B	C	D	E	F	G	H
38	A	B	C	D	E	F	G	H
39	A	B	C	D	E	F	G	H
40	A	B	C	D	E	F	G	H
41	A	B	C	D	E	F	G	H
42	A	B	C	D	E	F	G	H
43	A	B	C	D	E	F	G	H

Part 7

44	A	B	C	D	E	F
45	A	B	C	D	E	F
46	A	B	C	D	E	F
47	A	B	C	D	E	F
48	A	B	C	D	E	F
49	A	B	C	D	E	F
50	A	B	C	D	E	F
51	A	B	C	D	E	F
52	A	B	C	D	E	F
53	A	B	C	D	E	F

CPE R2

denote
Print Limited 0121 520 5100

DP691/191

UNIVERSITY *of* CAMBRIDGE
ESOL Examinations

Do not write in this box

Candidate Name
If not already printed, write name
in CAPITALS and complete the
Candidate No. grid (in pencil).

Candidate Signature

Examination Title

Centre

Supervisor:
If the candidate is ABSENT or has WITHDRAWN shade here ⬜

Test version: A B C D E F J K L M N   Special arrangements: S H

Centre No.

Candidate No.

Examination
Details

Candidate Answer Sheet

Instructions

Use a PENCIL (B or HB).
Rub out any answer you wish to change using an eraser.

Parts 1, 3 and 4:
Mark ONE letter for each question.

For example, if you think **B** is the
right answer to the question, mark
your answer sheet like this:

Part 2:
Write your answer clearly in CAPITAL LETTERS.

Write one letter or number in each box.
If the answer has more than one word, leave one
box empty between words.

For example:

Turn this sheet over to start.

Part 1

	A	B	C
1	☐	☐	☐
2	☐	☐	☐
3	☐	☐	☐
4	☐	☐	☐
5	☐	☐	☐
6	☐	☐	☐

Part 2 (Remember to write in CAPITAL LETTERS or numbers)

Do not write below here

7		7 1 0 u
8		8 1 0 u
9		9 1 0 u
10		10 1 0 u
11		11 1 0 u
12		12 1 0 u
13		13 1 0 u
14		14 1 0 u
15		15 1 0 u

SAMPLE

Part 3

	A	B	C	D
16	☐	☐	☐	☐
17	☐	☐	☐	☐
18	☐	☐	☐	☐
19	☐	☐	☐	☐
20	☐	☐	☐	☐

Part 4

	A	B	C	D	E	F	G	H
21	☐	☐	☐	☐	☐	☐	☐	☐
22	☐	☐	☐	☐	☐	☐	☐	☐
23	☐	☐	☐	☐	☐	☐	☐	☐
24	☐	☐	☐	☐	☐	☐	☐	☐
25	☐	☐	☐	☐	☐	☐	☐	☐
26	☐	☐	☐	☐	☐	☐	☐	☐
27	☐	☐	☐	☐	☐	☐	☐	☐
28	☐	☐	☐	☐	☐	☐	☐	☐
29	☐	☐	☐	☐	☐	☐	☐	☐
30	☐	☐	☐	☐	☐	☐	☐	☐

denote Print Limited 0121 520 5100

Exam countdown – top tips

Nine months before . . .

- You've already built up a good knowledge of English and now you're starting on the final year of preparation for the Cambridge English: Proficiency (CPE) examination. Work consistently, study conscientiously – and above all, enjoy learning!
- Establish good habits from the outset.
- Keep vocabulary lists in your notebook that include derivations, opposites, useful phrases, etc.
- Note down any word formations that might present a problem.
- Read widely outside the classroom. Use the resources of the internet to help you (online newspapers, magazines, etc) plus official Cambridge ESOL guidelines and advice.
- Make use of communication websites to listen to interesting talks in English in order to develop your listening skills further.

Six months before . . .

- Start looking back at what you've learnt over the previous three months. Constant revision is essential to successful learning. It's no use leaving it all until the last minute! The more often you study a new word or phrase, the more likely it is to remain fixed in your memory.
- Go through your written work. Are you developing your use of language sufficiently? Make a conscious effort to use new language in your written work.

Three months before . . .

- By now, you should have acquired a comprehensive understanding of the exam and its requirements and you should be completely familiar with all the exam tasks.
- Revise your vocabulary and word formation lists, highlighting any areas that you feel need special attention. Spend as much time as possible on your English.
- Start to practise the exam tasks under exam conditions: whenever you do an exam task, time yourself so that you can finish it within the time limit.

On the day . . .

- Make sure you take your identification. It must have your photo on it and must be the original document, not a copy.
- You will also need a pen, an HB or B pencil and an eraser.
- You should feel confident, knowing that you have prepared as well as you can for the exam.
- There will be a clock in the exam room, but wear a watch if possible and time each section of the exam very carefully. There won't be very much time to spare so it's important that you know exactly how much time you have. Try not to run over your timing for each part.
- Answer all questions as you work through the paper since you might not have time to check your answers at the end. Ideally, however, you should plan to spend time at the end of each paper checking your answers so that you can change them if necessary.

The day before . . .

- You should have a quick look through your most important notes, the highlighted points in your vocabulary and word formations, together with any other important areas. Do not try to cram in new material that you haven't managed to cover before.
- Know when to say enough is enough and get a good night's sleep. Your brain cannot work efficiently on five hours' sleep!

One month before . . .

- Having done so much exam practice and preparation, you should by now feel confident in your knowledge of the language and your ability to cope successfully in the exam.
- You know that lexical chunks (verb phrases, prepositional phrases, and so on) make up a large part of language learning. Revise all the phrases you have learnt, highlighting any particular ones that you find difficult to remember.
- Do a mock exam under exam conditions, whether through your school or on your own at home, if you are following a course of self-study. Check your performance according to timing, word count, etc.

Top twenty questions

1 How many papers are there in the revised CPE exam?

Four: Reading and Use of English, Writing, Listening, Speaking.

2 How long is the exam in total?

Just under four hours.

3 What has changed from the previous format of the CPE exam?

The Use of English paper and the Reading paper have been combined into a single paper with 7 parts. The summary task has been absorbed into the new Writing Part 1 task: summary and evaluation of two texts.

4 How much shorter is the revised exam?

About two hours.

5 How long is allowed for each paper?

Reading and Use of English: 1 hour 30 minutes

Writing: 1 hour 30 minutes

Listening: approximately 40 minutes

Speaking: 16 minutes

6 Is the level the same?

Yes.

7 What are the seven parts of the Reading paper?

Part 1: multiple-choice cloze (8 questions with 4 options)

Part 2: open cloze (8 questions)

Part 3: word formation (8 questions)

Part 4: key word transformations (6 questions)

Part 5: multiple-choice (long text, 6 questions with 4 options)

Part 6: gapped text (7 questions)

Part 7: multiple matching (long text or several short texts 10 questions)

8 What are the options for the Writing paper?

Part 1 is compulsory (summary and evaluation of two short texts).

Part 2 offers a choice of article, report, review, essay or letter, including a set text task. The set texts usually remain on the list for two years and the details can be found at *http://www.cambridgeesol.org/exams/cpe/index.html#wr*.

9 What if I exceed the word limit?

According to the Cambridge ESOL guidelines, the word count is a guide only. Candidates will not lose marks for exceeding the upper word limit. However, failing to reach at least the lower word count may mean that you have not answered the question satisfactorily.

10 If I have seen the film version of one of the set texts, but have not read the book, can I still answer Question 5?

Yes. It is possible to write about the film version of a set text, although reading the book as well is advisable, as it will give you more scope in what to write about in the exam.

11 Have any of the tasks in the Listening paper changed?

Yes. The task for Part 4 has changed and is now multiple matching.

12 Should I use a pen or pencil in the written exam?

A pencil should be used in all papers except the Writing paper, where a pen should be used.

13 Can I use correction fluid?

No. Correction fluid or tape may not be used. Any mistakes should be crossed out by drawing a line clearly through the word or phrase.

14 Will I be penalised for using American or other non-UK spelling?

No, but a certain amount of consistency is required. If you wish to use American spelling, for example, it is advisable to use it throughout.

15 Is there an age limit for candidates taking CPE?

No, but the examination contains some texts and tasks which are more suitable for candidates who are able to respond to abstract ideas and concepts in a mature manner.

16 Can *Cambridge English: Proficiency* also be taken as a computer-based exam?

Yes, from 2013.

17 If I take the computer-based exam, will I receive the same certificate as for the paper-based exam?

Yes. The certificate is exactly the same.

18 Who recognises the CPE certificate?

The CPE certificate is recognised globally by educational institutions, government bodies, professional and commercial organisations as evidence of a knowledge of English at near-native speaker level.

19 How long will it be before I receive my results?

Results are usually available online approximately 5–7 weeks after a paper-based exam, and two weeks after a computer-based exam. Certificates are usually sent out within three months.

20 Do I have to pass each paper in order to pass the exam?

No. The final mark you receive is the combined score of all the papers. The Reading and Use of English paper accounts for 40 percent of the final mark, with each of the remaining papers accounting for 20 percent each. If you perform poorly on one paper, you can make up for this by performing well on the other papers. If you do not achieve a pass at Level C2 of the Common European Framework of Reference for Languages (CEFR), but your overall result is within the Level C1, you will receive a certificate to confirm your ability at Level C1.

Writing: set texts

Requirements of the task

Questions 5(a) and 5(b) in Paper 2, Part 2 of the *Cambridge English: Proficiency* (CPE) focus on your knowledge of a set book. You will be required to write about the following, giving specific references to the text:

- the overall theme (or themes)
- the main characters: how they evolve, interact and impact on the development of the story
- the plot: key events, twists and turns, how it reaches a conclusion
- the language/stylistic devices: how the writer creates and conveys atmosphere or describes the characters' feelings and emotions

The task type may be an **article**, **essay**, **letter**, **report** or **review**. Where there is a film version of the book available, you can choose to write about that, if you wish. You will need to write between 280 and 320 words.

Studying the book

A Theme

As you read the book, make notes on the main themes, e.g. fear, loneliness, greed, courage, pride, shame, etc. Note down how the main character and at least one other character is affected by the themes, along with examples which illustrate this. You could do this by creating a table like the example below:

Theme	Character	Examples in the book
1 fear	1 James	1 .... 2 ....
	2 Alice	1 .... 2 ....
2 courage	1 James	1 .... 2 ....
	2 Alice	1 .... 2 ....

B Relationships

Make notes on the relationship the protagonist has with other characters in the book, and how those characters influence him/her. Make a list of examples in the book which illustrate this influence. You could do this by creating a diagram like the example below:

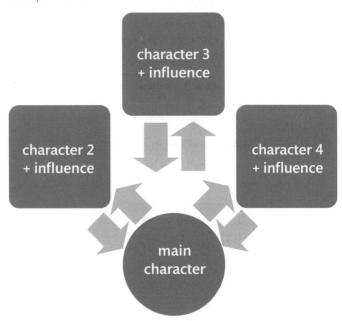

C Plot

Note down the key events in the book which affect the development of the plot. What are the turning points in the novel in which the protagonist makes an important discovery, or realises the truth about something or someone?

D Use of language

How does the writer use language effectively in order to build up suspense or give insights into people's characters? Note down any particularly effective metaphors or other stylistic and literary devices that you feel contribute to the overall success of the book.

Practice

1

The leader of your English language reading group has asked members to write a review of a book they would recommend including in a book exhibition at the library. You have decided to send in a review of a book you have enjoyed, describing why it made such an impression on you and how it would appeal to the reading public.

Write your **review**.

2

Your college's English language magazine is doing a feature on literature, and has asked readers to send in articles about the theme of *courage, pride, shame, trust, suspicion, secrecy, etc.* in a novel of their choice. You have decided to write an article about the book you have been reading, citing examples of how at least two characters display [courage, pride, shame, trust, suspicion, secrecy, etc.] in the story, and saying how this affects the development of the plot.

Write your **article**.

3

Your teacher has asked you to write an essay on the following topic, based on your reading of a novel: 'If the protagonist had not made certain decisions that directly influenced events, the story might have been a very different one.' Discuss this statement in relation to two major developments in the novel, giving your opinion on the decisions made and speculating how events might have turned out differently.

Write your **essay**.

4

You belong to a book club which has asked its members to write a report on whether a novel you have read recently is suitable for film adaptation. You should outline in what ways you think the book might be successfully adapted or not for the screen, giving your reasons.

Write your **report**.

5

You read this comment recently in a literary magazine about a book you enjoyed reading: 'The author's use of language to build up atmosphere and to give insights into the characters' thoughts and emotions is not as effective as it could be. This was a disappointing aspect of the book.' You disagree and decide to write a letter to the magazine, expressing your opinion.

Write your **letter**.

Answer Key

Vocabulary development 1 p. 6

1
1 sequel
2 stage fright
3 denouement
4 flashbacks
5 prequel
6 score

2
1 lead role
2 film adaptation
3 rave reviews
4 standing ovation
5 box office
6 silver screen

3
1 stretched
2 hobble
3 hoisted
4 clambers
5 glid
6 twirled

4
1 for/in
2 of/over
3 for
4 to
5 on
6 to

Use of English p. 7

3
1 D
2 B
3 D
4 D
5 A
6 C
7 B
8 A

Expert language
a Q6 gain a qualification
b Q2 to name but a few
c Q4 provides students with

Language development 1 p. 8

1
1 adores
2 Do you see
3 didn't notice
4 am enjoying
5 appreciates
6 was lacking
7 is being
8 promise

2
1 has been doing
2 haven't been attending
3 had been talking
4 have never performed
5 had told
6 had only been dancing

3
1 just now, later
2 currently
3 never
4 lately, since
5 still
6 occasionally

4
1 have also earned
2 trained
3 joined
4 did not/didn't exist
5 had given
6 were continually asking
7 became
8 embarked
9 came
10 believes

Use of English p. 9

4
1 such
2 out
3 more
4 if/when
5 Having
6 could/might/may
7 with
8 which

Expert language
a come (to a conclusion), have (a tendency), follow (a pattern)
b reach/arrive at a conclusion (preposition = at); show/demonstrate/display a tendency (no preposition required); conform to a pattern (preposition = to)

Listening p. 10

4
1 A
2 A
3 B
4 A
5 C
6 B

Expert language
a Q1 to hold out for
b Q3 to provoke a reaction
c Q3 benefited from

Vocabulary development 2 p. 11

1
1 on
2 for
3 into
4 back
5 toward
6 to

2
1 ring a bell
2 pulled out all the stops
3 blowing her own trumpet
4 went for a song
5 changed his tune
6 play it by ear

3
1 mediocrity, competitive, ruthlessness
2 subtleties, setbacks
3 deafening
4 outgoing, tendency

4
1 come
2 sampling
3 wider
4 significant
5 bar
6 dabbling
7 potential
8 ease

Reading p. 12–13

5
1 D
2 A
3 B
4 C
5 B
6 D
7 C
8 B
9 B
10 A

Expert language
a clamber, scramble
b leaping, flipping (themselves)
c handstands, leaps

6
1 doubles as
2 hands-on experience
3 letting myself in for
4 draws to a close
5 incredibly puny
6 a new lease of life
7 winds down
8 throw in the towel

Language development 2 p. 14

1
1	B	3	B	5	C	7	A
2	A	4	B	6	B	8	C

2
1	in	3	for	5	of
2	by	4	until	6	to

3
1 supposed
2 is expected
3 due
4 set
5 on the verge of
6 bound
7 might
8 should

4
1 is/was bound to be
2 was supposed to be
3 was (just) about to
4 was to
5 is set to be
6 stands to

5 *Suggested answers*
1 is/was bound to be a huge success
2 was going to cry
3 should have been here by now
4 is set to become very famous
5 the director was supposed to be here to answer them himself
6 she is on the point of giving up

Use of English p. 15

2
1 was the first time (that) | Luke had (ever)
2 there any improvement | in the cast's
3 as no surprise (to me) | to hear (that)
4 was on the point | of leaving
5 makes no | difference to Camilla
6 made an enormous | impression on
7 came to the conclusion | (that) he was
8 has no intention | of tolerating
9 of great | excitement to
10 difficulty (in) coming to terms | with the fact

Writing p. 16

1 In Text 1, the writer is implying that there is a mistaken assumption about comic books and animated films to the effect that they are much the same thing. On the contrary, the writer outlines the differences between the two genres showing that the viewer of an animated film does not really have to interact with the visual image at all whereas the reader of a comic book needs to actively use their imagination to interpret the images. Moreover, an animated film uses a sound track, a musical score and physical action in combination with the images; the comic book only has the images.

In Text 2, the writer expresses the opinion that it is unnecessary to worry or get upset about film adaptations of books because, whatever happens, nothing will actually change the book. It is also implied that cutting-edge developments in film technology can actually turn a book into something greater and more impressive.

2a
1 enhance
2 accessible
3 present
4 similarities
5 comparisons
6 demands
7 connection

2b Text 1 – E, C
Text 2 – F, A

2c
A	implies	D	underlines
B	suggests	E	emphasises
C	points out	F	questions

3 Students' own answers

4 *Model answer*
In the first text, the writer emphasises that comparisons between comic books and animated cartoons should not be drawn since they are very different in the demands they make on the viewer or reader: the reader has to make much more effort than the viewer. The writer also points out that there are elements to an animation that are not present in a comic book, such as music, movement and sound. I agree with the writer up to a point, since animated films, like all films, require less creative use of the imagination on the part of the viewer than reading a comic does. However, I have to say that there are undoubtedly similarities between these two genres, since their main element is the pictorial image. Whether one is actually better than the other is a matter of personal taste, I would say.

In the second text, the writer questions why people get so concerned over film adaptations of books since, whatever the film is like, the reader's connection to the book is not in any way affected. The writer also implies that modern digital technology can enhance a novel and bring other exciting dimensions to it. I'm not entirely sure whether I agree with the suggestion that film versions cannot possibly harm the original book. In my experience, many young people might watch a film and then feel that they needn't bother to actually read the book it was based on. This trend would be nothing short of disastrous for their overall intellectual development. Personally speaking, I agree that films are a great form of entertainment – but they can never, and should never, replace books.

Audio script

Extract One
F: I always say to drama students, you know, go to auditions even if you don't want the part, just for the experience. This profession can be good but they need to understand that everything won't always go their way – so you can't afford to think you can pick and choose and stuff like that – 'cos nobody wants to work with a diva.

M: Yeah – it's important to deserve the respect of your peers. The biggest audition that I ever flunked was when I went to work for a bank. I did an internship and at the end of it one of the guys said to me: 'Your heart doesn't seem to be in this,' and I felt like I'd failed to play the part well ... because I *was* only acting and I'd been busted! It was actually my dad who thought I should go into a more secure profession. I mean, he is a financier after all.

So, when I signed up for drama school, it was a bit of a let-down for him – but it was great when he came to see one of my first plays. I could hear raucous chuckles from the front row and I thought: 'He gets it now!'

Extract Two

F: Recently, I was asked to write and present a film that posed the question: 'Pop, what's it good for?'

M: That sounds provocative – how did you play it?

F: Well, I avoided a glib response like 'absolutely nothing' and got on with talking about some of my own favourite tracks.

M: Didn't the film need a bit more shape than just you sat in a room going through a list?

F: Sure. In the end I picked a dozen to represent the shifting sands of the genre over time and used that as a hook to hang it on.

M: Hardly a straightforward choice that dozen.

F: Indeed it wasn't. And, you know, I reckon if I'd made it at another moment, in another mood or whatever, it wouldn't have been the same twelve either.

M: Right. Pop's great for making lists of favourites . . .

F: .. you see them all the time on the internet

M: I guess they express something about your personality . . .

F: If you ask me, it's more about inventing yourself – along with the type of clothes, haircut and even car you go for.

M: But looking back on those lists, they kind of map out your changing dreams, your influences and your aspirations.

F: If you keep them!

Extract Three

M: Reality television really took off in the year 2000 when the idea behind the programme *Big Brother* went beyond its Dutch home market to be sold around the world and started a revolution in TV business models. In the ensuing decade, TV talent shows evolved into elaborate multi-platform profit engines, unlike anything the industry had ever seen. The most famous of these, *The X Factor*, is regarded in the industry as providing a masterclass in twenty-first century marketing techniques. By 2011, versions of the format were being produced in over twenty countries across the globe, whilst the final of the original UK version was watched by two-thirds of all households who switched on a TV that night. The show is alluring for brands: not only will massive audiences catch their thirty-second messages in the breaks but there's an entire suite of marketing opportunities both on air and off. Taking lessons from sports broadcasters, *The X Factor* uses gladiatorial on-air competition and encourages a running commentary on social media sites to build live audiences on a scale which advertisers find it increasingly hard to reach elsewhere.

Module 2

Vocabulary development 1 p. 17

1
1	decimation	4	evolution
2	desalination	5	proliferation
3	reforestation	6	evaporation

2
1	twittering	5	roar
2	crunch	6	claps
3	scrabbling	7	whistling
4	lapping	8	patter

3
1	scientific	5	hydroelectric
2	aquatic	6	euphoric
3	catastrophic	7	realistic
4	oceanic	8	domestic

4
1	evolved	5	contact
2	forces	6	captivity
3	grounds	7	treatment
4	variety	8	natural

Use of English p. 18

2
1	A	3	D	5	B	7	B
2	C	4	A	6	C	8	D

Expert language
sugar-cane (juice/biology), low-tech (methods), petrol-fuelled (vehicle)

Language development 1 p. 19

1
1	are currently being made	5	have been almost completely turned
2	to be restored	6	being cut down
3	have been devastated	7	is often removed
4	was formed	8	will also be cultivated

2
1	be	5	allowed/supposed/ permitted, etc.
2	being	6	been
3	Having		
4	needs		

3
1	something would be done	5	were/are thought to have been
2	was pointed out	6	have been/be considered
3	are said to be	7	were assumed to be
4	is rumoured to be carrying out	8	was estimated

4
1 have had their fields sown
2 had the fishing quotas increased
3 get/have that piece of wasteland converted
4 are currently having the project managed
5 will have had their application approved
6 getting/ having a wind turbine installed
* Note: *have* and *get* are normally interchangeable when they mean 'cause something to be done by somebody else' such as in Q3 and Q6. *Have* and *get* are not interchangeable in Q2 because *got* in this context is a reduced form of *managed to get*.

Use of English p. 20

2
1	would	3	are	5	with	7	which
2	If	4	could	6	puts	8	no

Expert language
to be avoided, to be carefully managed

4
1	expand	3	emit
2	threaten		

5 **1** *famine* affects a whole society and people die / *hunger* affects one person and is temporary

2 *foreseeable* means 'as far as can we can predict' / *foreseen* means something was predicted

3 *alleviating* means making something better / *aggravating* means making something worse

4 the meaning of both phrases is similar, but *not by any means* is more emphatic

Listening p. 21

3 **1** B **4** G **7** B **10** H
2 C **5** A **8** F
3 F **6** C **9** E

5 **1** G **4** B **7** E **10** J
2 A **5** I **8** D
3 H **6** C **9** F

Reading p. 22–23

2 *garbage* – is the US term for household rubbish; *refuse* – is the formal/technical term for rubbish; *compost heap* is a place where garden rubbish is left to rot

4 **1** B **3** B **5** A
2 D **4** C **6** C

Expert language
a miasmic, gnomic, civic, ironic
b conclusion, collection, regulations, infraction, prescription, medication, accommodation, instructions

Vocabulary development 2 p. 24

1 **1** manual **4** beneficial
2 superior **5** temporary
3 short-sighted **6** complicated

2 **1** f **4** a **7** b **10** d
2 c **5** h **8** i
3 g **6** e **9** j

3 **1** pros and cons, by and large, sick and tired, peace and quiet
2 pride and joy, length and breadth, safe and sound

4 **1** strut **3** wade
2 wallow **4** stalk

5 **1** general **7** absent
2 truly **8** magnetic
3 remotely **9** confined
4 apparently **10** visible
5 acutely **11** asymmetric
6 faint **12** precisely

Language development 2 p. 25

1 **1** a bring, b brought **4** a place, b placed
2 a met, b meet **5** a buy, b bought
3 a put, b putting **6** a took, b taking

2 **1** keep **4** taking
2 lending **5** get
3 taken, make **6** take

3 **1** In **3** On **5** in **7** On
2 with **4** at **6** by **8** at

4 **1** have *grave* doubts about
2 do significant *harm* to, having serious *consequences* for
3 gives *priority* to, have a clear *conscience*
4 give some *thought* to, do *without*
5 have an *informed* opinion on
6 does *wonders* for
7 give (people) the *impression* that
8 have no *scruples* about

Use of English p. 26

3 **1** accounts **5** inaccessible
2 unforgettable **6** highlighted
3 quickening **7** discouraging
4 rehabilitation **8** untouched

Expert language
in the hope of seeing, at an ever quickening pace

5 **1** flocking **4** on the brink of
2 in close proximity **5** demise
3 glimpsing **6** bleak

Writing p. 27

1 **a** readers of the magazine
b semi-formal/formal
c description of the event plus an evaluation
d use of interesting vocabulary, good introductory paragraph, address the reader, use of rhetorical questions, etc.
e descriptive, narrative, evaluative

2 Students' own answers

3 *Suggested plan*
Intro: challenging questions about issues to do with the environment: deforestation, endangered species, etc. to arouse interest
Para 1: description of talks/demonstrations
Para 2: description of practical workshops
Para 3: evaluation of the above
Conclusion: final assessment of usefulness of this type of event and possibilities of other similar events in the future

5 *Suggested answers* (although there is some overlap between categories)
Vocabulary
Precise descriptive: squawks, screeches, brightly-coloured
Verb phrases: make my way, attract attention, cross my mind, get involved in
Phrasal verbs: hand out

Collocations: loud noise, college lawn, member of the public, fly around freely, on loan (prep phr), in combination with (prep phr)

Topic vocabulary: in captivity, native habitat, bird sanctuary, endangered, conservation project

Advanced adjectives/adverbs: beautifully-kept, intrigued, ostensibly, well-researched

Grammar

Passive: could be heard, not being allowed, were kept, were being handed out

Appropriate tenses: here it is narrative as well as descriptive, so past tenses – mostly simple past / past continuous, also one example of reported speech (hastened to explain that the birds were on loan)

Register

Formal: use of passive, also phrases such as: hastened to explain, couldn't fault it

Sentence structure

Complex/varied: starting with -ing participle (Coming from one corner), with adjective (Intrigued), with adverb (Indeed), with prepositional phrase (In combination with), with impersonal verb (It was all fascinating). Complex: many sentences contain relative clauses (which was attracting, where they were kept, how the parrots' habitat is endangered, etc.) or subordinate clauses (but the people in charge).

6 *Model answer*

How can I learn more about sustainable energy? Where can I learn some bee-keeping skills? These were some of the questions that motivated me to attend a one-day event at the local college recently, focused on environmental issues. Upon arriving, I decided to attend a talk on sustainable energy. The speaker was a scientist of some renown and his talk was accompanied by fascinating slides of work being done in various countries around the world. I followed this up by taking part in a practical workshop on bee-keeping and I'm now thinking seriously about taking a proper course. I then moved outside the events tent in search of the exotic birds.

Coming from one corner of the college grounds could be heard a variety of loud noises: squawks, screeches and other animal noises. Intrigued, I made my way across the beautifully-kept college lawns. Indeed, there on its perch, was a lovely brightly-coloured parrot which was attracting a lot of attention from the younger members of the public. The thought did cross my mind as to why these birds were ostensibly here in captivity and not being allowed to fly around freely in their native habitat but the people in charge hastened to explain that the birds were on loan from a local bird sanctuary where they were kept in conditions similar to their normal surroundings. In combination with the bird attraction, leaflets were being handed out outlining how the parrots' habitat is endangered and how members of the public could get involved in conservation projects. It was all fascinating and well-researched. I couldn't fault it.

Generally speaking, the day seemed to be a resounding success: it was well-attended by local people, there was obviously a lot of interest in the issues presented, and I feel that this type of event is definitely the way forward for all of us who are concerned about the future of our environment.

Audio script

Speaker One

M: It's claimed that today's zoos are all about conservation – and first-hand contact with endangered species raises visitors' awareness. But the idea of animals being a form of entertainment always put me off, so I'd steered clear of the places. But when a year's pass to the local one arrived in my inbox out of the blue, courtesy of a grateful niece I'd done a favour, I decided to put my reservations aside and check it out. What really struck me was how much information there was attached to each enclosure and I wasn't the only person engaging with it either. And if I'd been expecting the animals to look forlorn in cramped cages, then I couldn't have been more wrong.

Speaker Two

F: Although I take animal welfare issues pretty seriously, I've always had a soft spot for our local zoo. I'd last been as a kid, but after stumbling across a really glowing write-up on a website – apparently the staff are involved in lots of research and captive-breeding programmes – I decided to give myself a nostalgic treat. But things had changed. The first thing I noticed was how tiny the cages were and you couldn't say the information about the animals was inspiringly presented. But the real eye-opener was the families there on day trips. I doubt if most of them even knew what animal they were looking at as they munched through their popcorn. It wasn't like that in my day.

Speaker Three

M: As a teacher, I've always seen it as my duty to present both sides of the argument but actually taking the kids to the zoo was anathema to me. I mean, some of them would be bound to behave inappropriately, maybe even upset the rare animals. But when the letter came formally asking us to participate in their research programme, I couldn't really say no. Actually, their paper-based educational resources leave a bit to be desired but the way the researchers interacted with the kids made up for that, going way beyond my expectations. Some of the kids still found the cages dirty and said the animals looked depressed – and produced some really impassioned written work about it.

Speaker Four

F: Never having been to a zoo for decades, my ideas about them were rather out-of-date. Locking animals up in pokey cages in an unnatural habitat just seemed too cruel to me. But when I got involved in a blog on the subject, a guy working in a zoo suggested I was just prejudiced. I bridled at the suggestion. So when he said I should go and see the work they did for myself, I could hardly refuse. It was an informal visit, and I saw behind the scenes, hearing about the conservation projects they're involved in. I was blown away by the state-of-the-art laboratories actually, much better than anything I'd expected. I ended up having to eat my words.

Speaker Five

M: I mean the animals don't have a lot of room to run around, I'll grant you that but I take issue with people who say the zoo's cruel. I mean, I couldn't believe how the monkeys all responded when the keepers called out their names and stuff – and they have a good life – no worries, no hunters coming after them or loggers cutting down their habitat. I only went actually 'cos I had to look after my sister's kids who were staying for the weekend. I thought it'd be educational for them. But I'd go again – they've got some really rare snakes according to a review I read on the internet – seeing them close up must be awesome.

Module 3

Vocabulary development 1 p. 28

1
1. Irrespective
2. non-confrontational
3. indecision
4. misconceptions
5. interpersonal
6. misunderstanding
7. illogical
8. disapproval

2
1. dissatisfaction, accomplishments, qualifications
2. appreciation, thoughtfulness, consideration
3. justification
4. intrusion

3
1. disbelief
2. incomprehensible
3. illiterate
4. irrational
5. disrespect
6. insecure
7. unstable
8. non-verbal

4
1. make-up
2. precursor
3. modify
4. insights
5. interact
6. premise
7. unconsciously
8. rationalise
9. revert
10. stance
11. manifest
12. control
13. analytical
14. dysfunctional

Use of English p. 29

2
1. D
2. B
3. A
4. A
5. C
6. C
7. D
8. B

Expert language
made up of, open up, catch up with

3
1. well-being
2. the latter
3. treadmill

4
A (competence) in
B (capacity) for
C (ability) to
D (expertise) in

Language development 1 p. 30

1
1. a, c
2. b, c
3. a
4. a, c
5. b, c
6. a, b

2
1. if
2. would
3. were
4. without
5. If so
6. what
7. whether
8. should

3
1. necessary
2. Even
3. would
4. won't/don't
5. happens
6. wouldn't
7. hadn't

4
1. without
2. whether
3. not
4. unless

Use of English p. 31

4
1. controversially
2. psychological
3. researchers
4. recognition
5. characteristics
6. tendency
7. doubtlessly/ undoubtedly
8. underlines

Expert language
bonding, finding

6
1. optimism
2. self-esteem
3. run in families
4. bonding
5. variant
6. symptoms

Listening p. 32

4
1. health resort
2. burnout
3. entities
4. skin type
5. moderate
6. bitter
7. mood swings
8. guilt
9. discomfort

Expert language
imbalance, inappropriate

Vocabulary development 2 p. 33

1
1. cranky
2. restless
3. wistful
4. resentful
5. tender
6. adamant

2
1. by
2. in
3. on/at
4. to
5. of
6. on
7. to
8. for
9. for/after
10. to
11. to
12. in

3
1. linked
2. overcome
3. recall
4. correlation
5. processing
6. disturbing
7. subconscious
8. light
9. conventional
10. suppress

4
1. am in no mood for
2. mood swings
3. lighten his mood
4. gets into the festive mood
5. when the mood takes him

Reading p. 34–35

2 a Jill Price is a 34 year-old housewife with an exceptional memory.
James McGraugh is an academic who specialises in the study of memory.
Marilu Hamer is an actor who has an exceptional memory.

b with amazement

c HM is a patient who suffered memory loss.

d It comes from the study of memory loss.

3 a It is an introduction to the topic and has information about Jill Price and how her gift came to light.

b It describes McGraugh and Price working together ever since.

c Paragraph B

4	**1**	B	**3**	H	**5**	A	**7**	C
	2	D	**4**	G	**6**	F		

Expert language
recall, misguided, reinforced, recollections, autobiographical, upbeat, invaluable

Language development 2 p. 36

1 1 In an office, it is easy to get into bad habits with regard to the way you sit at your desk, and this can lead to unnecessary tension and strain being placed on your neck and back.

3 Before sitting down at your desk it is important to consider how you are going to sit in order to avoid slumping or sitting at an awkward angle.

4 A lot of people forget how vital it is to have a good chair when sitting at a desk for long hours.

6 Remember it is essential that you keep your head, neck and back aligned as you work, otherwise you will create strain in these areas.

7 If you are working at a computer or laptop, it is a question of using your eyes to look at the screen, rather than leaning your neck and shoulders towards it.

8 You will probably find it difficult to maintain a good posture once you become absorbed in what you are doing, but it makes a difference if you do so.

9 Finally it is worth mentioning that you should keep both your feet flat on the floor and avoid the temptation to cross your legs.

2 1 It's a shame you missed the party on Saturday, as we had a great time.

2 I find it surprising that Karen's depressed, because she seems to have everything she could possibly want.

3 Once you've admitted that you need to make some changes in your life, it's a matter of getting started as soon as possible.

4 It suddenly dawned on me that I no longer felt tired in the morning.

5 It was Melanie who told me about Laughter Clubs.

6 It makes no difference to me who you go to see, as long as you get some professional help.

7 It's no good feeling sorry for yourself. You're the one to blame for this, and you know it.

8 It's a question of thinking 'outside the box' to solve this problem.

3 1 did she realise
2 she had
3 you should
4 have I
5 he had
6 was she
7 Howard was
8 should you
9 had she
10 had I

4 1 had we/I
2 was he
3 have I heard/has anyone given
4 could/was able to give/had given/gave
5 to have gone to see/to have seen/to have consulted
6 had you taken/if you'd taken
7 did I know/realise (that)
8 was his
9 did she show/betray/let on/was it apparent
10 she started
11 did I follow/listen to/take
12 been for

Use of English p. 37

3 1 (that) nobody | has any
2 it not | been for
3 there was no recurrence | of my back
4 can we account for | the fact
5 had been brought | to Ursula's attention
6 has been a | marked rise in
7 for fear of | scratching
8 he had no option | but to own

Writing p. 38

1 *Suggested answers*
a Both texts examine factors which affect the way people learn and study.
b Text 1 looks at the potential benefits of napping on people's short term memory, while Text 2 examines the possible effects drinking coffee may have on people's ability to concentrate for long stretches while studying. It suggests that caffeine does not boost a person's memory.
c Answers will vary.

2 Plan B

3 *Suggested plan*
Plan A
Paragraph 1: General theme of the two texts. 'Both texts examine factors which affect the way people learn and study'.
Paragraph 2: Summary – Text 1 – potential benefits of napping on people's short term memory – perform better after a nap; Text 2 – possible effects of drinking coffee on people's ability to concentrate for long stretches while studying. Says caffeine does not boost a person's memory.
Paragraph 3: Evaluation – Text 1 – limitations – doesn't consider people's different sleep patterns; Text 2 – short-term effects of coffee may be beneficial for people needing to complete a project. May help a person's ability to focus when cramming for a test, but prolonged consumption potentially detrimental. Text 2 recognises that coffee affects people in different ways, while Text 1 fails to examine the effects of different sleep patterns. Conclusion: Both texts – interesting points – more research needed.

Plan B

Paragraph 1: General theme of the two texts. 'Both texts examine factors which affect the way people learn and study'.

Paragraph 2: Text 1 – potential benefits of napping on people's short term memory – perform better after a nap. No doubt some benefits – limitations – doesn't consider people's different sleep patterns.

Paragraph 3: Text 2 – possible effects drinking coffee on people's ability to concentrate for long stretches while studying. Says caffeine does not boost a person's memory. Short-term effects of coffee may be beneficial for people needing to complete a project. May help a person's ability to focus when cramming for a test, but prolonged consumption potentially detrimental.

Conclusion: Text 2 recognises that coffee affects people in different ways, while Text 1 fails to examine the effects of different sleep patterns. Both texts – interesting points – more research needed.

4
1	advocates	5	beneficial
2	enhance	6	take into account
3	cites	7	uninterrupted
4	experiment	8	perform

5 *Model answer* (following plan B)

The two texts examine different factors which affect the way people learn and study, focusing on memory and concentration respectively.

Text 1 advocates taking a short nap during the day in order to enhance your memory, and cites a recent experiment which showed that people who napped after studying performed better on tests afterwards. Undoubtedly, a short sleep or rest during the day can be beneficial, but the writer fails to take into account the fact that people have different sleep patterns and needs according to their lifestyle. For instance, individuals who get at least eight hours uninterrupted sleep at night may not need to sleep during the day in order to perform well. Others may find that they wake up from a midday nap feeling tired and unable to work effectively afterwards. A lot depends on the way an individual sleeps, and how much rest he or she needs.

Text 2, meanwhile, looks at the controversy surrounding the effects drinking coffee may have on a person's ability to concentrate while studying. It recognises that caffeine does not boost a person's memory as such, but suggests that it may help people remain focused, thereby helping them retain information. The writer admits, however, that there is disagreement over the matter. It could be that the short-term effects of drinking coffee may benefit a person's ability to focus when cramming for a test, but prolonged consumption of caffeine is potentially detrimental, and could prove to have the opposite effect.

To my mind, there is certainly some validity to the points raised in both texts, but the writer of Text 2 holds a more realistic view that further research is needed before concrete conclusions can be formed.

Audio script

Hi there. I'm Amy and I'm a beauty editor by profession. But I haven't come along to talk about journalism – rather to tell you about my experience of going to the Maldive Islands in the Indian Ocean to investigate the benefits of ayurveda – the ancient, traditional Indian system of medicine.

The centre where I stayed was hardly like a hospital, however, and had more the look and feel of a health resort than a clinic. Although it had all the comforts of a five-star hotel, the centre was run according to ayurvedic principles, and the guests had the chance to try out some of the treatments. It had been recommended to me as a great place for anyone in need of silence, solitude and sleep. Well that was me. After a very hectic year at work, with a new baby at home and a new schedule in the office, to say I was stressed out would be something of an understatement. I was suffering from a very bad case of burnout – and clearly in need of rebalance if I was going to avoid a complete meltdown in my professional and private life.

Ayurveda is based on the theory that all living and non-living things are made up of five elements: space, air, fire, water and earth. They are all present within us, in the form of three entities, or doshas as they're known. Even though we are all made up of doshas, it is believed that each of us has one that is dominant. In order to establish which type I was, I had to fill in a short questionnaire.

This asked questions about my body – the usual things like whether I was large or small framed and how easily I put on weight, no surprises there – and then more intriguingly questions about my skin type – oily or dry, and the condition of my hair. Other questions focused on diet and exercise, personality and sleep patterns. This last question was a tricky one for a young mother. Clearly I'd become a light sleeper by necessity over the previous year, though my natural inclination was to place myself in the moderate category – I would hardly describe myself as a heavy sleeper, even if a long interrupted sleep was one of the things I was really looking forward to getting!

After further consultation based on the questionnaire, I learnt that my dosha type was predominantly in the category known as Pitta – and that I'd be eating foods to nurture that dosha type. These would be foods that would calm the heat inside the body and bring coolness to the system. I would be focusing on sweet and bitter flavours at the expense of spicy foods – and this suited me down to the ground as I have a famously sweet tooth and don't go in for spicy dishes. So I took immediately to the diet of vegetable soups with fresh fruit, millet and porridge that was recommended. Whilst ayurveda is not solely about diet, eating the right foods for your type is considered of the utmost importance. Get this wrong and your mind and body can be out of balance, resulting in physical problems such as fatigue, as well as mood swings and erratic emotions.

Next I met my therapist. The smell of incense permeated the room and a Tibetan singing bowl chimed in the distance. She asked me to choose one negative emotion to rid myself of. I pondered. Anger came to mind as did impatience but she nodded sagely when I plumped for guilt – it was always going to be either that or fear. This is where the Ayurvedic centre was unlike other spa treatments I've tried. A lot more is asked of you – you can't just lie back and drift off – there's a real sense of having to open up in order to allow your therapist to deliver the best she can in the guided yoga sessions. We worked on my stomach muscles and I experienced a real sense of relief as the usual tensions slipped away. Some people remarked on moments of discomfort, even assuming that everyone went through this as part of the experience – but I can safely say that didn't apply in my case. Indeed, I'd recommend these sessions and the whole experience without reservation.

So before I go on to . . .

Module 4

Vocabulary development 1 p. 39

1
1 mindset
2 sensationalise
3 expose
4 censorship
5 bias
6 scrutinise
7 objectivity
8 editorial

2 *Suggested answers*
1 What is your position on the government's proposal . . .
2 The journalist holds the view that . . .
3 Party members are deeply divided on what . . .
4 (I feel) I must take issue with the reporter's conclusion that . . .
5 The government has decided to adopt a tough stance on . . .
6 . . . but we should try and keep things in perspective.

3
1 **a** informative
  b informant
  c informed
  d misinformed
2 **a** representation
  b representative
  c representational
3 **a** inventive
  b invention
  c inventor
4 **a** like-minded
  b Mindful
  c mindless
5 **a** investigative
  b investigation
  c investigators

Use of English p. 40

2
| 1 B | 3 C | 5 D | 7 C |
| 2 A | 4 D | 6 A | 8 B |

Expert language
initially, simultaneously, eventually

3
1 feedback
2 likelihood
3 coincide

4
1 in (haste)
2 in (transit)
3 on (foot)
4 on (the move)

5
1 inclined/apt
2 liable
3 prone
4 apt/inclined

Language development 1 p. 41

1
1 mustn't
2 have to/must (more formal)
3 feel obliged
4 have to (someone else has imposed obligation)
5 don't have to
6 needn't
7 didn't need to reveal
8 are (more formal) / need

2 These modal verbs to be crossed out.
| 1 should | 3 would | 5 would | 7 could |
| 2 should | 4 would | 6 would | 8 would |

3
1 It's up to you to list . . .
2 The onus was on Sally to download all the notes . . .
3 I would browse . . ., if I were you. / If I were you, I would browse . . .
4 You had better not upload that . . .
5 You don't need to reveal . . .
6 Protective glasses are to be worn by all students . . .

4
1 needn't/shouldn't
2 had
3 had
4 might/could
5 wouldn't/needn't
6 should
7 had
8 mustn't/needn't/shouldn't

Use of English p. 42

2
1 deadline
2 undone
3 repeatedly
4 compulsive
5 continually
6 updated
7 understatement
8 sensible

Expert language
a the answer may be
b I urgently need to

4
1 assignment
2 get hold of
3 idly
4 get a grip on yourself
5 ration

5
1 *repeatedly* and *continually* mean doing something very often in a way that is annoying / *continuously* means doing something for a long time without stopping
2 to *update* is a verb / *an update* is a noun / *up-to-date* can be an adjective or an adverb
3 *state* tells us about the condition of something / *status* tells about how something is regarded
4 *sensible* means with good reason / *sensitive* means delicate or reacting to the senses

Listening p. 43

3
1 D	4 G	7 A	10 H
2 B	5 A	8 E	
3 F	6 D	9 G	

4 1 J   4 G   7 E   10 I
   2 A   5 B   8 F
   3 H   6 D   9 C

Reading p. 44–45

3 1 D   3 B   5 B
   2 A   4 C   6 D

Expert language

. . . never enjoyed such popularity . . . (Para 1) – a
Such defence . . . (Para 2) – b
.. such a project Work? (Para 2) – b
I believe such pessimism . . . (Para 4) – b
. . . are so committed to . . . (Para 4) – a
When they do so, . . . (Para 5) – b
So the challenge . . . (Para 6) – c

Vocabulary development 2 p. 46

1 1 B   3 C   5 A   7 B
   2 A   4 C   6 B   8 A

2 Possible answers
Newsagent, newsreader, newspaper, newsletter, newscaster, news bulletin, newscast, newsflash, newsgroup, newshound, newsroom, news agency, news blackout

3 1 mind-boggling   4 avant-garde
   2 breakthrough   5 diehard
   3 cutting-edge   6 mind-blowing

4 1 inspiration   6 inject
   2 conceived   7 blueprint
   3 realise   8 alternative
   4 stagnating   9 innovative
   5 bleak   10 generate

Language development 2 p. 47

1 1 ✓
   2 You might not be able to/can't use your mobile phone here, . . .
   3 Can/Could you lend me a flash drive?
   4 ✓
   5 Gill can't help checking her emails . . .
   6 Hey, Sal! I can't find the earphones for my . . .
   7 ✓
   8 I'd appreciate it if you could send me an email . . .

2 1 might buy   7 can't/couldn't have
   2 should have received   been
   3 might not get   8 should/could/
   4 should have   might be
   5 could/might be   9 might not have
   6 can be, might/could have forgotten

3 1 can   7 are likely to
   2 may   8 can
   3 are able to   9 may
   4 can   10 might
   5 are able to   11 could
   6 may   12 are no more likely to

4 1 I must have deleted the . . .
   2 . . . up, so that can't be the answer.
   3 . . . in my inbox, so it must be in my spam folder.
   4 . . . so it can't/couldn't have been him you saw . . .
   5 Without you/without your contribution, we couldn't have made the breakthrough/found a solution.
   6 It must have been Christine I saw . . .

Use of English p. 48

2 1 Simon's friends who talked him | into buying
   2 of fixing the computer myself | never crossed my
   3 rumoured to be | on the verge of
   4 (left) up to the customer | to choose
   5 chances of the new laboratory | being ready for
   6 was drawing | a clear distinction
   7 was not alone | in taking
   8 time (that) Sally | made up her mind
   9 to the database | is restricted to
   10 never tires | of playing

Expert language

smartphone, breakthrough, laptop, password

Writing p. 49

1 *Suggested answers*
   1 **a** college professors, administrators and students
     b semi-formal
     c how attractive the website is, how useful and relevant the news and information on the website is, and how easy it is to navigate round the site in order to find what you are looking for.
     d possible recommendations: more visually stimulating, brighter colours, personal stories from students, advice/problem page for students, help for new students, shorter chunks of text

2 Students' own answers

3 Students' own answers

4 Students' own answers

5 Model answer
Introduction
The aim of this report is to assess the value of the college website in terms of its visual appeal, the quality and relevance of the information it provides and how accessible that information is. It will also make some recommendations for improvement.

Visual appeal
Generally speaking, the home page of the website is attractive, making use of lively photos and bright colours to highlight different sections. A major drawback, however, is that you find little artwork or colour throughout the rest of the site to break the monotony of text.

Quality and relevance of information

The site offers students news of upcoming events, advice and useful information about using college services. One particularly positive aspect is its help page, written by students for new incoming students, containing valuable tips on finance and accommodation. There is a section where students can post books and furniture for sale, and where bargains can usually be found. Nevertheless, the information is presented in rather long and wordy texts, which many students find off-putting.

Ease of navigation

Another area which needs attention is that of navigation. While there is a useful drop-down list of the various sections on the home page, the long texts and lack of colour make all the sections appear the same. They are not tagged clearly either, which can be confusing.

Recommendations

In light of the observations made above, there are several things that could be done to improve the appeal of the website. One suggestion would be to colour-code each section, using the colours shown on the home page. This would make it clear to students which section they were navigating through at any time. Another idea would be to use bullet pointed headings with shorter texts. Including stories of students' personal experiences at college would also be appealing. If such alterations were made, the website would become both more appealing and easier to navigate.

Audio script

Speaker One

F: I collect antique jewellery. Half the fun's browsing in antique shops, so I'd never looked online. It was a colleague who put me onto the site. When I logged on, I was amazed at the range of stuff there – reasonably priced too. When I spotted the brooch, I had to have it. I paid by credit card without so much as a glance at the small print. The postage and packing seemed cheap actually, perhaps that's why it took ages to arrive. I was beginning to panic, so I called them. They said it had been despatched and I should've insured it – they only gave a refund if you actually returned it. Luckily, next day it turned up!

Speaker Two

M: I collect silver but never usually buy online. I like to see the marks close up and always get my wife to double-check them for me. But since moving to the island, we're quite a hike from the nearest antique dealer, so I was tempted when I saw this cup on a website. I should've checked the courier company was willing to deliver up here though. I ended up having to pick it up from their depot on the mainland. And to think, before paying, I'd been through everything with a fine toothcomb. You know, the returns policy if I wasn't satisfied with the condition, insurance in case it got damaged in transit. But you can't think of everything!

Speaker Three

F: Buying period clothes online isn't usually recommended. You can't know what the condition's really like till you see the garment, and you can't always trust sellers to pack things properly – so stuff gets crumpled in the post. Anyway, after breaking my wrist, I couldn't drive, so was at a loose end at home. That's when I saw a lovely coat on an auction site and put in an impulse bid. It was only later I discovered they don't accept debit cards – that you have to sign up for this complicated online system instead. So when the email came saying I'd won it and here was my invoice, I got a bit of a shock. It took me ages to sort out.

Speaker Four

M: I collect *Star Wars* figurines and don't have a lot to spend on my hobby. But when I saw one I haven't got advertised online, I had to go for it – it's such a rare item. I know you can easily get ripped off online – especially on auction sites and you're recommended to take out accidental damage insurance, which costs an arm and a leg but still I seemed to be getting a bargain. So imagine my disappointment when it arrived and it wasn't the right one. There was no discussion about the refund itself – they were clearly at fault but I then got into a lengthy argument about who was going to pay the postage to send it back. Never again.

Speaker Five

F: I collect football programmes and other memorabilia. I go to collector's fairs with my mate Petra – because I can never make my mind up whether I'm getting a good price or not. I've been doing a lot of overtime at weekends lately – so I was in funds, but not free to go to the fairs, so I went online. The World Cup Final programme I ordered was a bargain but the postage and packing seemed a bit steep so I queried it – and guess what? They'd made a mistake! It was a bit dog-eared when it arrived but they'd never said it was perfect or anything – so my request for a refund was turned down. Petra says it serves me right for not asking about that before buying it.

Module 5

Vocabulary development 1 p. 50

1
1 jargon
2 Estuary
3 lingua franca
4 dialect
5 slang
6 burr

2
1 undeniably
2 misleading
3 inaccessible
4 inaccuracies
5 impressive, memorable
6 illiteracy

3
1 brains
2 head
3 inch
4 fool, play
5 stock
6 nails

4
1 minority
2 official
3 word
4 translation
5 transcribe
6 linguist
7 consonants
8 spelling
9 print
10 tongue

Use of English p. 51

2
1 B
2 C
3 B
4 C
5 A
6 D
7 D
8 C

Expert language
misspelling, remarkably, phenomenally

3
1 ubiquitous
2 wacky
3 acronym
4 mainstay
5 phenomenally

4
1 ubiquity
2 relentlessness
3 durability
4 constancy

Language development 1 p. 52

1
1 abandon
2 differ
3 equivalent
4 necessity
5 chance
6 launched
7 proposed
8 value

2
1 a negligible
  b negligent
2 a disposable
  b disposal
3 a expanding
  b extend
4 a censored
  b censured
5 a insistent
  b persistent
6 a varying
  b variable

3
1 illustrious
2 shoulders
3 insight
4 confined
5 precedent
6 heady
7 inspirational
8 gamut
9 pickings
10 attend

4
1 weather
2 sights
3 pored
4 quay
5 weigh
6 serial
7 feat
8 through

Use of English p. 53

2
1 holds
2 when
3 come
4 goes
5 order
6 Together/Along
7 whose
8 what

Expert language
getting your tongue around, goes by the name of

4
1 trickiest
2 perennial
3 pilot

5
1 wholly
2 enough
3 whose

Listening p. 54

3
1 D
2 D
3 B
4 A
5 C

Expert language
a devote (themselves) to, combine with, distracted from, do research into, concentrate on, deal with
b secure the support, meet the challenge, develop a (loyal) following

4
1 B
2 C
3 A
4 E
5 D

Vocabulary development 2 p. 55

1
1 Don't/Never judge a book by its cover!
2 I can read him like a book
3 reading between the lines
4 I'm in my tutor's good books
5 take a leaf out of Dan's book
6 speaks volumes

2
1 coaxed
2 muttered
3 murmured
4 rave
5 insinuate
6 rabbiting on

3
1 babble (on about) (speak quickly in a way that is difficult to understand or sounds silly), gabble (say sth so quickly that people cannot hear you clearly or understand you properly), rabbit on (about) (talk for a long time in an uninteresting or annoying way)
2 coax (sb into/out of doing sth or to do sth) (persuade sb in a kind, gentle and patient way), wheedle (sth out of sb or wheedle sb into doing sth) (persuade sb by saying nice things that you do not mean)
3 rant (complain in a loud, excited way), mutter (has connotations of complaining), whine (complain in an annoying voice about sth, often of children), whinge (keep complaining in an annoying way)
4 insinuate (suggest that sth unpleasant is true, without saying it directly)
5 mumble, murmur, mutter

4 **1** prolific **4** discerning
2 attentive **5** voracious
3 fluent **6** celebrated

5 **1** speechless **7** tête-à- tête
2 conversations **8** put forward
3 picked up **9** phenomenon
4 input **10** dialect
5 imitative **11** identify
6 colloquialisms **12** communication

Reading p. 56–57

4 **1** A **4** C **7** A **10** A
2 C **5** B **8** C
3 A **6** D **9** D

Expert language
outselling, overstated, interactivity, interface, transform, unfailingly, unknown

5 **1** bibliophile **6** add-on
2 be on board with **7** cornerstone
3 multi-faceted **8** inception
4 blurring **9** unfailingly
5 think tank **10** scrawled

6 **1** delightful **5** congregate
2 imminent **6** exaggerate
3 incorporating **7** annotated
4 collaborative **8** commentators

Language development 2 p. 58

1a **1** All **4** Having
2 What **5** thing
3 There **6** reason

1b Students' own answers

2 **1** What JRR Tolkien is really admired for is his creative imagination. / What people really admire JRR Tolkien for is his creative imagination.
2 There wasn't much that Colin didn't know about English idioms.
3 Producing a novel a year is quite difficult, but many authors do it.
4 The only quotation I know from Shakespeare is *To be, or not to be!*
5 All the tutor wanted was for us to give our work in on time. / All the tutor wanted was that we gave in our work/gave our work in on time.
6 The person (who/that) Liz really wished she could meet/to meet was JK Rowling.

3 **1** what **5** why
2 whoever **6** how
3 where **7** when
4 which **8** Whichever

4 **1** sign of success **5** offer of help
2 point of view **6** lapse of memory
3 waste of time **7** time of day
4 price of fame **8** matter of opinion

Use of English p. 59

2 **1** diplomacy **5** significantly
2 reluctance **6** sharpen
3 Irrespective **7** onset
4 cognitive **8** bemoan

Expert language
mother-tongue speakers, English-speaking countries

3 **1** a mixed blessing **4** ageing
2 lingua franca **5** susceptible
3 across the board **6** given a hearing

Writing p. 60

1 Three Gold Spoons, Trentbridge

This is a review of the Three Gold Spoons restaurant which recently opened in High St, Trentbridge. Managed by the celebrated cookery writer, Ben Adams, the restaurant claims to live up to the standards of his recipes by providing fresh, locally-produced ingredients and offering its clients the highest quality dining experience. Last Saturday, we went to find out.

Upon entering the restaurant, which was set in a small courtyard just off the High Street, the first thing we saw was a huge array of flowers – it was almost like going into an exotic garden! We were welcomed by Ben's wife, Anna, who was most pleasant. She escorted us to our table by the window. The restaurant was small but the individual tables were in private alcoves, which gave a certain amount of privacy – a nice touch, I thought.

The menu was impressive, not so much because of the number of dishes on it but with regard to their originality. Before ordering, I produced one of Ben's cookery books at the table and everyone in our group had a good look at the fantastic illustrations! We all hoped that the food when it came, would be as good as the photos! Fortunately, we were not disappointed; everything was cooked to perfection and was of the highest quality.

Personally, I felt very relieved that a chef who could produce such wonderful books hadn't let me down. My only slight criticism would be that the menu was a bit over-priced: the bill for a starter, main course and dessert came to quite a lot more than I would normally be prepared to pay in a restaurant. However, it was a superb evening, made even more memorable by the appearance of Ben Adams himself at the end of the meal. He was amused to see a copy of one of his books on our table!

So Three Gold Spoons: thoroughly recommended – but save up your money first!

Note: the last sentence could be incorporated into the previous paragraph, making a total of four paragraphs.

2   The student had not fully dealt with the aspect of the service, so a sentence or two could be incorporated to deal with that. For example, a sentence could be added onto the end of Paragraph 3 relating to the service, e.g. The service was also very commendable: the waiters were attentive but at the same time they left us alone to enjoy our meal in peace.

3   *Suggested cuts*
This is up to the students, but perhaps a sentence from Paragraph 4 (the bill for a starter . . .)

4   Other possible criticisms of the sample: the student deals with the price at some length but doesn't go into much detail about the actual food they ate. However, the overall standard and the ambiance are included in the answer.

2   Students' own answers

3   Model answer with suggested amendments as outlined above
This is a review of the Three Gold Spoons restaurant which recently opened in High St, Trentbridge. Managed by the celebrated cookery writer, Ben Adams, the restaurant claims to live up to the standards of his recipes by providing fresh, locally-produced ingredients and offering its clients the highest quality dining experience. Last Saturday, we went to find out.
Upon entering the restaurant, which was set in a small courtyard just off the High Street, the first thing we saw was a huge array of flowers – it was almost like going into an exotic garden! We were welcomed by Ben's wife, Anna, who was most pleasant. She escorted us to our table by the window. The restaurant was small but the individual tables were in private alcoves, which gave a certain amount of privacy – a nice touch, I thought.
The menu was impressive, not so much because of the number of dishes on it but with regard to their originality. Before ordering, I produced one of Ben's cookery books at the table and everyone in our group had a good look at the fantastic illustrations! We all hoped that the food when it came, would be as good as the photos! Fortunately, we were not disappointed: everything was cooked to perfection and of the highest quality. The service was also very commendable; the waiters were attentive but at the same time they left us alone to enjoy our meal in peace.
Personally, I felt very relieved that a chef who could produce such wonderful books hadn't let me down. My only slight criticism would be that the menu was a bit over-priced. However, it was a superb evening, made even more memorable by the appearance of Ben Adams himself at the end of the meal. He was amused to see a copy of one of his books on our table!
So Three Gold Spoons: thoroughly recommended – but save up your money first!

Paragraph plan (if required to help students):
1   Introductory information
2   Description of restaurant – ambiance
3   Standard of food – service
4   Assessment – personal comment
5   Final concluding recommendation

Audio script

Int = Interviewer, S = Simon, N = Naomi

Int: With me I have two writers, Simon Chirk, author of fifteen best-selling novels, and Naomi Glenn who writes fiction for teenagers. Simon, the image we get of authors these days is of media-savvy youngsters making a quick fortune. Is it really that easy?

S: Well, we've all got stories in us, whether it's family secrets, grand passions or quirky comedies. But it's quite another matter knowing how to tap into them. To my mind, the desire to make pots of money is scarcely the best starting point. You've got to be up for the challenge of creating a fictional world; one that wouldn't exist if you didn't put your particular energy and talent into it – and that's got to be there in no small measure. Otherwise you're unlikely to have the resilience, patience and sheer willpower to get it finished, let alone get it published in some form. Unless, of course, you're already in the public eye for some other reason, in which case you'll have the commercial publishers falling over themselves to sign you up.

Int: Would you go along with that, Naomi?

N: I remember my first novel, getting up at six every morning to write before putting in a full day at the office. It was gruesome but that's still the norm for a lot of young unpublished writers. It's a real effort, you get drained of energy, but I look back on it with a certain pride. Because if I got stuck, which everyone does at some point, I'd no choice but to keep at it – that can be painful. Suddenly the idea of tidying up your bedroom becomes incredibly attractive but you've got to resist the urge – writers are past masters at displacement activities! The other thing I'd say is avoid being beguiled into spending a fortune on high-tech kit – you just need a basic software package to bash the stuff out – getting to grips with anything else just wastes time.

Int: So what's the ideal subject matter to start off with?

S: Well, there's a lot to be said for the old adage: write about what you know. But if what you know's a fairly uninspiring job, it'll hardly be the right context for mass-market readers. They'll be hoping for something more aspirational, like the world of fashion or horseracing or whatever. I mean your characters can do those humdrum jobs but that shouldn't be the background against which the whole story is set.

N: And another thing to avoid is jumping on the bandwagon. Just because last year's number one blockbuster was a thriller set in the world of high finance, doesn't mean that the market wants a whole raft of inferior imitations. It's an easy trap to fall into. So yes, it's best not to stray from familiar ground.

S: But whatever genre you go for, you've got to be giving the reader some sort of added value, some kind of insight into another world, as well as just a cracking good story. I mean, the other thing to mention is that if you don't have an inspirational idea buried somewhere inside you, then research can take you there. If you explore another world in depth, then inspiration can stem from that and you can share your new found enthusiasm with your readers.

N: Well, there's something in that but again I'm rather inclined to think that that comes later, when you've played out your own ideas and you need to go somewhere else – so you don't just keep repeating the same old stuff. You're beginning to contradict yourself actually, Simon.

S: Am I? Oh well – it was ever so!

Int: But you write for teenagers Naomi, which must have its own challenges.

N: Well it's a whole different ballgame. I mean fundamentally there's kids' literature on the one hand and then there's mainstream adult stuff on the other – and because of that narrow window, there's not actually a vast amount on the market that's specifically aimed at teenagers because they quickly move on. But whilst initial volume of sales can be a lot lower than with the big adult genres, the shelf life of your work can extend over the generations, meaning income stacks up. But, it's also difficult to hit the right note. Teenagers are quick to let you know if anything you've written feels patronising or dumbed down – yet they aren't quite ready for the complexities of adult fiction – so you're walking a bit of a tightrope. I sometimes think there must be easier ways of earning a living!

Int: There we must leave it. Naomi, Simon – thanks for . . .

Module 6

Vocabulary development 1 p. 61

1
1	cumbersome	7	overcrowded
2	incompatible	8	lightweight
3	indispensable	9	beaten
4	high-altitude	10	chosen
5	multi-purpose	11	reliable
6	makeshift	12	negligible

2
1	rugged	4	sprawling
2	vibrant	5	fertile
3	sun-kissed		

3
1	hike	5	traverse
2	wade	6	negotiate
3	traipse	7	emerged
4	trek	8	trudging

Use of English p. 62

2
1	B	3	B	5	D	7	D
2	C	4	A	6	A	8	C

Expert language
reinvented, reconnect

3
1	whims	5	niche
2	decommissioned	6	craze
3	redundant	7	urbanites
4	defunct	8	flares

Language development 1 p. 63

1
1	No matter what	4	come what may
2	Be that as it may	5	Far be it from me to
3	so be it	6	suffice it to say

2
1 being given ('demand' is not followed by a gerund)
2 to be checking (infinitive continuous not suitable in this context)
3 that she take out; should take out – (possible structures after 'urge' - 'Jenny urged that Mandy (should) take out . . .')
4 to contact (the subject must be mentioned in this context to clarify who 'their' refers to in the second clause)
5 for guests being charged – gerund is not acceptable here
6 to shop around ('for him to shop around' would be OK); that he would shop around ('would' is not acceptable here)
7 would be vaccinated ('would' not acceptable here); being vaccinated (gerund not possible after 'that . . .')
8 will provide ('will' not acceptable after 'that' here)

3 *Suggested answers*
1 . . . I be given/you move me to another room immediately.
2 . . . we be refunded/you refund us part of the cost of the holiday.
3 . . . you make sure a replacement warden . . . .
4 . . . as it may, you should be able to provide alternative activities . . . .

4
1	B	3	A	5	C
2	C	4	B	6	A

5
1	insisted/demanded/requested	3	if/though it was/were
2	would stop/wouldn't keep (on)/wouldn't insist on	4	you had been
		5	were
		6	had/showed/had shown

Use of English p. 64

2
1	What	5	something
2	Even	6	brought
3	other	7	As
4	into	8	way

Expert language
invisible, disequilibrium, disappeared

3
1	ledge	5	vertigo
2	discarded	6	disequilibrium
3	borne aloft	7	being stricken by
4	jagged	8	gingerly

Listening p. 65

3
1	B	3	A	5	C
2	B	4	C	6	A

Expert language
a outdoor (pursuits), overriding (feeling), money-raising (target)
b gain an impression, increase awareness, question assumptions

Reading p. 66–67

2 a Gandhi's birthplace in India
b to prove that you can live without money
c none

4	**1**	A	**3**	D	**5**	E	**7**	G
	2	H	**4**	B	**6**	F		

Vocabulary development 2 p. 68

1	**1**	intrinsic	**4**	watchdog
	2	carbon	**5**	informed
	3	conscientious	**6**	community-based

2	**1**	food buffs	**4**	quench your thirst
	2	work up an appetite	**5**	culinary expertise
	3	local cuisine	**6**	locally sourced

3	**1**	under	**5**	round/on
	2	down	**6**	against
	3	off	**7**	along
	4	about	**8**	through

4	**1**	offset	**5**	globe
	2	power	**6**	intercontinental
	3	spanning	**7**	epic
	4	circumnavigation	**8**	voyage

Language development 2 p. 69

1	**1**	C	**3**	C	**5**	A
	2	B	**4**	A	**6**	B

2 1 No matter what you (may) say about solar-powered flight, . . .
2 Whatever made you decide to go on holiday with them, . . .
3 Whether they like Prague or think it's too much of a tourist trap, most people agree that it's . . .
4 Expensive though it may be, a taxi ride . . . / Though it's expensive, a taxi ride around . . .
5 . . . I can contact him wherever he is/may be.
6 . . . tour guide like that, whoever you are! / Whoever you are, you have . . .

3a 1 Whatever
2 how
3 wherever
4 whether
5 whichever
6 though

3b *Suggested answers*
1 No matter how attractive they may be, personal subs will prove detrimental to the environment.
2 However rich you are, spending two million dollars on a plaything seems irresponsible.
3 Innovative though they may be, personal subs present a further threat to an already fragile marine environment.
4 Whether they like it or not, even the rich should accept responsibility for protecting the oceans.

5 Whatever the commercial gain, we should not put our marine ecosystems under further unnecessary strain.
6 Whichever way you look at it, the personal sub will adversely affect marine biodiversity by making the underwater world a tourist spot.

Use of English p. 70

2	**1**	therapeutic	**5**	connection
	2	tickly	**6**	miraculous
	3	unacceptable	**7**	ailments
	4	prescription	**8**	remoteness.

Expert language
Whatever it was

3

	1	steeped	**5**	melancholy
	2	ran contrary to	**6**	sheer
	3	hang on to	**7**	salve
	4	haunting	**8**	wounded

Writing p. 71

1 *Suggested answers*
The main theme of both texts
Text 1 talks about the latest apps you can get for your mobile phone, which allow you to pinpoint your position, and which can replace maps to a certain extent. Text 2 talks about paper maps as works of art, having artistic and historical value.
The opinion each writer expresses
The writer of Text 1 welcomes the development of digital mapping devices, arguing that it is easier to find your way with them. The writer of Text 2 believes that interest in paper maps is not dead, but has shifted to focus on them as representational works of art, and as historical evidence.
Students' own opinion
Ideas will vary, but one point may be to consider the limitations of apps – what happens when there is no signal for the smartphone and you are stuck on a mountain, for example. In this case, the paper map is much more reliable. The writer of the second text might be seen as having a slightly idealistic view of paper maps, for interest in the artistic and historical value of maps is likely to be limited to a relatively small group of collectors. Nevertheless, it could be argued that paper maps are not totally obsolete just yet.

2 *Suggested answer*
The two texts consider the value of digital as opposed to paper maps. The first text supports the view that smartphone navigational applications have superseded paper maps, making walking and hiking a lot easier, and enabling even those inexperienced in orienteering to find their way. The second text, on the other hand, while agreeing that traditional paper maps have become outmoded, makes a case for the latter by pointing out that they have great value both as historical evidence and as works of art.

3 Students' own answers

4a While statement (a) could refer to either text, (b) clearly refers to Text 1.

4b Students' own answers

5 *Suggested answer*

While the two texts make valid points with regard to the value of both types of map, there are certain important aspects of the paper map they ignore. One thing they both fail to recognise is its intrinsic reliability. The second text dismisses its navigational value in today's society altogether. The first text recognises its continuing appeal for hikers, yet more in a sentimental sense than a practical one. It ignores the fact that in remote, mountainous regions, both weather and the terrain can make it difficult to obtain a signal for digital tools to work. In such cases, the paper map remains a vital piece of equipment to the walker. Furthermore, visually, a paper map is easier to look at, if you want to see the kind of terrain you'll be passing through at a glance. Screens are too small to do this effectively. So, for serious hikers trekking through mountains, the paper map is far from obsolete.

6 *Model answer*

The two texts consider the value of digital as opposed to paper maps. The first text supports the view that smartphone navigational applications have superseded the paper map, making walking and hiking a lot easier, and enabling even those inexperienced in orienteering to find their way. The second text, on the other hand, while agreeing that traditional paper maps have become outmoded, makes a case for the latter by pointing out that they have great value both as historical evidence and as works of art.

While the two texts make valid points with regard to the valu e of both types of map, there are certain important aspects of the paper map they ignore. One thing they both fail to recognise is its intrinsic reliability. The second text dismisses its navigational value in today's society altogether. The first text recognises its continuing appeal for hikers, yet more in a sentimental sense than a practical one. It ignores the fact that in remote, mountainous regions, both weather and the terrain can make it difficult to obtain a signal for digital tools to work. In such cases, the paper map remains a vital piece of equipment to the walker. Furthermore, visually, a paper map is easier to look at, if you want to see the kind of terrain you'll be passing through at a glance. Screens are too small to do this effectively. So, for serious hikers trekking through mountains, the paper map is far from obsolete.

To my mind, while digital tools have indeed revolutionised the art of navigation, there is still a place for the traditional paper map, and the writers of both texts are rash to dismiss it out of hand.

Audio script

Extract One

F: Empuriabrava's hardly the sort of place you'd expect to offer an adrenalin rush. This sedate development on Spain's northeastern coast was built by German developers for boating types who like a mooring right outside the villa door. So what you get is a kind of villa resort cut by twenty-five miles of glinting tranquil canals. As a place it's not without its charms.

Extract Two

M: So next you went to India?

F: Yes, I had that urge to escape again. A family friend was working on a leprosy station in the Himalayas and I settled in so easily to the pace of life – it was blissful. But I wanted to find out what was going on in my mind too. I'd been roaming for years and thought I'd love to spend time tucked away from it all – see where my brain would take me. With the benefit of hindsight, that was the bit I got most out of actually.

What you've got right on the edge of town, however, is Europe's busiest skydiving centre and the summer sees in excess of a thousand fliers a day drop from the skies, thrill-seekers all. Having hopped over from London with a brochure entitled Skydiving Discovery Weekend in my bag, I duly fetched up at the airfield and introduced myself to a man called Ritchie Pym, who promised to show me the ropes. Ritchie's an Australian world champion skydiver with a handsome face and a curious line in jokes. He assured me that: 'Gravity works, and if nothing else does, we're going to die, ha-ha-ha!'

So I went to bed last night in a hotel on the edge of the airfield, feeling less than a hundred percent sold on the idea of what I'd let myself in for.

M: And you did a travel programme in the Irish language. How was that?

F: Weird. I wanted to express the ideas of unlimited elation I'd found in India – the boundlessness of it all – but whereas Irish is great for expressing concepts of hardship and oppression, it lacks the words to go far into the sort of stuff I was experiencing in India – so I tended to let the images speak for themselves.

M: I know what you mean. Before you go travelling, your world view's kind of conditioned by the confines of the particular mindset you're part of. My understanding of how humans interrelate came from seeing other cultures, rather than from observing my own.

F: No doubt about that.

Extract Three

F: Hi Keith. Tell us how you're feeling right now.

M: Well, at the moment, I feel like I've got very bad jet lag. I seem to have lost all sense of balance and though I'm on dry land, in a hotel in Barbados, and the trip's over, the only place I feel normal is on a boat. Strange that, considering I've just spent sixty-three days rowing across the Atlantic and the one thing I never intend to set foot in again is a boat! Don't get me wrong, I'm incredibly proud of the money we've raised for charity. That said though, the idea of setting foot on another waterborne vessel fills me with dread and horror. It's not just my hands, cracked and flaky from holding the oars, nor my lips burnt and sore from the sun. It's the memory of endless hours slumped in the back of the boat in the heat of the day; I can only liken it to being laid out in a hot, wet coffin. We did our best to stick to a routine. One of us would row for two hours, then the other would take over and for the most part we'd try and stay awake to keep each other company – in the hours of daylight at least – it was a way of keeping ourselves sane.

Module 7

Vocabulary development 1 p. 72

1
1 unprecedented step
2 tribal communities
3 neighbourhood watch
4 dramatic shift
5 government policy
6 vested interest

2
1 what gets me is
2 I'll give you that
3 gets things done
4 get me wrong
5 get-up-and-go
6 give and take
7 give as good as you get
8 give it a go

3
1 community projects
2 challenge
3 perceptions
4 initiative
5 inspire
6 marginalised
7 communal
8 anti-social behaviour
9 stronger
10 community spirit

Use of English p. 73

2
1 B
2 C
3 D
4 D
5 A
6 D
7 B
8 C

> **Expert language**
> a overwhelmingly
> b wellbeing

3
1 I'm often struck . . . by
2 seedling
3 breeze
4 row of ticks

4
1 in
2 in
3 up

Language development 1 p. 74

1
1 that/which
2 many of whom
3 by which time
4 that/which
5 in which case
6 to whom

2
1 Seeking a solution to the financial crisis of 2012, citizens of the Greek town . . .
2 Known as TEM Magnesias, the group took its name . . .
3 Serving all individuals and businesses in the Volos region, the organisation began . . .
4 Based on similar systems operating in Britain, Canada and Germany, the TEM initiative spawned local currency initiatives in . . .
5 Anyone wanting to join the group should visit their website.
6 Alternatively, the place to enrol at is the group's main exchange point, situated in the town centre.

3
1 –
2 –
3 who
4 who
5 –
6 –
7 –
8 whose

4 Crystal Waters Permaculture Village, (1) situated on the subtropical east coast of Queensland, Australia, is a working sustainable community project with over two hundred permanent residents. Permaculture, (2) a term coined by the Australian designer and environmentalist, Bill Mollison, is a form of ecological design (3) aiming to develop sustainable human communities, by integrating ecological engineering, housing and sustainable agriculture. Crystal Waters, (4) founded in 1985 on six hundred and forty acres of land, was the world's first permaculture settlement. Designers collaborated to produce sustainable homes (5) made from natural materials such as straw bale, rammed earth and mud. The village received a UN World Habitat Award in 1996, (6) gaining it worldwide interest.

Use of English p. 75

2
1 but/except
2 hardly/scarcely
3 Little/No
4 Once/Previously
5 in
6 apart
7 whether
8 account

> **Expert language**
> self-imposed hardships, group fitness competitions

3
1 hardship
2 ardent
3 taking off
4 once/previously
5 in their droves
6 in roughly equal proportions
the domain of

Listening p. 76

4
1 ambassadors
2 safety
3 escort(s)
4 whistle
5 brakes
6 one-stop shop
7 lockers
8 (easily) accessible
9 (annual) leave

Vocabulary development 2 p. 77

1
1 lifestyle
2 home-school
3 home town
4 homemade
5 lifetime
6 life coach

2
1 irresistibly
2 unsustainable/non-sustainable
3 disrespectfully
4 unconventional
5 misguided
6 incomparable
7 impractical

3
1 strapped
2 simple
3 Concerned
4 undeterred
5 invigorating
6 self-sufficient
7 ambience
8 manner
9 awe-inspiring
10 artificia

4
1 of
2 to
3 with
4 to
5 of
6 in
7 to
8 in

Reading p. 78–79

4	1	B	4	B	7	C	10	B
	2	A	5	C	8	D		
	3	D	6	B	9	A		

Expert language

rat race, house husband, job description, stay-at-home dad, labour market, birthday, reserve player, star striker, playground, roundabout, supermarkets, laptop

5	1	enlightened		5	inequities
	2	smugness		6	muddle through
	3	the rat race		7	complied
	4	disquieted			

6

1 It suggests progressive attitudes.
2 This is a rather pejorative word.
3 It conjures up a good mental image of people who continually compete for success and have a lot of stress in their lives.
4 It rather understates the feeling he's trying to conceal.
5 It is more usual to use this word in the plural – unfairness is an abstract noun.
6 A 'muddle' suggests disorganisation.
7 There is irony in the use of this formal word.

Language development 2 p. 80

1	1	Now that		5	While
	2	✓		6	Before
	3	until		7	No sooner
	4	Ever since		8	✓

2	1	E	3	F	5	D	7	H
	2	G	4	B	6	A	8	C

3	1	otherwise		4	hence
	2	consequently		5	in which case
	3	in such a way as to		6	That being the case

4	1	Nevertheless		5	All the same
	2	so as		6	Although
	3	Much as		7	Be that as it may
	4	However		8	though

Use of English p. 81

2

1 for anyone wishing | to file a complaint is
2 to keep his options open | as far as
3 set the day apart | was
4 of the factory would have | (serious/grave) repercussions for
5 no account | should this window (ever) be
6 nothing | stand in her
7 mind, Henry | should never have put
8 intents and purposes, | Tim has put the business
9 went to great lengths | to make
10 was on the point | of serving lunch

Writing p. 82

1 *Suggested answers*

a the editor of the magazine
b You are writing in response to the request for readers to express their opinion about the level of litter on the streets of their home town, and suggest ways to improve the situation.
c You must describe the current levels of rubbish in your town, assess the situation and think of ways it could be improved.

2 Students' own answers

3a Questions 1–5 ask about the current situation, and so logically, should form one paragraph. So, the break should come between 5 & 6.

3b Students' own answers

4 *Suggested answers*

1 Our neighbourhood is fairly clean. Be that as it may, we do get quite a lot of litter in the High Street, particularly on Saturdays.
2 The litter bins are emptied every Tuesday and Friday, which I don't think is sufficient.
3 One problem being ignored is that a group of teenagers hanging out in the park vandalise the children's playground and leave bottles lying around.
4 A neighbourhood volunteer group cleans up the park once a month, in this way helping to reduce the problem.
5 A park keeper looks after the park during the day. Nevertheless, at night patrols are needed to prevent damage being caused.
6 The teenagers should be provided with their own meeting place, otherwise they will continue to damage the park area.

5 *Model answer*

Dear Editor,

I am writing in reply to your magazine's invitation to readers to express their opinion about the question of litter in their home town. I live in a suburb on the outskirts of a provincial town, and while we don't have many problems with litter, there are a few in the town centre which certainly need attention.

My own neighbourhood is fairly clean, as are most of the residential areas in the town. Be that as it may, we do get quite a lot of litter in the Town Centre, particularly on Saturdays. The street cleaners do not clean up until Monday morning, and neither are rubbish bins emptied until then, leaving the centre looking dirty and unattractive over the weekend. Another problem being ignored is that a group of teenagers hanging out in the local park vandalise the children's playground and leave bottles lying around. This makes it both unpleasant and dangerous for young children to play there.

One obvious solution to the problem of litter in the Town Centre is to have street cleaners and rubbish collectors operate on Saturday evenings. This would benefit the town, as more people would be attracted to the bars and restaurants in the centre on Sundays if the area were cleaner. With regard to the park, a volunteer group cleans up the park once a month, in this way helping to reduce the problem, and there is a park keeper looking after the park during the day. Nevertheless, the damage is caused at night. Night patrols are costly, so a more realistic solution might be to provide teenagers with their own meeting place, thus eliminating their need to hang around the playground.

If these few simple steps are taken, I believe that the problem of litter in our town could be dealt with fairly easily, making the town a more pleasant place to visit at weekends.
Yours faithfully,

Audio script

Hi there. I'm Jerome Wilby and I've come along to tell you about the work of *CycleAware*, an organisation that promotes cycling as an environmentally-friendly method of commuting to work.
The government is now backing initiatives to encourage this kind of cycling and that's where organisations like *CycleAware* have a part to play. So what do we do? Generally speaking, we're working with companies and acting as specialist advisors to the management, as well as providing hands-on assistance to individual employees. This generally begins with a visit from one of our ambassadors who will hold meetings in-company to assess how cycling to work can be facilitated and encouraged amongst the staff. Once an action plan has been drawn up, then our team of cycling mentors goes in to help with the promotion itself.
The action plan will look at whether people cycle to work at the moment and if they do, what facilities are available to them. And if they don't, we try to identify what it is that puts them off. There are issues of cost, of course – buying, maintaining and insuring a good bike requires quite an investment, and convenience is also an issue. Is there a good route? Where can bikes be parked? – and so on. But actually safety is usually the overriding concern amongst those who need convincing.
This is where our cycling mentors can actually be of practical help to anybody thinking of taking up cycling to work. By acting as what we call an escort – cycling alongside the person, advising on the best routes and potential hazards – the mentor can make sure the cycle-commuter gets off to a good start. The mentor will also help with the choice of kit – giving advice about the most comfortable type of helmet and other practical considerations. Like, for example, bikes used to be sold with bells to attract the attention of other road users but these aren't effective in modern traffic and some bikes are now fitted with horns instead. Whereas *we* actually think a whistle is best because the sound is much more penetrating and so more likely to be heard.

CycleAware also provides a range of other services to cycling employees. For example, regular maintenance checks on bikes. Often adjustments are made to saddles, gears and wheels to improve the cycling experience, although it's most often the brakes that need seeing to most urgently.

Anyway, those are just some of the things we do – but there's lots more. As a specialist agency, we aim to provide companies and employees with the necessary support at all levels – we're like a one-stop-shop for all their cycling needs, especially where there are subsidies and incentives available from the government. We can advise companies on the kind of infrastructure they need to put in place to support cyclists at work. Most firms provide cycle parking areas, some even go as far as providing showers and other facilities for cyclists but often overlooked is the need for lockers in which employees can store helmets and other cycling gear. These are inexpensive and take up very little space but can make all the difference when commuters are considering switching to cycling.
Companies also need to put thought into the positioning of cycle racks and facilities. Racks need to be as easily accessible as the employees' car park, because cyclists should never be made to feel that they are the poor relations. These places also need to be clean, secure and preferably under cover. *CycleAware* can also advise on incentive schemes to encourage cycling to work. There are, for example, financial and other perks that can be offered. Some companies offer executive company bikes instead of company cars as part of the remuneration package, or allow claims for travel expenses that include cycle mileage. One company, which offered extra annual leave to those who regularly cycle to work got an immediate response at all levels and would seem to provide a useful model.
Anyway, before I go on to . . .

Module 8

Vocabulary development 1 p. 83

1
1	into		
2	in	**8**	from
3	of	**9**	of
4	with	**10**	away
5	into/to/of	**11**	of
6	at	**12**	in
7	under		

2
1	monument	**4**	aqueduct
2	fortress	**5**	dungeon
3	landmark	**6**	edifice

3
1	drop	**4**	draw
2	draw	**5**	dropped, drew
3	draw	**6**	draw

4
1	handwriting	**6**	letters
2	patterns	**7**	images
3	rounded	**8**	sketchy
4	straight	**9**	signs
5	boxes	**10**	shading

Use of English p. 84

2
1	D	3	A	5	B	7	A
2	C	4	B	6	C	8	D

Expert language
Only after living with it for a while would you . . .

3
1	daunting	7	bogus
2	out of place	8	in situ
3	size (it) up	9	hoodwinked
4	on approval	10	disappeared without
5	backfire drastically		trace
6	confidence tricksters		

4
1	off	2	by	3	by

Language development 1 p. 85

1
1	good	5	advantage
2	view	6	prone
3	committed	7	fear
4	possibility	8	prospect

2
1	up	6	better
2	tired	7	despite
3	Instead	8	help/stop
4	point	9	mind
5	regrets	10	for

3
1 The art tutor at my evening class complimented me on executing my first sketch pretty well.
2 Jack prides himself on never doing anything less than a really good job.
3 I hate the thought of that lovely old building in the centre being knocked down.
4 I have no intention of ever buying a brand new car.
5 In addition to buying painting materials, Yvonne (also) bought a sculpting kit.
6 I have to take responsibility for breaking the plate.

4
1	of (our) getting away	6	for planning
2	with looking after	7	about studying
3	to owning	8	of forging
4	on renovating	9	about spending
5	into maintaining	10	for missing

Use of English p. 86

2
1	increasingly	5	efficiency
2	typically	6	minimise
3	counterpart	7	storage
4	likelihood	8	overlooked

Expert language
struggle to accommodate, a need to minimalise

3
1	called into question	4	knack
2	cramped	5	voids
3	clutter	6	tucked away

Listening p. 87

3
1	G	4	D	7	H	10	D
2	F	5	H	8	C		
3	B	6	E	9	A		

4
1	C	4	E	7	J	10	B
2	F	5	I	8	A		
3	G	6	H	9	D		

Reading p. 88–89

2 a It marked the beginning of a new marketing trend.
b Blogs started out as a form of alternative culture.
c These were once regarded as eccentric and avant-garde, but have now become mainstream.

4
1	C	3	E	5	F	7	H
2	B	4	G	6	D	8	A

Expert language
Coincidentally, Before you could say ..., Within a week, In the past, When they blogged, At the end of the day

Vocabulary development 2 p. 90

1
1	part with	6	build up
2	take up	7	stashed away
3	get into	8	looking to
4	pick them up	9	put them up
5	root them out	10	kicking off

2a Positive: effortless, flawless (= perfect), spotless
Negative: characterless, clueless (= (disapproving) having no understanding or knowledge of sth), hopeless, meaningless, useless, worthless
Neutral/Could be either: endless, timeless (= remaining attractive and not becoming old-fashioned; (literary) (= continuing for ever), speechless (= unable to speak because you feel very angry, surprised, etc), stainless

2b
1	stainless	4	speechless
2	endlessly	5	worthless
3	characterless	6	effortlessly

3
1	keep, appearances	4	keep, tidy
2	wear, tear	5	casual wear
3	keep, word	6	keep

Language development 2 p. 91

1
1	being able	4	to fork out
2	to portray	5	to make
3	having	6	displaying

2
1	to change	4	in understanding
2	for pulling down	5	to convince
3	of coming up with / to come up with	6	of succeeding

3
1	bound	4	ready, willing, anxious
2	apt, liable	5	capable
3	accustomed	6	guilty, accused

4
1	setting up	11	spending
2	being	12	watching
3	to try	13	to get
4	making	14	becoming
5	to teach	15	drumming up
6	to make	16	to be introduced
7	making	17	to learn
8	having	18	to stamp
9	to study	19	showing
10	working	20	carving

Use of English p. 92

2
1 was nowhere | to be seen
2 he drew the line | at her
3 son's reluctance | to go dancing down
4 little/not much prospect of | the new stadium being
5 for singing | could not make up
6 to popular belief, | Harry has no intention of
7 to the family enclosure | is restricted to
8 the museum was | (certainly/definitely/well) worth a
9 we were under no obligation | to attend
10 goes without saying (that) | all complaints are taken

Writing p. 93

1 The texts express opposing points of view. Phrases that particularly show this are:
Text 1 – the complete freedom of expression that modern-day artists enjoy; without having to conform to outdated rules about perspective; art represented no sense of challenge
Text 2 – Any comparison between the great artists of earlier centuries and those of today cannot fail to come down on the side of the past masters; give the person viewing that art a sense of satisfaction; I hardly think they inspire in us respect or a feeling of reverence for the creative artist's skill.

2 Text 1 – D ('complete freedom of expression', 'without having to conform to outdated rules'), F ('It is up to the person viewing that painting or work of art to interpret the artist's message as they see fit', 'in previous times, . . . art represented no sense of challenge')
Text 2 – A ('a recognisable scene'), C ('a feeling of mild amusement', 'I hardly think they ims[ire in us respect . . .')
Extra: B, E

3
1	As	4	as
2	commonly/generally	5	begin/start
3	true	6	reference/regard

Sentences 2 & 5 are not suitable since these are categorical statements not based on fact. Students need to be aware of the dangers of making sweeping statements that might sound impressive but are unsupported by any evidence.

4 *Model answer*
In Text 1, the writer outlines the importance of a type of art that is no longer rule-bound. Thus modern art, in the writer's view, is more creatively challenging, both for the artist and for the viewer: for the artist, in that they can create images that represent reality as they see it personally, and for the viewer in that a particular work of art can have multiple meanings of which they can choose the one that suits them most. In essence then, the writer supports the idea of art as being something that requires a certain amount of thought.

In Text 2, the writer argues in favour of an art form where the subject matter is clearly depicted. With regard to earlier art forms, the focus then was very much on a realistic portrayal of what artists saw around them and it is this that the writer finds eminently praiseworthy. A distinction is drawn between the technical mastery shown by these artists and what the writer sees as the 'dumbing-down' approach shown in contemporary works of art: the writer makes the point that abstract art may inspire ridicule.

Just as fashions in clothing belong to different periods of time, so styles of art go in and out of fashion. It may be true that much of modern art does not depict reality in a way that is easily comprehensible. However, as I see it, modern art has a particular attraction simply because of the freedom of interpretation that it offers each individual. For example, you might hang a picture of modern art on your wall and how many hours of interesting discussion about its meaning or symbolism might follow?

Audio script

Speaker One
M: I'd never really been into ceramics but during a wet family holiday, I was talked into visiting an art pottery studio. I thought we'd just be viewing stuff but the potter was there, large as life, and that's how I came to see this vase emerge out of a piece of clay. Impressed by her skill, I ordered one on an impulse, just as a souvenir really – not as an investment or anything – though looking at reviews on the net, she's obviously quite highly thought of. People ask what I see in it and I agree it doesn't really stand up to close inspection – but it's kind of striking in a way that I find aesthetically pleasing. I never tire of it.

Speaker Two
F: It's a painting – rather an abstract one at that. I'd never have known it existed if I hadn't bumped into a friend one day at the local gallery. It was tucked down a back corridor – I found out later that the critics had really slammed it, so it was on sale at a giveaway price. And I admit it's quite puzzling really – spooky almost – yet I could spend hours just looking at it wondering what the artist was trying to say. Anyway, this friend hated it and wanted to tell me why – we'd been on an art appreciation course together once. So I'll never forget the look on his face when I told him I'd been back and bought it.

Speaker Three

F: I was fortunate enough to get the drawing as a wedding present. I love it to bits because it's so brilliantly executed. I knew of its existence, of course because my mother sat for the artist and had often talked about the experience, though not about specific works. I remember her talking about the thrill of watching him draw. I came across a critical appraisal of his work online which listed the main pieces and one was called simply 'Emma' – my mother's name. Quite how my friend managed to get hold of it is a mystery to me but it was a wonderful surprise. I really don't like to think about how much it might be worth.

Speaker Four

M: People think it's a photo but it's actually a computer enhanced painting. It's one of those pictures where the longer you look, the more you see but it's not so much the detail that draws me to it, though it must've taken ages to do, it's more the way it takes me back to my childhood. It just brings it all back. And to think, if I'd never signed up for that evening class in software design, I'd never have met Alice whose work it actually is. When I said how much I liked it, she wanted to give it to me as a present but I said no way and made her accept a fair price.

Speaker Five

F: The thing about silver from India is that it's very finely decorated with an intricacy that I find irresistible. People in Europe admire the craftsmanship but I can see from their reactions that they aren't really in tune with the aesthetics of the objects, which is a shame – but at least it means the stuff is less collectible here, which stops prices getting out of hand. The elephant's my personal favourite because it was presented to me at my graduation party. An antique-dealer friend advised my parents where to look for pieces in their price range but of course they needed no help in choosing the one that I'd fall in love with.

Module 9

Vocabulary development 1 p. 94

1a 1 **d** iv 3 **e** iii 5 **a** i
2 **f** ii 4 **b** vi 6 **c** v

1b 1 below par
2 below the belt
3 in the same league as
4 backing the wrong horse
5 go off the deep end
6 time out

2 1 inconsolably
2 outshone
3 underestimated
4 outstanding
5 inconsistently
6 unparalleled

3 1 circumnavigation
2 controversy
3 epic
4 undertaking
5 ensued
6 challenges
7 resourceful
8 isolation

Use of English p. 95

2 1 A 3 B 5 D 7 C
2 C 4 A 6 B 8 C

Expert language
a aims to ensure, hopes to make, hopes to raise
b is designed to make

3 1 sponsored
2 at grassroots level
3 enabling skills
4 thereby
5 cross-section

4 1 compound nouns where the first element is a preposition.
2 downside/upside
3 underpin, uphold

5 1 subsidise
2 subsidy

Language development 1 p. 96

1 1 Incredible
2 Funnily
3 Generally
4 Believe

2 1 b 2 a 3 b 4 a

3 1 perfectly capable
2 highly unlikel
3 stunningly beautiful
4 meticulously tidy
5 purely coincidental
6 ridiculously expensive

4 Words to be crossed out
1 genuinely
2 perceptibly
3 patently
4 unbearably
5 deceptively
6 stupidly

5 1 widely
2 sheer
3 seriously
4 somewhat
5 painfully
6 reluctantly
7 utterly
8 truly

Use of English p. 97

2 1 repeatedly
2 empathise
3 setbacks
4 inescapably
5 intricacies
6 insight
7 multiple
8 opponent

3 1 gripping
2 triumphs
3 palpable
4 duel

4 1 popularise
2 mechanise
3 neutralise
4 criticise
5 legitimise
6 emphasise
7 analyse
8 hypothesise
9 digitise
10 energise

Listening p. 98

4
1 competitive anxiety
2 intense
3 (public) announcements
4 process
5 elbows
6 visualisation (techniques)
7 commitment
8 butterflies
9 anger

Expert language
reporting verbs, no

Vocabulary development 2 p. 99

1
1 incorporate
2 eliminate
3 water
4 Acquire
5 whet
6 crave
7 Chew
8 savour

2
1 B 2 C 3 A 4 C

3
1 E 3 H 5 B 7 F
2 D 4 G 6 A 8 C

4 *Suggested answers*
1 calmly
2 got angry
3 crazy
4 was too busy
5 silly
6 one of the best students
7 easy
8 in difficulty
9 take back what he'd said earlier

Reading p. 100–101

2 Den Hague: an abiding first memory of a football match
Carlisle United: a club that inspired one fan's lifelong devotion
Arsenal: fans attracted to a club with a safe and comfortable stadium
Chelsea: a club with a transient fan base
Calciopoli scandal: something which puts fans off a club

3
1 C 4 C 7 A 10 A
2 D 5 B 8 C
3 A 6 B 9 D

Expert language
some are, most aren't, very few, nor are most

4
1 hooked
2 diehards
3 attendances
4 lapse
5 deters
6 crooked
7 slump
8 ominous
9 lucrative
10 pull out

Language development 2 p. 102

1
1 attributes . . . to
2 subject to
3 imposed . . . on
4 contribute to
5 confused by
6 comply with

2
1 with, at, for
2 for, to
3 for, on, in
4 in, from
5 for, on
6 of, at

3
1 in
2 on
3 without
4 out of
5 for
6 In

4
1 of
2 for
3 from
4 by/about
5 of
6 to
7 on
8 of
9 with
10 of
11 in
12 for
13 over/about
14 to
15 to
16 of
17 of
18 in
19 on
20 on/about

Use of English p. 103

2
1 so
2 which
3 as
4 when
5 under
6 clear
7 put
8 beyond

Expert language
a Doctors do . . . sometimes prescribe
b start prescribing

3
1 assertion
2 head on
3 circulation
4 tackle
5 ailments
6 in short

Writing p. 104

1 *Suggested answers*
Students should choose from the following points: 1, 2, 3, 5, 6, 7, 8, 10
Points 4 and 9 are in danger of becoming irrelevant, as they move away from the central message of the statement.

2 *Suggested answers*
Points for: students should include 3 of the following – 1, 6, 7, 8, 10
Points against: students should include 2, 3, 5

3a Nevertheless, it takes a great deal of courage and determination to recover from defeat, and not everyone succeeds. [= point being made] There are many stories of athletes abandoning professional competition as a result of being unable to cope with defeat. This is particularly hard for champions, [= example given] who may find it psychologically hard to bear defeat after having experienced the glory of success.

3b Students' own answers

4 *Model answer*

People often feel that their greatest achievements occur after disappointment, simply because the determination and fortitude they had to show to overcome failure has made them appreciate their success more. So, although there is a lot of truth in the statement above, it is really a matter of attitude.

There is a popular myth that some people are born to succeed in life, while others are doomed to fail. However, the truth is that success or failure is not simply a matter of fate. How an individual deals with failure will determine whether or not they then go on to succeed in the future. Making mistakes is a natural part of the learning process in life. Failing at something is an opportunity to reflect on the mistakes one has made, and correct them for the future. Suffering a setback teaches us humility, and not to take our situation for granted. If we accept the value of our mistakes in this way, this can help us become more determined to succeed. The feeling of success is always greater if it is the result of considerable effort.

Nevertheless, it takes a great deal of courage to recover from defeat, and not everyone succeeds. Many athletes suffer from a loss of confidence and even despair, abandoning competition altogether as a result. Similarly, in the working environment, professionals are sometimes unable to cope. They may view failure as a personal deficiency, rather than a stepping stone on the road to success.

Undeniably, for many, it may be necessary at some point to recognise that they have little ability or talent in their ch osen profession. Yet admitting this to oneself is itself a step in the right direction, since having done so, the necessary changes that may ultimately lead to success can be made. This, therefore, reinforces the statement that greater success comes after disappointment.

Audio script

Hi there. My name's Graeme Walcott and I'm a sports psychologist. I'm going to be telling you how psychologists like me can help top sportspeople to have the right approach to their training for major events.

Now much of psychology is of interest to sports coaches but the studies with the greatest appeal and practical application for them are those in the field of competitive anxiety. This looks into the techniques that athletes can use to maintain control and optimise their performance. Once learned, such techniques allow an athlete to relax and focus his or her attention on the event in a positive manner.

The demand for concentration, however, does vary with the sport. What's known as sustained concentration's required for sports like tennis and squash, whilst short bursts of concentration are more useful for cricket and golf, and some sports, such as bobsleigh and skiing, call for intense concentration. But whatever form of concentration they're after, sportspeople are prone to getting put off by external factors. Learning to ignore these can pave the way to success. Common distractions for sportspeople include, predictably, their own mistakes, the weather and the behaviour of opponents. Weirdly, public announcements often get under the skin of even the most seasoned sportspeople, however, and fatigue of course always has a part to play.

Strategies to improve concentration vary. Although the athlete will have set him or herself an overall goal – usually winning or beating a personal best time – I generally suggest they also identify process goals for each stage in their preparation. These focus on specific aspects of the task, rather than just on the outcome. For each of these, the athlete can then use a trigger word – that's one word which instantly refocuses concentration to the immediate goal. For instance, a sprinting technique requiring the runner to focus on being relaxed, smooth and to drive with the elbows – might use that one word as the trigger to achieving concentration on the right technique.

Another psychological issue that sports coaches can work on is self-confidence. Confidence is a belief that you can meet the challenge ahead – it's also a feeling of being in control. To improve self-confidence, in my opinion nothing beats visualisation. It's a technique whereby the athlete creates a mental image of a previous good performance and so recalls how it looks and feels to do well – this does wonders for self-esteem.

Of course, stress on the day of the event is an issue, no matter how confident and focused an athlete is. Athletes often ask me how they can avoid race-day nerves but to be honest those feelings are just a part of the excitement that surrounds the event. Not to experience them might well reveal a low level of commitment that would actually detract from performance. It's well known that sportspeople develop routines to help them cope in these situations, and these certainly have their place, but they may still suffer from what are generally referred to as butterflies – a range of symptoms including excessive sweating, feelings of nausea and that strange tightening in the stomach from which the term gets its name.

Emotional control is the key. An athlete's ability to maintain this in the face of adversity and remain positive is essential to success. That's why sportspeople often shed tears immediately after the event – these are not tears of disappointment or frustration, they're just a release of pent-up emotions that have been suppressed in the run-up and during the event itself. The emotion most often associated with poor performance, however, is anger. When an athlete feels this, whatever's causing it often becomes the focus of attention, leading to a loss of concentration, and a downward cycle is established.

So before I go on to . . .

Module 10

Vocabulary development 1 p. 105

1
1. financial backing
2. learning curve
3. target market
4. comfort zone
5. business acumen, career ladder
6. consumer behaviour

Note: obviously other combinations of words can theoretically be made but the collocations here have to fit the context of the individual sentences.

2
1. trumps
2. ceiling
3. box
4. door
5. ground
6. scratch

3
1. strike
2. drive
3. carving out
4. have
5. launching
6. have
7. coming
8. get

4
1. indecisively
2. inconceivable
3. Undeterred
4. insignificant
5. unachievable
6. inexplicably

Use of English p. 106

2
1. C
2. B
3. D
4. A
5. C
6. D
7. A
8. B

> **Expert language**
> 1 marine safety helmet
> 2 niche watersports market
> 3 innovative heat-retaining helmet
> 'heat-retaining' is a compound adjective that describes a different quality to 'innovative'.

3
1. product offering
2. a whole new ballgame
3. paid off
4. in the long run

4
1. concentrate on
2. focus on
3. target (no preposition)

Language development 1 p. 107

1
1. He claimed that he'd never spent a minute of his life regretting things he could have bought.
2. He explained that if you happened to see something that looked like a good bargain, it was only natural you were going to try and buy it. / If you happen to see something that looks like a good bargain, it's only natural you're going to try and buy it.
3. He emphasised that his latest deal would probably go down in history as one of the best that had ever been done.
4. He admitted that his biggest battle had been won in that boardroom the year before / the previous year.
5. He assured me that he wouldn't ever / would never make a bid for a company unless he was sure of its worth.
6. He acknowledged that he had been lucky and had received some really good training in the early years.

2
1. spoke out against
2. would (only) touch on
3. to dwell (too much) on (the mistakes) he'd made and (that it was best to) move on
4. blurted out (that she) was not very happy in her job.
5. couldn't get through to
6. filled Ben in on (what) had been happening while he'd been away.

3 These options to be crossed out
1. to set up
2. All options are correct
3. I should take, my taking
4. to go
5. he didn't act, his not acting
6. that I agree, agreeing

4
1. Tim made a comment about the conference but . . .
2. She is alleged to have been involved . . . no one has confirmed that officially / nothing has been officially confirmed
3. The Minister of Education will make a statement . . .
4. I feel that the criticisms (which were made) of her conduct were quite . . .
5. It has been rumoured that some cheating . . .
6. I'm afraid I have no recollection of writing down . . .
7. He denied (having) any involvement in match-fixing.

Use of English p. 108

2
1. other
2. even
3. Take
4. out
5. despite
6. stand
7. which/that
8. into

> **Expert language**
> be a thing of the past, nowhere to be seen, devoid of

3
1. lavish
2. a thing of the past
3. consensus
4. timeless
5. thrive
6. tighter budgets
7. stand the test of time
8. accentuates

Listening p. 109

2
1. A
2. A
3. B
4. D
5. C

> **Expert language**
> dread the prospect of, problems arise, lead to difficulties, jump to (unfair) conclusions, ideas have shifted, lend weight to

3
1. D
2. F
3. H
4. E
5. G
6. B
7. C
8. A

Reading p. 110–111

3
1. D
2. D
3. C
4. C
5. A
6. B

> **Expert language**
> by no means uninitiated, far from uncommon.
> In both examples, they add emphasis to the positive idea.

Vocabulary development 2 p. 112

1a 1 in response to
2 on the off-chance
3 at a loose end
4 out of his depth
5 to my liking
6 under her belt

1b 1 on the strength
2 to no purpose
3 under discussion
4 at a disadvantage
5 In place of
6 On no account
7 out of character
8 at a stretch
9 under her belt

2 1 dissertation
2 tuition
3 bachelor's
4 tertiary
5 scholarship
6 disciplines
7 graduates
8 Faculty

3 1 sandwich degree
2 foregone conclusion
3 last straw
4 plain sailing
5 loaded questions
6 easy option

Language development 2 p. 113

1 1 to worse
2 no surprise
3 no notice
4 the board
5 for granted
6 (swift/speedy) recovery
7 of business
8 best of
9 on board / heed of
10 a decision / his senses
11 the opportunity
12 to terms
13 into account / consideration
14 without saying

2 1 disposal
2 comparison
3 aback
4 obligation
5 access
6 making
7 concern
8 an attempt
9 requirements
10 ease
11 signs
12 advantage

3 1 drawbacks
2 feedback
3 upturn
4 breakthrough
5 setback
6 turnout
7 intake
8 outlay

Use of English p. 114

2 1 to pay your bill | may result in your
2 involved in a | collision with
3 in recognition of | all the charity/charitable
4 was rejected | out of hand by
5 got/developed/acquired a taste for | seafood after
6 with (a) complete disregard | for the
7 no/not a decline in sales | the shop has
8 is the likelihood of | the company('s) making
9 no circumstances | must/should/may employees
10 could have knocked Bruce | down with a feather

Writing p. 115

1a *Suggested answers*
Text 1: learning only takes place early on in life, through school and higher education. Later on, the time for learning has gone and other things such as work and families take priority.

Text 2: learning should not be confined to one period of our lives, it should be seen as a continuous process. Many older people show evidence of learning new skills and a maturity of their intellectual powers later on in life.

Pros and cons of ideas in text 1 (suggested): pros – obviously, children, teens and young adults devote their early years to learning and education and it could possibly be the only time in their lives when they have the luxury of being able to do that; cons – depending on the quality of the education young people receive, the learning process isn't always that enjoyable and some young people resent the fact that they are forced to learn certain subjects that they are not interested in. This can have a negative effect and block the learning process, to a greater or lesser extent.
Pros and cons of ideas in text 2 (suggested): pros – certainly people should carry on with the learning process throughout their lives, it would be sad to think that learning came to an end when formal education stops, Yes, most people at the head of companies and academic institutions, etc are not people in their youth; cons – lack of time and possibly other resources means that it's more difficult for adults to do in-depth educational courses at a later age.

1b Students' own answers

2a 1 I
2 D
3 H
4 G
5 A
6 F
7 J
8 B
9 G/H/E
10 C

2b 1 take priority, settling down
2 devote, time
3 came/comes, to an end
4 expresses, the view
5 lay the foundations
6 undertake, formal education
7 put, to good use
8 develop, one's capabilities
9 have, a negative effect

3 *Model answer*
The writer of the first text suggests that the years when learning takes place are in school and higher education since this is the only time in a person's life when they can be fully committed to the learning process. The writer also implies that in later years, other matters can sometimes take priority, such as finding a job or settling down and starting a family. In my view, this is true to a certain extent. However, depending on the quality of the education young people receive, the learning process isn't always that enjoyable and some young people resent the fact that they are forced to learn certain subjects that they are not interested in. This can have a negative effect and block the learning process.
The writer of the second text on the other hand, expresses the view that lifelong learning should be encouraged. Rather than being confined to one period of our lives, learning should be seen as a continuous process. For example, many older people show evidence of learning new skills and a development of their intellectual maturity later on in life. As far as I'm concerned, it would be sad to think that learning came to an end when formal education stops, particularly because this suggests that adults cannot develop any further once they have completed their academic studies.
In conclusion, I would agree with the second writer insofar as one of the goals of life should be to develop one's capabilities as far as possible. However, I admit that lack of time and possibly other resources means that it's more difficult for adults to do in-depth educational courses later in life.

Audio script

Int = Interviewer, J = John, L = Lois

Int: In the studio tonight, I have the sociologist John Farrendale and philosopher, Lois Granger and we're going to be discussing attitudes towards work. Tonight's discussion was prompted by an email from a listener who, amongst other things, asks why people tend to become depressed if made redundant – as if work were the be all and end all – rather than seeing that situation as an opportunity to do something else. John?

J: Well, it can't be denied, I'm afraid, that unemployment is one of those misfortunes, like soured relationships and chronic pain, that most affect long-term happiness. Work is good because it gives people meaning, self-respect and the chance to make a contribution; unemployment conversely robs them of all that, which can come as a blow. So while I don't doubt, as our listener suggests, that there are people out there who might cope well with redundancy – see it as a chance to change direction or whatever – for the majority the opposite is the case. I mean, that's the reality, isn't it, Lois?

L: Well, one rarely meets anyone embracing redundancy, John. But I guess what our listener is getting at is the fact that paid employment isn't the sole provider of purpose, self-worth and engagement and I'd go along with that to an extent. Indeed, a job can work against us if the experience is tedious and it feels irrelevant. Work is vital to your happiness if work is what you want and if it's fulfilling. But we mustn't forget that tying too close a knot between meaningful activity and paid employment can be perilous, as we know from people who lose all sense of meaning when they retire. And this can affect those who love their jobs just as much as those who see them as a means to an end.

J: And indeed, there are people like that – who view work simply as that, a way of funding other things they want, as opposed to something that holds intrinsic value. Doing a well-paid job that lacks excitement but one which allows you to do exciting things in your spare time, might work perfectly well for some – and I'd say good luck to them as long as they get on with the job whilst they're there. Where's the harm in it? But I'd say it's preferable to earn less doing something you love, because work actually takes up an awful lot of your waking life. But if you want the good things in life and haven't found the kind of meaningful work that can provide them directly, then you have some thinking to do: the trade-offs are treacherous, and some of what you value may have to be sacrificed along the way.

Int: You mention attitudes to work John, we do tend to come down heavily on slackers – people who don't pull their weight – don't we?

J: We do. And amongst the many career options we have to choose from, one is almost taboo. As the listener who suggested this week's topic put it, someone tempted to work as little as possible is likely to be 'afraid of being judged as a useless slacker'. This taboo seems to have grown as our work options have multiplied. Now work is no longer destiny, determined at birth by the social standing of your parents; how we earn a living reflects more of our individual qualities and choices, and we're judged accordingly. But perhaps these judgments are distorted by confusing sound reasons for thinking work is important with the false belief that honest labour is inherently virtuous.

L: That's right. I mean think of Freud, the famous psychoanalyst, who's widely attributed with the quote: 'Love and work are the cornerstones of our humanness.' – although it's actually a paraphrase by Erikson. What Freud actually said is that 'the compulsion to work' was 'created by external necessity'. In other words, the imperative to work springs from practical demands, not immutable psychic needs. There's nothing valuable in work per se. Indeed, the philosopher Bertrand Russell went so far as to claim that immense harm is caused by the belief that work is virtuous – that if we work more than we need to, we deprive ourselves of the time and opportunity for learning, self-development, relationships and many other things that make for a better world. If we must work, or choose to do so, what matters is that it serves the goal of living well, rather than detracts from it.

Int: At that point, I'd like to bring in . . .

Practice exam

Reading and Use of English p. 116–125

Part 1

1 B	**3** C	**5** D	**7** A
2 C	**4** D	**6** C	**8** B

Part 2

9 what	**13** into
10 something	**14** could/might
11 as	**15** for
12 due/owing/thanks	**16** Despite

Part 3

17 identification	**21** update
18 Apparently	**22** timely
19 accompanying	**23** painstaking
20 checkout/check-ou	**24** offenders

Part 4

25 no circumstances will/would I ever/am I ever going to
26 come to terms with
27 took absolutely no notice of the/any/any of the
28 had led John to believe
29 long as there is no/is not a(ny) sudden deterioration
30 to popular belief, the island was not

Part 5

31 A	**33** C	**35** C
32 B	**34** D	**36** D

Part 6

37 H	**39** G	**41** D	**43** A
38 B	**40** E	**42** F	

Part 7

44 A	**47** D	**50** D	**53** C
45 B	**48** B	**51** C	
46 C	**49** A	**52** B	

Writing p. 126–127

Part 1

1 *Model answer*

The two texts deal with the issue of what constitutes a work of art, but look at the issue from two quite different perspectives. The first text seeks to provide a definition of the term 'work of art' and begins by suggesting that anything created by a human being has the potential to be considered one. But the text then goes on to suggest that objects created by hand, which are therefore unique in themselves, may have more inherent artistic value than objects which are designed and then produced on a large scale for mass consumption.

I would take issue with this contention because so many creations which are clearly 'works of art' are also widely available. A Jane Austen novel is unequivocally a work of art, but the term can be applied to any copy you might read – even one delivered online to your e-reader. The same, surely, must go for the coffee pot the writer mentions?

The second text is more contentious. It calls into question the integrity of certain modern artists, suggesting that their work does not have true artistic value, and that gullible patrons are hoodwinked into paying large sums for works that are not even well executed. I think this is unfair. The fact that modern art is often ground-breaking, challenging our very ideas of what art is, provokes this sort of reaction in people, and this is perhaps to the artist's credit. What's more, if enough people agree that a work has artistic value, then it will command a high price, and this has always been the case.

Clearly, what constitutes a work of art will always be, to a certain extent, in the eyes of the beholder.

Part 2

2 *Model answer*

Doing research on the Internet often makes me feel like a sailor in a little boat adrift on a sea of information. An Internet search yields a wealth of varying data and explanations, and it's all too easy to lose your bearings and find yourself in a place at some considerable distance from your starting-point, where you can become side-tracked and waste a lot of valuable time, and sometimes even money. To give a very banal example, when searching for information about what constitutes a healthy diet, I came across all manner of information regarding essential vitamins and minerals – including the dire consequences of not getting enough of them. Before I knew what was happening, I found myself the proud owner of a five-year supply of supplements I never knew I needed – and on reflection perhaps don't need after all.

So, if you're researching a particular topic, you need some sort of criteria to help you sift through the masses of information online. Bear in mind that nobody may have verified the content of a site before it's made public and, as a researcher, it's your job to evaluate what you locate, in order to determine whether it suits your needs and also whether it's reliable. Going to a reputable site can save you a lot of time.

This was brought home to me when I was considering attending a university in the UK and needed certain precise details about the language requirements. An Internet search took me straight to my local British Council website, which provided me with all the information I needed regarding which exams were recognized for which courses, and where and when I could sit them locally. Having found the correct qualification, I was able to follow a link to a site where I could view the syllabus and some past papers. Unlike, the vitamins, this information all turned out to be accurate and useful.

3 *Model answer*
This report will explain why the Soccerstyle website is superior to other soccer sites, but also suggest some improvements.

1 The advantages of Soccerstyle over other similar websites

1.1 Content
Like many other soccer fans, I regularly log on to the Internet to get the latest news about the sport. Soccerstyle is my first choice of website because it features content about a wide range of clubs, not only those in the higher divisions of the national league. Although other websites include some information about non-league soccer, only Soccerstyle does this in a systematic way. Also, unlike some other websites, it doesn't favour clubs or leagues in the capital city, but carries news about all aspects of the provincial game. For example, I can get results within minutes of the games ending, and access team listings and match reports from a wide range of local leagues, whilst keeping up-to-date on individual club news and events.

1.2 Layout
Another big plus point of Soccerstyle is ease of navigation. I can move around the site quickly and easily and the search facility really does take you to the information that you're looking for – in sharp contrast to its main competitor Matchplay, where you can waste a lot of time clicking and scrolling without ever finding anything useful. The design of Soccerstyle is also very clean and modern compared to some of its rivals that have a rather garish, unprofessional appearance.

2 Criticisms of Soccerstyle
My only criticism of the site concerns the advertising. I appreciate that this is necessary for financial reasons on a free site, but sometimes the pop ups and banners cause the informational content to move around, as they gradually open on the page. What's worse, if I inadvertently click on one of these adverts, I get taken out of the site on a link. If these two irritating features could be redesigned, it would make the site much more pleasurable to use.

4 *Model answer*
The Abruzzo region, situated on the Adriatic coast of Italy, offers a wide choice of places to eat and a time-honoured culinary tradition. The restaurant I intend to talk about is located inside a medieval building originally used for storing salt, which is borne out by the name 'La Corte del Sale.' The interior is tastefully furnished and there is the typical terracotta floor and vaulted ceilings which people expect in a place serving really traditional cuisine. A colleague had recommended 'La corte' to me, and when I mentioned his name, the owner welcomed us warmly. Needless to say, the service was impeccable; the owner himself served us and kept a discreet distance while we ate, appearing only now

and then to enquire whether all was well.
I'm not a great fan of the popular traditional local cuisine, with its heavy meat-based sauces and thick pasta, but this restaurant prides itself on a 're-visitation' of tradition. So I was prepared to be pleasantly surprised. And surprised I certainly was, as dish after carefully chosen dish, arrived at our table. There were little balls of ewe's cheese stewed in a light tomato sauce, aubergine stuffed with herby rice, and vegetable shoots with beans – and those were just the starters! These were followed by a pleasantly spicy risotto, then a perfectly plain piece of angler fish with fresh local vegetables. And to finish, the most delicious tiramisu I have ever tasted.

The arrival of the bill, which had been in and out of my thoughts all evening, came as another pleasant surprise, dispelling any fears I'd had. I can definitely say that the whole experience was excellent value for money.

In recommending this restaurant to visitors from other countries, I would judge the tasteful mix of tradition and novelty to be a winner, revealing as it does, that flair for originality and imagination in full respect for traditional which is a typical Italian trait.

5 *Model answer*
Born of the Sun by Gillian Cross

I chose this book to read in English because I knew it had been written with younger readers in mind, and I thought that would make both the ideas and the language more accessible. I also liked the fact that the book is set in South America, which I know well, and so I was interested to see the continent through the eyes of an English writer. The writer, by the way, has won several literary prizes for her novels, which I always think is a useful recommendation.

The book tells the story of a girl called Paula who goes on the journey of a lifetime, and it is a dramatic and powerful story told from her perspective. After years of planning, Paula and her father go to South America in search of a lost Inca city. As they descend into the jungle, the dream turns into a nightmare and Paula begins to suspect that something is terribly wrong because her father is acting strangely. Gradually, she becomes convinced that they are being followed.

I would recommend this book to students of English because it's an exciting story and the main character is very appealing. At the same time, the themes explored in the story – the lost city itself and the travelling healers called Kallawaya – do have a basis in fact, and the writer has done her research into these areas very well.

The book is relatively short at 230 pages and the language is accessible and modern. Even so, students of English will find plenty of new words and idiomatic phrases to add to their vocabulary notebooks. As there is plenty of dialogue, however, and the story moves on very fast, you never get bogged down. I would recommend this book to anyone who wants to improve their English. It was also be useful for a group of friends to read and discuss as it raises interesting issues about a variety of engaging topics.

Listening p. 128–131

Part 1

1	C	3	B	5	A
2	C	4	A	6	B

Part 2

7	invasive	12	mathematicians
8	(sandy) desert(s)	13	reaction time(s)
9	(slight) pink	14	(mobile-phone) ringtones
10	secondary cavity (nesters)	15	dialect(s)
11	worms		

*In Part 2, bracketed words do not have to appear in the answer.

Part 3

16	D	18	A	20	A
17	C	19	B		

Part 4

21	A	24	F	27	B	30	C
22	C	25	G	28	D		
23	E	26	E	29	A		

Audio script

Part 1 Extract 1

PR = Presenter, D = Denise

Pr: Now, when we last spoke to Denise Redshank, she'd just taken up bee-keeping. I visited Denise earlier this week to see how she was getting on.

D: Well, as readers of my online beekeeping diary will know, I faced the disaster that every beekeeper dreads: the collapse of the colony. People assume that this was due to disease or some failing on my part, but I'm afraid it was just the way things worked out. A beehive needs a queen bee, and mine disappeared on me. I ordered a replacement from the bee dealer, but for some unknown reason, the worker bees rejected her. I don't think there was much anyone could've done about it. Anyway, it did give me the chance to reinvest – and I went for what's called a beehaus rather than a beehive. Now, a traditional beehive's a kind of wooden box at the bottom of a tower that gets taller and taller as summer progresses and it fills with honey. It's quite a big job taking it apart to see what's going on. The beehaus is different. It's a plastic trunk and instead of the tower, the bees store their honey in small light boxes arranged horizontally along the top – so instant access!

Part 1 Extract 2

So people ask me, you know, in the nicest possible way: 'So how come a well-established rock guitarist like you decides to join an unheard-of band like *The Ashes*?' But it wasn't like that. When the guys first contacted me, I didn't know whether they wanted me to produce them, write with them or what. I went over for ten days and it was like we were kids getting together and starting a group at fifteen or something – I got caught up in it.

I found myself thinking: 'I'm not having someone else recording my guitar parts, we're on to something great here. I'll do it myself.' I'd got absolutely attached to the music in such a way that the rest of my life and other concerns became secondary. To have that captivating feeling come back is pretty exciting. So it would've been weirder for me not to take the next step, to pull out and not play the tour, than it was to be in the band and help propel forward the stuff that we'd all worked on. And it's nice not having to be in charge for a change – I can put my intensity into being a guitarist – because it was never my intention to change the group's sound.

Part 1 Extract 3

Int = Interviewer, W = Woman

Int: You fed the novel called *The Kilburn Social Club* into a text analysis program on the computer. Why?

W: I wanted to see how a computer program that's usually used to analyse and summarise factual texts such as government reports or legal documents would cope with a work of fiction. The program I used was called Alceste, which works by looking at how often words occur near each other. It managed to identify the central themes of the novel – football, business and romance. But it couldn't distinguish between setting and plot; the fourth theme it picked out was 'walking in London', as the characters spend a lot of time doing that as they discuss philosophical ideas. As a reader, we'd hardly register the setting as we'd be concentrating on the dialogue, but the computer considers both equally. Basically, the program's only capable of telling you what the book's about. That's fine for factual prose or some works of fiction when the book's actually about what it's nominally about, but many novels have multiple layers of meaning. Often the most obvious theme is hardly the most important, and this is completely missed by a computer.

Part 2

Hi there. My name's Phil Asterton and I've come along this evening to talk about a bird that will be quite familiar to many of you. It's called the common European starling, and it is indeed one of the commonest birds in Europe, and one which is instantly recognisable from its appearance and behaviour. Because it is such a familiar bird, however, many people are surprised to learn that it's quite an important species, with some amazing characteristics that are quite widely studied. Anyway, more of that later.

First of all, a little information about the species. The Common European Starling is a member of a family of birds that are native to Europe, Africa and Asia. Some starlings are migratory by nature – moving south and west to avoid the worst winter weather in Europe for example, whilst others stay put. Although found in the Americas and Australasia, they are officially listed as invasive rather than native species there because they were introduced by European settlers.

Starlings are just as happy living in urban areas as they are in the countryside, where they are to be found in areas of both farmland and woodland. Indeed, with the exception of the sandy deserts, the birds may be found in all types of habitat.

The common European starling is essentially a medium-sized black bird. The plumage is speckled white in the winter months, taking on an iridescent sheen in the spring with hints of green and purple. The sexes are generally alike, with only a slight pink colouration around the beak in the female differentiating it from the male, where the same area has a blue colouring. Starlings generally build their nests in holes in trees. They are not excavators though, preferring to use existing holes. In other words they are 'secondary cavity nesters', to use the proper jargon. They do clean out the holes before using them, however, especially nesting material left by other species.

In terms of diet, starlings are omnivorous, famous for eating almost anything, although they do generally prefer fruit, insects and other small creatures. What I didn't realise though, was that they are much fussier when it comes to feeding their young, who are invariably given worms. In fact you often see the adult birds hunting for these on lawns.

So that's the basic information about starlings. But there's much more to them than that, because they are incredible birds in two quite different ways. Firstly, there is what's called the murmuration, where on winter evenings literally thousands of starlings come together as a flock and fly around together in tight formation. This behaviour has been the focus of extensive scientific study, not just by biologists, but also by mathematicians and engineers, in an attempt to understand how the birds manage to do it.

Because it is an incredible sight – so many birds, so close together, forming beautiful patterns in the sky as they all move together like one wave. But why do they do it? And how does each bird know what to do and how to avoid bumping into the others. Researchers who've studied the phenomenon identify the incredible speed of the birds' reaction time as the explanation. Without having a leader, each bird seems to know what to do – it seems they all just follow each other and it just works.

The other incredible thing about starlings is the sounds they can make. Indeed, starlings are famous imitators. Although they don't have a beautiful song as such, they make a lot of noise and reproduce the sounds they hear around them – typically the calls of other birds, but also electronic ones. Apparently mobile-phone ringtones have now taken over from car alarms and bleeping pedestrian crossings as the favourite sounds to imitate! Quite why they do this is unclear, but researchers have noticed that individual flocks of starlings have their own repertoire of sounds, around twenty of them, and that this helps individuals to recognise others in their group. It's a bit like human dialects that allow us to recognise people from our home area apparently. Incredible – you almost wonder if the young ones have their own slang expressions!

So, you see – starlings are wonderful birds. Now before I go on to …

Part 3

Int = Interviewer, M = Marc, E = Elena

Int: On this evening's programme, we're talking about identity, what makes us what we are. And joining me here in the studio to discuss the issue is the philosopher, Marc Jerome and the psychologist, Elena Berensen. Marc first of all, is that OK – calling you a philosopher – or would you prefer another label?

M: Hi. No, that's fine by me. But I'm also British, a parent, a teacher, an amateur photographer and a keen squash player – all categories I fit into at different moments in my everyday life, and which sometimes overlap. But the one you've gone for is arguably the most appropriate in the context of this programme, though the others might be more valid in another context. Because, it's useful to capture our identity in a handful of labels that we can show to the world, isn't it? 'Look, this is who I am,' we say. It's also reassuring. Being able to describe ourselves with a string of concrete nouns creates an illusion of solidity, and a sense of belonging, binding us to people in the same group or as we've said, to different groups at different times.

Int: Would you go along with that, Elena?

E: Oh yes. What's more, and perhaps surprisingly, this comforting effect can surface even when a label points to something negative – seeing yourself as a victim of an economic downturn, for instance, at least puts you in the company of others.

Int: But people don't always like them, do they Elena? I mean, am I 'pigeonholing' you by calling you 'a psychologist'?

E: Hardly! And when people use that term – 'pigeonholed', it does have negative connotations. But I think it's not because those people resist labels per se, it's just that they don't want others to do the labelling for them. Left to our own devices, we happily categorise ourselves in any number of ways, probably because, as Marc says, our identities give us a feeling of belonging and, at the same time, a sense of self. But that doesn't mean any of us fits neatly, one-hundred percent, into one pre-ordained category, and neither do we share all the characteristics of the other people within one category.

M: And too strong a sense of identity can feel restrictive and judgmental, can't it? I mean, what starts as a convenient label, can become too rigid – leaving a big gap at the centre of your existence if it's taken away. Feeling loss of identity is a common experience for many people who retire after spending a lifetime married to their job, for instance, and, of course, even more common for mothers whose children have left home.

E: And defining the edges of who we are too sharply can also undermine flexibility. You may end up avoiding situations that you perceive as 'not you' and miss out on opportunities – whether professional or recreational - that could expand your identity. When we use sweeping generalisations to draw attention to important aspects of ourselves, we'd do well to remember that what's important can change, and we also contain shifting, unlabelled potentialities that may be yet to emerge.

Int: But what about labelling by the media?

E: Well, at the end of the day, whatever labels of identity we wear, we are all unique individuals. Labels indiscriminately applied cannot capture that. The moment we start referring to, say 'university students' or 'road users' as a homogeneous group, sharing some core element of identity, we end up crudely lumping together all sorts of people who are actually quite unalike – except that they share that one thing in common. After all, labelling is only a short step away from stereotyping – making out that all the people in a group share other characteristics – and that can be divisive in society. Yet ironically, it is exactly because labels of identity can only refer to what we have in common with others that they can never capture our uniqueness.

M: And that's as it should be. To sum up, I'd say you can't understand what it means to be a human individual unless you understand the extent to which we live in a shared social world, whilst at the same time having a private view of it. Labels of identity help us to make sense of this. Each identity we take on is shared with others, but together they form a set which, if not quite unique, is at least highly personalised. Our multiple identities are like an incomplete list of ingredients in a recipe, but one which doesn't specify how much of each to use – or even how they should be combined.

Int: Marc, Elena – there we must leave it. Thank you.

Part 4
Speaker One

I kind of walked into my current job thanks to contacts I'd made doing postgrad research, and I've never attended many job interviews. So, when this headhunter emailed me, suggesting I might like to go for a vacant post in a rival lab, I felt flattered, but at a bit of a disadvantage. I imagined a panel of interviewers firing really tough questions at me, but what I got was a cosy one-to-one with the departmental head. He was dead keen to have me, but to be honest, the post itself didn't sound that enticing. Even though it's a well respected company, it would hardly represent a step up in career terms, so I'm staying put.

Speaker Two

I've been to plenty of job interviews in my time and thought I'd seen it all, but this latest one was beyond a joke! I came away quite upset actually. Given that my current post is disappearing in a departmental reshuffle, I had little choice but to apply – it was either that or redundancy – although with more staff under me, I could expect a bonus. I knew it would be tough; that I could expect no favours from the panel, but their questions were fair and I didn't put a foot wrong. But the group task all the applicants had to do at the end really backfired, because it made us all look really silly – I mean what's the point of that!

Speaker Three

When our manager resigned, we were told we needn't bother applying; that they wanted to recruit new blood. That got my goat. It wasn't the extra money I was after, still less the stress of being in charge, no – there was a principle involved! So I applied, and, incredibly, got an interview. How I ever managed to convince myself I was in with a chance, I don't know, but I was gutted when they announced the post was being re-advertised. I guess I was buoyed up because when the panel asked really searching questions, I wasn't thrown at all, and to be honest the other applicants I met were anything but high-flyers. Never mind. I'll chalk it up to experience!

Speaker Four

I go to pieces in interviews, and never get the job. But I'm always scanning the media for vacancies I can apply for. At more reputable firms, where interviews are well set up, you get an idea where you're going wrong – it's all good practice. When I got one at a fashion house, I barely took in the details of the job itself – instead agonising over what to wear – eventually plumping for the posh dress I'd worn to my sister's wedding. Imagine my horror when I arrived to find the panel lounging about in jeans. Fortunately, they saw the funny side of my gaffe, and what could've been an unsettling experience turned into something surprisingly relaxed and positive. I start next Monday.

Speaker Five

It's a big deal an interview at a multi-national, and I'd psyched myself up for it. Even if the company doesn't always get a good press these days, they have an impressive website, and I thought I'd done my research. The interview panel seemed a bit uncoordinated at first, lulling me into a false sense of security – but once they got into their stride, I was really put on the spot. I can't get over how searching those questions were. Anyway, I'd set my sights on getting into the big league in terms of remuneration and bonuses – and I had to show I was worth it. Some of the other applicants actually fell by the wayside as the day progressed, and the pressure mounted.

Pearson Education Limited
Edinburgh Gate
Harlow
Essex CM20 2JE
England
and Associated Companies throughout the world.

www.pearsonelt.com

© Pearson Education Limited 2013

The right of Megan Roderick, Carol Nuttall and Nick Kenny to be identified as the authors of this Work has been asserted by them in accordance with the Copyright, Designs and Patents Act 1988.

All rights reserved; no part of this publication may be reproduced, stored in a retrieval system, or transmitted in any form or by any means, electronic, mechanical, photocopying, recording, or otherwise without the prior written permission of the Publishers.

Photocopying: The Publisher grants permission for the photocopying of those pages marked 'photocopiable' according to the following conditions. Individual purchasers may make copies for their own use or for use by the classes they teach. Institutional purchasers may make copies for use by their staff and students, but this permission does not extend to additional institutions or branches. Under no circumstances may any part of this book be photocopied for resale.

First published 2013
Second impression 2014

ISBN: 978-1-4082-9900-5

Set in Amasis and Mundo Sans

Printed in Slovakia by Neografia

The publisher would like to thank the following for their kind permission to reproduce their photographs:

(Key: b-bottom; c-centre; l-left; r-right; t-top)

Alamy Images: Jake Lyell 20br, Mar Photographics 99cr, PhotoAlto 9b, Q-Images 90cl; **Corbis:** Aristide Economopoulos / Star Ledger 75br, Bob Sacha 18br, Jeffrey Rotman 69cr, Joel Knight / Arcaid 86bl, Radius Images 70b; **Fotolia.com:** 26bl; **Getty Images:** Ariel Skelley 79cr, Geri Lavrov 40br, Image Source 104bc, John Rowley 101tl, Matt Cardy 67cr, Paper Boat Creative 108br, Peter Dazeley 23br, PhotoAlto / Frederic Cirou 53br; **Rex Features:** Broadimage 89tl, Image Source 45cl, London News Pictures 13tr, MC Films 91br, Startraks Photo 89tc, Tim McKenna 64br; **Shutterstock.com:** 27br, 29br, 38br, 51br, 60cl, 111tl; **SuperStock:** Cultura Limited 7br, Flirt 97bl, imagebroker.net 57cl, Science Picture Co / Science Faction 35br; **TopFoto:** 58cl; **www.imagesource.com:** Powerstock 82br

All other images © Pearson Education

We are grateful to the following for permission to reproduce copyright material:

Text

Article on page 8 adapted from http://www.telegraph.co.uk/culture/theatre/dance/8480719/Lift-the-mind-and-the-body-will-follow.html, Telegraph, Rupert Christiansen, 30 April 2011, copyright (c) Telegraph Media Group Limited; Article on page 11 adapted from http://www.independent.co.uk/arts-entertainment/classical/features/a-virtual-seat-for-a-galaxy-of-virtuosi-2313752.html, Independent, Jessica Duchen, 15 July 2011, The Independent; Article on page 16 adapted from http://www.independent.co.uk/arts-entertainment/books/features/play-it-by-the-book-one-day-shows-that-bestsellers-dont-make-great-films-2342592.html, Independent,Gillian Orr,24 August 2011, The Independent; Article on page 16 adapted from http://www.guardian.co.uk/film/2011/jun/16/how-to-film-a-graphic-novel, Guardian,Marjane Satrapi,16 June 2011, Guardian News and Media Ltd; Article on page 17 adapted from http://www.independent.co.uk/environment/nature/whales-and-dolphins-are-so-intelligent-they-deserve-same-rights-as-humans-say-experts-7237448.html, Independent,Steve Connor,21 February 2012, The Independent; Article on page 19 adapted from http://www.telegraph.co.uk/earth/environment/conservation/9276915/Botanists-launch-bid-to-rescue-the-worlds-threatened-habitats.html, Telegraph,Richard Gray,

20 May 2012, copyright (c) Telegraph Media Group Limited; Article on page 24 adapted from http://www.independent.co.uk/environment/nature/nature_studies/nature-studies-by-michael-mccarthy-sense-and-sensibility--birds-have-lots-of-both-7544484.html, Independent,Michael McCarthy,8 March 2012, The Independent; Article on page 74 adapted from http://www.telegraph.co.uk/lifestyle/9319601/Commuter-Spy-half-term.html, Our man on the train Telegraph Media Group Ltd. Jun 8th, 2012, copyright (c) Telegraph Media Group Limited; Article on page 83 adapted from http://www.telegraph.co.uk/culture/art/architecture/9287621/Supporters-bid-to-preserve-Sir-Arthur-Conan-Doyles-home-but-do-we-read-too-much-into-writers-houses.html, Daily Telegraph,Philip Hensher,24 May 2012, copyright (c) Telegraph Media Group Limited; Article on page 98 adapted from www.brianmac.co.uk/psych.htm, BrianMac.co.uk; Article on page 99 adapted from http://www.helpguide.org/life/healthy_eating_diet.htm, Helpguide.org Maya W. Paul, Melinda Smith, M.A., and Jeanne Segal, Ph.D, Helpguide.org; Article on page 102 adapted from http://www.independent.co.uk/life-style/health-and-families/health-news/the-raw-meat-diet-do-you-have-the-stomach-for-the-latest-celebrity-food-fad-493908.html, Independent newspapers, Steve Bloomfield, 12th. June, 2005, The Independent; Article on page 109 adapted from Is it important to work?, *FT Magazine*, 22/10/2011, p.58 (Macaro A & Baggini J), © The Financial Times Limited. All Rights Reserved.; Article on page 2 adapted from Ten years on, and still the brightest light in space' *Independent on Sunday* 07/11/2010, p. 15 (Rodgers P), The Independent; Article on page 6 adapted from Tech Music School's new Repertoire, *Evening Standard*, 04/07/2012 (Chesworth N), Solo Syndication (Daily Mail, Mail On Sunday, ; Article on page 13 adapted from Acrobatics: Cirque Mandingue, *FT Magazine*, 17/03/2012 (Janina Conboye), © The Financial Times Limited. All Rights Reserved.; Article on page 10 adapted from How Reality TV transformed the industry's business model, *Weekend Financial Times*, 08/09/2011, © The Financial Times Limited. All Rights Reserved.; Article on page 10 adapted from *The Independent on Sunday*, 07/10/2010 (Gilbert G), The Independent; Article on page 10 adapted from Rousing and arousing – the story and glory of pop, *Sunday Telegraph Severn Magazine*, 06/01/2008 (Morley P), copyright (c) Telegraph Media Group Limited; Article on page 6 adapted from Goodbye to all this, *Financial Times Magazine*, 26/06/2010, p.26-27 (Vanderbilt T), Vanderbilt, Tom; Article on page 11 adapted from *NatWest Sense Magazine* Summer 2009, p.78-81 (Potter M); Article on page 18 adapted from A Tank of Sugar: Brazil runs on Biofuel, *FT Magazine*, 28/04/2012 (Cookson C), © The Financial Times Limited. All Rights Reserved.; Article on page 15 from Fiction for Robots, *New Scientist*, p. 46 (Griggs J), New Scientist; Article M3Paper1.12 adapted from Should we worry about status?, *FT Magazine*, 13/11/2010 (Macaro A & Baggini J), © The Financial Times Limited. All Rights Reserved.; Article on page 35 adapted from The Amazing Memory Marvels, *New Scientist* (Sukel K), New Scientist; Article on page 18 adapted from A popular Enlightenment, *New Scientist* (Nattrass N), New Scientist; Article on page 57 adapted from The Book is Dead: Long Live the Book, *New Scientist* (Grossman L), New Scientist; Article on page 62 adapted from Smokestack Sightings, *Financial Times Weekend*, 19/05/2012 (Dickie M), © The Financial Times Limited. All Rights Reserved.; Article on page 65 adapted from Up in the Wild Blue Yonder, *The Times Activity/Travel*, 03/04/2004 (Roe N), News International Syndication (NI Syndication) 55; Article on page 67 adapted from Step this way for an alternative economy, *The Guardian*, 14/02/2008 (Van der Zee B); Article on page 70 adapted from Destination, *Heathrow Traveller Magazine* Autumn 2010, P.38 (De Botton A), Heathrow Traveller and Magazine and Alain de Botton; Article on page 67 adapted from Failure to make it was never an option, *Telegraph Weekend*, 11/02/2012 (Portal B), copyright (c) Telegraph Media Group Limited; Article on page 73 adapted from Is Simple life better?, *FT Magazine*, 18/05/2012, P.51 (Macaro A), © The Financial Times Limited. All Rights Reserved.; Article on page 78 adapted from Daddy Daycare *FT Magazine*, 07/04/2012, p.34-35 (Holt R), © The Financial Times Limited. All Rights Reserved.; Article on page 85 adapted from Why not try this at Home?, *Weekend FT*, 02/12/2006, p.12 (De Burton Simon), © The Financial Times Limited. All Rights Reserved.; Article on page 89 adapted from Stars, stripes and Selling Clothes, *Financial Times Weekend*, 16/12/2011, p.1 (Green L & Friedman V), © The Financial Times Limited. All Rights Reserved.; Article on page 97 adapted from Literary Aces inspired by Tennis', *FT Weekend* 23/06/2012, p.2 (Sunyer J), © The Financial Times Limited. All Rights Reserved.; Article on page 101 adapted from Why we follow football', *FT Magazine*, 28/04/2012 (Kuper S), © The Financial Times Limited. All Rights Reserved.; Article on page 111 adapted from The Technology of Trust', *FT Magazine*, 07/04/2012, p.54 (Tett G), © The Financial Times Limited. All Rights Reserved.

In some instances we have been unable to trace the owners of copyright material, and we would appreciate any information that would enable us to do so.